GARGOYLE

EDITOR/PUBLISHER: Richard Peabody

DESIGN/COPYEDIT: Nita Congress

LAYOUT: Stephen Caporaletti

WEBMASTER/EMT: John Barclay-Morton

STAFF/INTERNS:
Jenn Bennett-Genthner
Matthew Blasi
Elena Botts
Rebecca Conway
Kristy Feltenberger Gillespie
Abby Frucht
Victoria Gaffney
Ivy Grimes
Jessica Harper
Victoria Horton
Beth Konkoski-Bates
Raima Larter
Lia Milgrim
Tova Seltzer

Gargoyle is on the web at www.gargoylemagazine.com.

Founded 1976
Gargoyle is published annually in the USA by Paycock Press.

Contact us:
GARGOYLE
3819 13th Street North
Arlington, VA 22201
Phone: 703-380-4893
Email: rchrdpeabody9@gmail.com

Our next reading period will begin July 1, 2020, and we accept/reject until we're full. Please use the Submittable tool on our website.

Price per single issue varies.

Subscriptions: $30/two issues to individuals; $40/two issues for institutions

ISBN-10: 0-931181-75-5
ISBN-13: 978-0-931181-75-7
ISSN 0162-1149
Copyright © 2020, Richard Myers Peabody Jr.

Photos of Pamela Moore on the cover and p. x by courtesy of Kevin Kanarek.

Gargoyle is distributed by:

- Direct from us through our website
- Amazon.com
- Sundial Books, 4065 Main Street, Chincoteague, VA 23336
- NewPages Magazine Webstore, www.newpageswebstore.com

Copies are also available from Bell and Howell Information and Learning.

Printed by Main Street Rag Publishing, Charlotte, NC.

People who do not write will tell you that they haven't gotten around to it yet because they know they can do it. They just need to get the kids in school, hire a lawn service and spend weekends writing, recycle their notebooks into usable material, make a concerted effort to remember their dreams. It can be done tomorrow. Anytime. They are just about to get to it that thing that comes so naturally to all of us, that thing we've all done through school and with great elan in our love letters. The books they could write, their plots based on something that happened to them, that are more exciting than le Carre's. Tomorrow. tomorrow. I'll see you tomorrow. They are not writing because they can. You are writing because you can't.

—Ann Beattie

’ll begin by appreciating local writer/scholar Robert Nedelkoff for resurrecting Pamela Moore’s history and reputation via his exhaustive essay in *The Baffler*, and also for steering me to her son. Unfathomable that his work about her was the only one in forty years up to that publication in 1997.

And without Pamela Moore’s son, Kevin Kanarek, the keeper of the flame, none of this would have happened. Absolutely gobsmacked that he allowed us to reprint his mother’s work from two of her published novels, plus allowing us to print the notes for her unpublished second novel.

I was fortunate that old friend James Harper was available for chauffeur service and heavy lifting when #70 was delivered.

Hats off to Cynthia Atkins, Mark DeCarteret, Sean Dougherty, David Keplinger, and Susan Tepper for steering folks our way during the last reading period.

Additional thanks to Rotem Banai and everybody at Bethesda Urban Alliance for making me useful.

And special thanks to Nita and Steve, Jimmy and Rose, Blair and Mary, Andrew Gifford, M. Scott Douglass, Margaret Grosh, Twyla and Laurel, my Salmon Poetry family, and all my Frostburg and Delaware friends.

IN MEMORIAM

Lee K. Abbott
Julie Adams
Warren Adler
Bibi Andersson
Jo Andres
Dominic Argento
Diana Athill
Russell Baker
Nanni Balestrini
Jonathan Baumbach
Birch Bayh
Joe Bellino
Keith Birdsong
Hal Blaine
Verna Bloom
Bill Brundige
Neus Catala
Carol Channing
Larry Cohen
Tim Conway
Doris Day
Stanley Donen
Milena Dravić
Denise DuBarry
Francine du Plessix Gray
Carol Emshwiller
Georgia Engel
Ethel Ennis
Richard Erdman
Roky Erickson
Rachel Held Evans
John Falsey
Conxita Julià i Farrés
Alvin Fielder
Albert Finney
Jim Fowler
Kathleen Fraser
Bruno Ganz
J.D. Gibbs
Tony Glover

Forrest Gregg
Linda Gregg
Skip Groff
John Guernsey
Bonnie Guitar
Barbara Hammer
John Havlicek
Victor Hayden
Maida Heatter
Susan Hiller
Mark Hollis
Tony Horwitz
Susannah Hunnewell
James Ingram
Joseph Jarman
Dan Jenkins
J.O. Jeppson (aka Janet
   Asimov)
Donald Keene
Kevin Killian
Chuck Kinder
Clydie King
Florence Knoll
Patrick Lane
Honey Lantree
Niki Lauda
Andrea Levy
William F. Levy
John L'Heureux
Peggy Lipton
Gene Littler
Dušan Makavejev
Barry Malkin
Tania Mallet
Gino Marchetti
Vonda N. McIntyre
Mark Medoff
Jonas Mekas
W. S. Merwin
Sylvia Miles

Les Murray
Willie Murphy
Don Newcombe
Ken Nordine
Mary Oliver
Amos Oz
Alan R. Pearlman
I.M. Pei
Rosamunde Pilcher
Stanley Plumly
Andre Previn
Mac Rebennack (aka Dr.
   John)
Leon Redbone
Frank Robinson
Sara Romweber
Bernice Sandler
Sam Savage
Bob Schloredt
Carolee Schneemann
John Singleton
William E. Smart
John Starling
Bart Starr
Peter Tork
Tomi Ungerer
Skip Van Winkle
Agnes Varda
Patricia Nell Warren
Guy Webster
Peter Whitehead
June Whitfield
Paul Williams
James Calvin Wilsey
Gene Wolfe
Morgan Woodward
Herman Wouk
Pegi Young
Perry Deane Young
Franco Zeffirelli

CONTENTS

FEATURE: PAMELA MOORE

Richard Peabody   Invoking Pamela Moore   1
Diana   6
The Horsy Set   18
Prophets Without Honor   30

NONFICTION

Amy Issadore Bloom   The Rose   57
Patricia Henley   Beds   59
Jelena Kecmanovic   Pita from Home   61
Randi Gray Kristensen   Miss Peaches   63
Stephanie Leow   Alice's Adventures in Wonderland: A Coming-of-Rage Story   64
Christopher Linforth   Island Boy   68
Trish MacEnulty   The Trump Supporter Who Peed on My Mattress   71
Daniel Mueller   The Way They Do in Movies   76
K.P. Taylor   Garden of Weeds   84
Mark Terrill   The Director   87

POETRY

Amy Alfier   Amelia's Ultimatum   90
JC Alfier   Morgan City Fragment   92
In Wabbaseka   93
Tobi Alfier   Man as Broken Levee   94
Linette Marie Allen   The Bridge by Penn   96
Casting Crowns at Memphis   97
Nancy Allen   Mexico   99
King of the Dogs   100
Resort   101
David Alpaugh   Roo–Zuh–Velt/History   102
Rose Mary Boehm   Summerfest   103
Ace Boggess   Advice for Killing a Spider   104
Paula Bonnell   Knowing   105
Instruments of Purpose, Considered   106
Shirley J. Brewer   Accounting   108
Marilyn Speaks   109
Joan Colby   Floating   110
Dia de los Muertos   111
Gail Braune Comorat   In This Dream of Endless Aisles   113
Robert Cooperman   Worse   115
Melvin Dickson, the Girl Scouts, and Pot Shops   116
Barbara Crooker   Crow Mischief   117
Moon   118
Black and Purple Petunias   118
Mark Danowsky   Grace   119
Bird in a Box   119
Heather L. Davis   Because of Poetry   120
Robin Dellabough   Oz Redux   121
All Our Stories   121

Margaret Diehl	Women Remember	122
	Why I Write Novels	123
Alex McRae Dimsdale	Diplodocus	125
	Kiwi	126
Catherine Fahey	Seal Eyes	127
Gary Fincke	Miracle Fish, Los Angeles	130
Michael J. Galko	The Protective Eye	132
Kathleen Gillespie	The Ballad of Lovecraft County	133
James Grabill	In a Sleep-Dive Swoon	134
	Out of Unfathomable Time	135
James Gross	Vibe-branded	136
Hedy Habra	Allegro Ma Non Troppo	137
Chloe Hanson	Your Body, The Afterlife	138
Donald Illich	Success as the Rain	139
	Crabgrass	140
Mike James	Ghazal 1	141
	Ghazal 2	141
Brad Johnson	World Forgetting by World Forgot	142
	Northern Aggression	143
George Kalamaras	So We Can Teach Ourselves Not to Bleed	144
	Arthur Waley's Deathbed Photo	145
Rodger Kamenetz	Homer and Penelope	147
	Nekiya	147
Lilah Katcher	Invasion	148
	Winter Landscape with Ice Skaters	148
Sandra Kolankiewicz	Snow on the Mountain	149
Kathleen Kraft	Cumulative Rainfall	150
Andrew Lafleche	Forget the Rest	151
Susan Lewis	Dumb Lucks	152
	Valor Added	152
Miles Liss	Folding up Nets	155
Kristian Macaron	The Ways I Hold My Floods	156
Joyce Enzor Maust	Making a Cigarette Run with a Trio of My Homeless Friends	157
Mark Melnicove	Uncle B would say	158
	If weeds made noises	158
Nancy Mercado	Catcalls to My Brain	159
Michael Milburn	~~Strong~~ Silent	161
Liz Minette	Piano	162
Miles David Moore	Grandma and the Hurricane	163
Elisabeth Murawski	From the Station	164
	Urn with Hummingbird	165
Jordan Pérez	Wild Cactus	166
	Theodore Roosevelt Island	167
David Romanda	Before I Move In	168
Mark Rubin	Mouse and Fox	169
Leslie M. Rupracht	Whirled Peas, Man	170
Beate Sigriddaughter	Emily Watches Him Sharpen Kitchen Knives	171
	Rosemary Honey	171
	On Ice	172
Noel Sloboda	Progress Report	173
Ellen McGrath Smith	Shaken 19: Devouring Time blunt thou the lion's paws	174
	Shaken 22: My glass shall not persuade me I am old	174
	Shaken 25: Let those who are in favor with their stars	176

J.D. Smith	Mushrooms	177
	A Vanishing	178
Maya Sonenberg	The Lost Poem, 1978	179
Shenandoah Sowash	Dave Announces He's Made Partner, So I'm Thinking Maybe I Should Too	182
Marilyn Stablein	The Baths	183
	A Hard Read	184
Kurt Steinwand	Settlers	185
	Rick Sunshine	186
Marjorie Stelmach	Unjust	187
Joseph Stern	Global Reports and Analysis	188
Gail White	The Aging Process	189
Sally Wilde	Snow Day	190
	XVI: The Tower: Drunken Jenga Night	192
Paula Yup	My Apartment	193

FICTION

James Armstrong	Locks	195
Jonah Marlow Bradenday	The Playwright	201
Jody Lannen Brady	Anything You Need	208
Gerri Brightwell	Mr. Sweet Pie	216
Kathryn Chiariello	Doctor Delacruz Meets Her Match	226
Chris Cleary	Perspective	231
Katie Cortese	Before There Was Light	239
Daniel Coshnear	Proximity	242
Zane deBlosat	Cupid, Valentines, and LSD	247
Gabriel Don	Extraordinary Rendition	257
Aaron Emmel	The Listeners	279
Greyson Ferguson	The Woman by the Sea	291
Shelby Settles Harper	Feather	297
Thomas Hrycyk	Blood of a Different Color	301
Beth Uznis Johnson	Wild Turkey	311
Stephanie Joyce	Nos Morituri	327
Karan Madhok	New Mutiny	335
Ryan Masters	Everyone Negotiates	349
Hannah Moloney	The Water	362
Alastair Murdoch	The Chalet	365
Donají Olmedo	Between Autumns	372
Colleen Kearney Rich	Wild Horses	381
Dawn Ryan	My Own Divine Motility	386
Marija Stajic	Sirens	397
David A. Taylor	Humane Society	399
Varsha Tiwary	A Pear a Day (and Other Proverbial Truths)	405
M. Kaat Toy	Entering Atlantis	409
Andrea Wyatt	He's Crazy, Everybody Said	418
Vonetta Young	As Far Away	420
McKenzie Zalopany	Stamp Bingo	430

ART

Franetta McMillian	Six photos	iv, 56, 89, 194, 326, 437
Contributors		438
Last Words		454

Richard Peabody
INVOKING PAMELA MOORE

(September 22, 1937 – June 7, 1964)

"This book is a sexier, more cosmopolitan Bell Jar*–young girl, manic depression, New York, LA. It is amazing. Everyone who loves* The Dud Avocado *will go crazy for this novel." —Emma Straub, author of* Laura Lamont's Life in Pictures

I find it difficult to process whether or not Pamela Moore's badass reputation and success balances in any way with her early death and the subsequent neglect her books received. Touted as "America's Françoise Sagan" (in part by the French press) for a variety of reasons—young, sophisticated, writing about sex, but publishing industry marketing above all.

French author Sagan was eighteen when she splashed onto the scene in 1954 with *Bonjour Tristesse*, and it's possible to imagine American publishers acting like football coaches—*they've got a hot young babe who writes about sex, find me a hot young babe who writes about sex.* Moore appeared at precisely the right time to fit the bill.

Chocolates for Breakfast was published in 1956 when Moore was eighteen years old and became an international bestseller. The from-innocence-to-experience-with-the-jaded-set plot follows a fifteen-year-old girl named Courtney as she shifts from coast to coast—Rosemary Hall (now part of Choate) in New England, to the Garden of Allah in Hollywood, to establishment landmarks of midcentury Manhattan such as P. J. Clarke's. (I love the "Garden of Allah" as a possible nod to F. Scott Fitzgerald.)

Moore began the semi-autobiographical novel when she was fifteen. And it's believed to be based on her life from 1953–54. What a life. She is heartbroken after her crush on her boarding school English teacher, sleeps with a bisexual Hollywood actor who abandons her, leaving her to sleep with a debauched European aristocrat in a luxurious Manhattan hotel.

This was something new. A young woman exploring territory that had primarily been the domain of the boys. Who let her in the treehouse? And what a dynamite movie her first book could have been.

A timeline for perspective:

- Korean War—1950–53
- *Catcher in the Rye*—1951
- *Bonjour Tristesse*—1954
- *The Deer Park*—1955
- *The Body Snatchers*—1955
- *Lolita*—1955
- ***Chocolates for Breakfast*—1956**
- *Peyton Place*—1956
- *On the Road*—1957
- *West Side Story*—musical 1957 [film 1961]
- *Candy*—1958
- *To Kill a Mockingbird*—1960
- *Tropic of Cancer*—1961 [1934 in France]
- *The Carpetbaggers*—1961
- *Catch-22*—1961
- *Naked Lunch*—1962 [1959 in France]
- *The Bell Jar*—1963
- *The Group*—1964
- *Valley of the Dolls*—1966

She was a prodigy with a lost childhood owing to her parents' early divorce. Both parents were writers. I don't know if it was expected that she would continue in the family business but it seems to me that she couldn't wait to go to Barnard or to Europe to escape her family. And that movement does impact her books—the divorced semiprivileged kid surrounded by wealth. The bicoastal travel to see her father in LA then back to NY to see her mother. Something of a timeless recipe for many young writers both before and after.

We know now from her son Kevin Kanarek's afterword to the *Chocolates for Breakfast* reprint edition, which was published in 2013, that her relationship with her lesbian-ish? teacher and Euro lover, plus time spent in Europe, grew her up quickly in regard to the publishing industry and its role in maintaining the status quo. Learning that she self-censored her writing to avoid conflicts, she anticipated when it was time for a literary career and then a year later added new material to the French "nouvelle edition" of *Chocolates*, material that shifts the axis of the book away from sexual awakening and more toward political awakening. She was naïve about the publishing biz with *Chocolates*, but after enduring corporate handlers, the greedy marketplace, and forced celebrity, she rebelled biting the hands that fed her.

Her second novel, "Prophets Without Honor," written after her marriage to Adam Kanarek, was rejected by Knopf, which canceled their contract in 1959. It has never been published in any form. We are grateful to present the synopsis/outline/working notes in this issue. Moore returned to this material on several occasions, and the manuscript was called variously "Kathy on the Rocks," "Tho All the World Betrays Thee," and "My Sister Kathy." Dell even had a working contract in 1964 for the book entitled "Debut."

Comparisons to J.D. Salinger and Sagan are frequent, but her young teen protagonists are closer in age to Nabokov's *Lolita*. Consider that there were very few young women writers and, at that time, maybe four young women songwriters—Jackie DeShannon, Carole King, Ellie Greenwich, and Laura Nyro. Moore was a forerunner with a European sensibility wedged into a gap between the ending of the McCarthy era and the coming of the Beatles and the British Invasion. Yet, many people compare her to those more successful writers who followed her after Moore opened the gate.

Her photos display a mercurial personality. She seems older than her years in some, like Grace Slick in her European photos, and honestly the photo shoot for *The Horsy Set*, with Moore in her equestrian garb holding a cigarette holder, seems more akin to satirist Florence King.

The best of her prose for me is in her attention to detail and her snarky takes on marriage and relationships. The excerpts from *Diana* reprinted here have one foot in the New York Beat Scene and the other planted in an ethnic Polish/Jewish/Puerto Rican neighborhood.

The Horsy Set takes aim at her wealthy upbringing. The novel reads like a sexed-up version of *National Velvet*. Seventeen-year-old Brenda's ex-showgirl mom wants a divorce from her stodgy Wall Street husband so she can continue boinking the stud master of the stables. Brenda, still a virgin, has a laser focus on everything happening around her—drinking, cuckholding, lust, and philandering. Before she escapes Horse World she gives us a peek behind the steamy curtain

While much of her language and subject matter were eye opening during her lifetime, the intervening years have dulled the shock value. Moore's writing often seems hurried or careless. Dialogue is seriously riddled with exclamation marks. There are moments, but *The Exile of Suzy-Q* makes for slow going. Though I do love how it pokes and prods Hollywood and dude ranches like some amalgam of *Lolita*, *Rancho Deluxe*, and *Hannah Montana*.

It's not difficult to read Moore now as a pre-Brat Pack novelist with one foot in the trashy romance *Peyton Place* tradition. As if Jay McInerney, Bret Easton Ellis, Mary Gaitskill, and Tama Janowicz wrote a group novel.

Moore gave birth to her son in 1963, and nine months later committed suicide by .22 rifle at age twenty-six. Her baby was asleep in the next room.

The WHY? resonates. Some think postpartum depression. Kanarek has said that in some ways she saved him. And, of course, the first year with an infant is life changing and nothing really prepares anybody for the stress and lack of sleep. A writer's work often must take a backseat.

Those who see a link with Sylvia Plath believe Moore would be diagnosed as bipolar today given her symptoms. Moore was suffering from depression and self-medicating with alcohol and nicotine. She didn't have a lot of options in the 1950s as psychotropic drugs were in their infancy.

By 1964, she was also reworking "Prophets Without Honor," focusing on the life of a failed writer. (F. Scott comes to mind again.) Washed up at twenty-six. The age most contemporary writers are graduating with their MFAs in hand.

What I'm left with is a talented young writer (so young!) who wasn't nourished by the right people in her era's publishing world. And that seems a real pity. Pamela Moore had talent to burn. If anybody had stepped in and edited her excesses, helped her escape her Stockholm Syndrome devotion to her Svengali husband, perhaps things would have turned out differently. And it's that loss of potential that eats away at me. (Can you imagine her as a YA writer today?) Given a little more time, a little less pressure? Who's to say whether or not it would have helped? Her growing political awareness could have morphed into something else entirely.

At least, after forty years of neglect, *Chocolates for Breakfast* lives on.

Notes the Chocolates for Breakfast website maintained by Kevin Kanarak: "Since its publication in 1956, *Chocolates for Breakfast* appeared in 11 languages, including French, Italian, Spanish, Hebrew, Swedish, and German. According to the Bantam paperback edition, the book went through 11 printings in the U.S. and sold over one million copies." Kanarek adds, "The eighteenth edition of the Italian translation, *Cioccolata a Colazione*, lists the total number of copies sold in Italy as of 1966 at 408,000."

About time a new generation discovered her.

WORKS

- *Chocolates for Breakfast*—1956 [circa 1952–56]
- "Prophets Without Honor"—rejected by publisher [circa 1957–59]
- "Are American Men Afraid of Sex?"—*Playboy*, February 1957
- *The Pigeons of St. Mark's Place*—1960 (France); aka *East Side Story*—1961 (England); aka *Diana*—1964 (United States) [circa 1959–60]
- *The Exile of Suzy-Q*—1962 (France) [circa 1961–62]
- *The Horsy Set*—1963 [circa 1962–63]
- "Kathy on the Rocks" [circa 1963–64; never completed]

ONLINE REFERENCES

Pamela Moore site, Wikipedia, https://en.wikipedia.org/wiki/Pamela_Moore_(author)

Fitch, Janet, "Great Girl Trash," *Salon* April 10, 2000, https://web.archive.org/web/20080612162218/http://archive.salon.com/books/bag/2000/04/10/fitch2/index.html

Kevin Kanarek's site about his mother and her books, with photos, book covers, and tons of info, http://chocolatesforbreakfast.info/

The Rumpus Interview with Kevin Kanarek, https://therumpus.net/2013/07/reading-backwards-from-the-end-the-rumpus-interview-with-kevin-kanarek/

Dan Visel, "Writers No One Reads" guest post, http://writersnoonereads.tumblr.com/post/51746581871/pamela-moore

Pamela Moore's papers at Columbia University, https://findingaids.library.columbia.edu/ead/nnc-rb/ldpd_13202800

PRINT REFERENCES

Koa Beck, "The Sylvia Plath You've Never Heard Of," *MarieClaire*, February 26, 2016.

Joseph Gerard Brennan, *The Education of a Prejudiced Man* (Scribner, 1977).

Dina Gachman, "The Girl with the Sequined Chip on Her Shoulder," *LA Review of Books*, September 23, 2013.

Whitney Matheson, "*USA Today* Review," June 26, 2013.

Robert Nedelkoff, "Pamela Moore Plus Forty," *The Baffler* (10): 104–17 (1997).

New York Times, "Novelist, 26, Found Dead at Her Home in Brooklyn," June 8, 1964.

Hope Reese, "Review: 'Chocolates for Breakfast' by Pamela Moore," *Chicago Tribune*, July 5, 2013.

Emma Straub, "Foreword," *Chocolates for Breakfast* reprint (New York: HarperCollins, 2013).

DIANA

FROM CHAPTER 1

A FLOCK OF FLUTTERY PIGEONS soared high over the flat roofs of St. Mark's Place. As the dusky bluebirds rose beyond the spindly crosses of the television antennae, the light of the morning sun on their full-spread wings made them as white as the snow on the roofs. When suddenly the pigeons furled their wings and shot downwards over the hazy orb of the sun and against the light, they turned ominous black. Then they settled, chortling, back onto the sooty New York rooftops.

"Ooh, just look at that, Casimir!" Evelyn exclaimed, pointing with a brusque and awkward gesture towards the chink of sky that overhung the narrow street.

"Watch your step instead, it's icy," said Casimir, and he profited from the moment to slip his arm beneath hers.

"Did you see those pigeons?" Evelyn asked. "White and then black and then white again, turning so fast into..."

"Makes me think of your older sister," Casimir said drily.

"Ruth did very well for herself," Evelyn said, "and her wedding tomorrow is going to be absolutely gorgeous!" Evelyn held her dark head high.

"That's what I mean," Casimir said with a vague gesture. He still had not figured it out: Evelyn's older sister had got up out of Casimir's bachelor bed one morning with hair all distraught and face flushed from his attentions, and had announced, "You'll see, you big Polack! You think you can do what you want with a girl and she'll never leave you. Within a month I'll be engaged. Just to show you! And...and," she had spluttered, "to a doctor! I have him all picked out, so there!" Then she had put on her prim nurse's uniform and stalked out, never to enter his apartment again. Casimir wondered if all the Epstein sisters were capable of such abrupt about-faces, and he looked over at Evelyn appraisingly. She had the same dark, petulant beauty as Ruth...

"All your family must be celebrating," said Casimir. "How would you like me to pick you up tonight after work, and take you out to dinner? We'll toast your sister's happiness together."

He could not keep the note of smug anticipation out of his voice, but she seemed not to have noticed.

"OK," she said, surprised and flattered. She even tottered a little on the slick sidewalk: she had actually been asked for a date by her sister's old boyfriend, the handsomest man in their whole apartment house! The fact that her older sister had warned her against this Pole only contributed to her excitement. "You know where the hospital is..."

Casimir glanced down at her firm legs clad in white nurses' stockings, and a smile broke over his hawklike features. "I know," he said. "I've been there before."

Over the heads of the group that trudged to work along the sidewalk of St. Mark's Place there on the Lower East Side of New York, the pigeons wheeled and swooped and soared with abandon against the dusty sun. It was eight o'clock and soon the block would be empty, its men and children reclaimed by school and factory. Up and down the peeling faces of the four- and five-storey apartment houses, windows were pushed open. The housewives, stocky and peasant-faced and imperturbable, laid out their bedding to air on the snow-encrusted fire escapes, then leaned on plump elbows to watch their husbands go off to work.

It was Friday: tonight the men's wallets would be full and so would the bars. Some would come home with hearts so laden with joy and anguish that their wives dreaded the hour. Tonight the ramshackle apartment houses would shudder with the sound of glasses smashed against the walls and a fearful female scream or two, useless against the heavy-throated Slavic curses of their husbands. But the women who now stared out at the icy New York street knew that the night would end in urgent and clumsy caress and perhaps, when their menfolk fell asleep, they would succeed in hiding whatever remained of the weekly paycheck. That was the way of the world on St. Mark's Place, but the men were men and their women did not complain.

Stefan Jasinski rested his sinewy arms on the windowsill high over St. Mark's Place and the sun fell full on his broad-featured, high-cheekboned face. He smiled at the sky with yearning in his gentle blue eyes, and concentrated hard in an effort to banish the chimneys and the sooty roofs and replace them with a broad, snowy plain that stretched undulating to empurpled infinity. If only the vision in his mind were a little sharper or more specific he would be able to set it down on canvas. But it didn't work, and his dreaming gaze traveled down to the street. Then he chuckled.

"Say, Maggie," he called to his wife behind him. "There's Casimir arm in arm with little Evelyn from downstairs! But no... she's moving away now, she's a coy one! Well, I don't think it'll be long before Casimir's bed will be warmed by another virgin."

His friend Casimir and the girl passed out of sight around the corner of Second Avenue, and Stefan scrutinized the sky once more. He sighed heavily. Was it a sin that for him the loveliest thing on earth was what never bloomed on St. Mark's Place, a tree with the heavens caught in its uplifted branches? If only he were able to dissect that tree of his imagination into intersecting lines and shifting planes and helter-skelter blotches of garish color, his paintings would be on exhibit in the East Tenth Street galleries, and they would sell! But what critic or buyer these days got excited over a rigidly accurate landscape? They wanted wild innovation, and if only he were capable of that, poor Maggie would have a new dress or two and they could even eat meat every day! But it was idle to think of what might have been. Stefan's wandering gaze fixed on a flock of pigeons describing swift, graceful circles around the sun in flashes of black and white, and his eyes lit up. It was, after all, a beautiful day for painting!

"The air is so clear today, Maggie!" he called to his wife. "I'm going out to Central Park. Do you mind, Maggie?" He hesitated. "Maybe you could come with me and sit next to me while I paint, the way you used to?"

There was no response. Stefan turned back to the dim apartment. "Maggie? Will you come with me, Maggie?" he asked eagerly, but once more was met with silence. He rose, walked from the little living room that was cluttered with his easel and festooned with his landscapes, passed through the kitchen and stood at the door to the narrow back room.

"Maggie? Come with me today," he said tenderly.

She looked up from her housework, but only for a moment. The rough cloth of her bathrobe clung to her rounded haunches as she leaned back over the bed and pulled taut the bottom sheet. She hadn't yet brushed her hair, and the shining chestnut locks fell in confusion over her face, and down to her shoulders. She had been a prim and cocky American girl when he had met her, always dressed in slim and severe secretarial suits, with the straight hips and long legs of a boy. He had set about to make her look like a Polish girl, plump and healthy and easy-going, but Maggie Smith had a mind of her own, and had determined to maintain her trim, career-girl figure. Still, the hips had filled out nicely and the pert breasts had swelled and softened, all, he had smugly pointed out to her, the natural result of being his woman. He was a Pole and ardent; he had placed his stamp on this American girl, and she had not minded a bit.

"What's wrong?" Stefan asked. "Something's on your mind. I was talking to you for a good fifteen minutes, and you didn't hear a word I said."

"Oh." She straightened up and brushed the wayward hair from her eyes.

"Don't," he said. "I like to see your hair that way, tumbling over your face."

"Well, you get someone else to do the housework and I'll be your artist's model, all right?"

"Please tell me what's bothering you."

"Nothing," she said and with nervous motion she tucked the blankets in at the bottom of the bed. It was silly to get upset this way, when four years had passed since the conversation that she had been remembering just before her husband walked in. It had started, that talk so long ago, when she announced to her mother that she and Stefan had decided to marry. Her mother had taken her aside then, and with eyes all full of tears had stroked her daughter's hands and said, "Maggie, I don't want to see these pretty fingers all red and shaky from scrubbing a floor that will never get clean, I couldn't bear to see your eyes that look so loving and trusting turn just weary and hopeless…"

Maggie looked up at Stefan, who stood in the doorway gravely waiting for her to speak, and then she busied herself again. with the bedmaking. She recalled how her mother had become more and more worked up, saying that her life would end right there in the Bronx, but she had always wanted her daughter to have an easy time of it, with a nice house and a maid and happy children and never a worry about making ends meet. Maggie, inexperienced and in love, had listened with half an ear…

"What are you thinking about, Maggie? I don't want to have to ask you again."

"Then I'll tell you! While I was making the bed I was thinking about what my mother said to me just before we got married. She ended up a long lecture with, "Go ahead and marry your immigrant painter, and spend the rest of your life in four walls with an unmade double bed!" Maggie smiled half-heartedly, but she was trembling. "And I was thinking…"

Stefan dreaded the words.

"…that in the end Mother was right."

"What can I say!" Stefan smashed his fist into his palm and, disgusted more with himself than with her, spun around so that his back was to her. In the beginning she had thought that these three tiny rooms were heaven on earth; she had sat at his feet inside these four cracked walls and every one of his damnably unsalable canvases had been a glorious love offering…

"You know that it's always going to be this way, Maggie," he said to the kitchen where the dishes waited to be washed. "Don't you fool yourself like the others that live here: I'll never be able to carry you away from the slums. My paintings haven't sold yet and never will. But I won't keep you here with me if you can't take it. You're free to go, Maggie, as free as...as the pigeons I was watching from the window. You can fly far away from St. Mark's Place and come to earth in some comfortable nest where..."

He turned around, enraged and miserable that she had confronted him with his failure. But she had slumped down where she had been standing and lay now inert across the bed with her chestnut hair swirled around the pillow and her narrow shoulders shaking with absolute silent sobs. He sat down beside her and lifted her chin between his broad fingers.

She turned brimming and reddened eyes upon him. "I'm sorry I... You don't mean that, you don't...want to get...rid of me..."

"No, oh no! I love you, Maggie! But don't you understand me by now? I'm an artist and I know only one way to paint. I don't care that nobody wants my work, I've got to keep on painting and in my own way, otherwise I'd... be through as a man, I wouldn't be able to look at myself in the mirror! Don't make me choose between my work and you, Maggie, because I'm afraid..."

"I...I don't want to leave you," she murmured desperately as though crying out against a certain fate.

"Maggie, Maggie, poor Maggie," he said. "You are a child."

But he had to take care of her. He could blot out the dinginess of St. Mark's Place and silence the protest in his stomach as the eternal plate of spaghetti was set before him by his wordless wife: he had only to glance over at the unfinished work on his easel and he would lose himself in the whispering sweetness of some secret glen of a blue-green forest. His life at least made sense, he knew who he was and had no fear of the future. Yesterday, today and tomorrow merged all in a single patch of delicious color there in the corner of the paintings that brooded over his daydreams. But the shaking and submissive girl in his arms could justify her misery only in the name of love, and that must bring her little comfort when her lover cared more for an image or a brushstroke than for her happiness. Abruptly he rose from her side, the faithless husband, for he could not bear the accusation of the love in her eyes.

Maggie said nothing, only got up, dried her face on the sleeve of her bathrobe and walked into the kitchen. Stefan heard her turn on the water tap and start the washing of the breakfast dishes.

"I am going into the park today," he announced aggressively, "and you can come with me if you want."

She did not deign to answer, and why should he have expected her to? She would not be a participant in his betraying her. Stefan hung his head and sat down wearily on the bed. He had no heart for painting now. Maggie always held her emotions in firm check, whether out of devotion or fear of his temper he neither knew nor cared. Her outburst, brief as it had been, was a dangerous sign. But there was nothing he could do to make her life easier! She had married a painter, that was all there was to it.

FROM CHAPTER 3

IF THE SUN SHONE ON St. Mark's Place, inside the coffee house it was always evening. Burlap had been stretched behind the plate glass to keep away the stares of the squares. A boy with a magnificent bush of black beard strummed a plaintive folk-song on the guitar. Ralph Stetson sat cross-legged on the floor, listening to the folk-singer and sketching him. Diana helped herself to another cup of coffee from the Espresso machine, and then made a mark beside her name on the blackboard over the counter. Two couples were sitting on the floor upon orange pillows, with elbows resting on a very low white table. They all stared into space, listening to the low and thin song. Against the other wall three slim young men were sprawled in various graceful poses on a double bed that served as café sofa by day and the bed of the folk-singing owner by night. The young men were playing chess. As Diana walked back to Ralph she did not look at the three. The boy in the middle, Bobbie, lived across the hall from them and the other two were his present crushes. Bobbie had taken a liking to Ralph—not that Ralph did anything to encourage him—and as a result he never exchanged a word with Diana, greeting her only with icy, jealous stares. Diana didn't care; it only annoyed her that they all met in such close quarters here in the café.

"Sssss! The snake walks on two feet and has eyes that scan the ceiling!" Bobbie muttered as she passed, but she ignored him.

Diana sat down next to Ralph on the floor, and glanced over at his sketch. It wasn't much of a likeness: Ralph had never learned to draw, but his splatter-work achieved startling effects in color and was all the rage at the East Tenth Street galleries. Even here in the café, everybody looked up to him as a master. "Everybody but me," thought Diana. That fellow Stefan who lived downstairs was a better artist to her mind. Diana had studied fine arts before she left Radcliffe to live with Ralph, and she had a high respect for draughtsmanship.

"You can't draw the side of a barn," she said, and stretched out her leg clad in tights, nudging Ralph with her shoeless toe.

"The side of a barn, yes, because it's only color. But the whole barn; there you've got me," Ralph said with good humor. Ever since his abstract work had caught on a few months ago, his artistic confidence had been unshakable and he was no fun to tease anymore.

Diana fell silent and hugged her knees under her chin, pressing the legs against her flat stomach. She wondered when she would start to get heavy. With tall and thin girls like herself, you usually couldn't tell right up to the last months. How idiotic of Ralph to have done this to her She remembered the night when he had become her lover. Looking back now, she was convinced he had been a virgin. But he had been the first for her, and it had taken her weeks and weeks to realize how clumsy he had been that first time in the Cambridge hotel. And now he played the man of the world, assuring her that what she knew to be true just couldn't be. Living side by side with these manly Slavs had given him new ideas of how women should be treated, but he didn't carry off arrogance very well.

She ruffled his reddish hair with her fingers, and he leaned back against her knees, "You're just a little boy, Ralph, you know that?"

He sighed with contentment and continued sketching. But it was the little boy in him that had from the first attracted her: he was rebellious and full of delightful fantasy.

This year together had been the happiest of Diana's life; it was one long and beautiful thoughtless escapade. In the beginning she had figured it would not last over a month, but living and sleeping side by side with him for all these days and nights, she had grown accustomed to him. Still, she had felt herself ready at any minute to leave him should another man come into her life. Ralph had wanted to marry her, and she had been steadfast in her refusal. Now that she was convinced she was expecting a baby, the natural thing would be for them to marry. They had been contented together, and yet she felt that there must be more to love than the casual pleasure and amusement that he had given her. She wanted to be swept off her feet by a man, and Ralph had not known how to do that. Marriage was in her mind irrevocable and she was not ready to bind herself now, at twenty, to Ralph Stetson. But she had to face the blank fact that she was, quite simply, pregnant and unmarried.

Outside the café the afternoon waned, and inside nobody moved. The singer ran through his whole repertory, but it seemed that nobody listened. Diana Marcher wrestled with herself in silence and isolation; her face was drawn and pale. Her hand rested on her stomach and the fingers twitched convulsively. Ralph did not look up from his sketching.

Saturday night settled lazily over St. Mark's Place. The rejoicing of Friday was over and done with, and in most of the households the remainder of the paycheck had been hidden away by the vigilant wives. Behind the lighted windows, the men of the family nursed colossal hangovers. The bar of the Polish National Home was half-empty. Not even Casimir was there; he stood lingering across the street from Ratner's restaurant on Second Avenue, listening to the music and laughter that issued from the wedding celebration. The festivities must eventually come to an end; Ruth must sooner or later escape with her doctor, and the guests would trickle out.

FROM CHAPTER 7

THE FIRST LIGHT OF DAWN awakened Diana Marcher. She did not stir, for fear of rousing Ralph, who slumbered beside her with one leg thrown across her thighs. The apartment was freezing. Usually this was the hour when the furnace was briefly turned on, but there was not even the knocking in the pipes that presaged a couple of hours' warmth. She didn't care; it was cosy there in bed with the bodily warm of both of them. The pale sun was reflected off the corner of the neighboring building and into their narrow bedroom with a dull glow. But over in the living-room, she could see the rays of morning illuminate clearly Ralph's easel and the fresh paintings all around it. Suddenly, the delight with which she greeted each new day was snuffed out.

Ralph had been painting furiously all of these last two weeks, as though he felt that on some unnameable day of the near future his talent would somehow disappear. Diana understood it all. This burst of work had begun the morning after she had told him she was pregnant. He had not touched her all that night. Instead, as she had perceived vaguely through her fitful sleep, he had sat on a chair beside the bed, smoking endless cigarettes as the pile of angrily squashed butts in the morning had testified. When she had awakened he had taken in silence the coffee that she made for him, and only after the two of them had sat across from each other over coffee for almost an hour, had he finally spoken. She had not urged him. She had been too fearful, and her fear proved justified.

"Diana," she heard his rough-edged, sleepy voice even now in the silence of a later dawn. "Diana," he had said, "I've been thinking all night."

"I know."

"Then of course you know about what."

"Of course."

"Diana, tell me honestly, do you really want to go through with this? I mean, there's only one way that I could see it making sense for you to keep the baby, and that's if we got married."

"You're proposing to me?" she had asked icily.

"Well, yes, if you want to put it that way, but I know you're just making this harder on purpose, and I don't see why you should."

"Do you think it's easy for me? Do you think it was easy for me to make the decision, all alone?"

He had wet his lips nervously, and she had felt sorry for him. When he had a paintbrush in his hand, Ralph was brilliant. But dealing with life, dealing with her... Ralph was after all only twenty, and every psychology textbook would tell you that at this age a man was not as mature as a woman. What they didn't seem to say anything about was that a man of twenty was a man, and if he inadvertently found he was about to become a father, then what, O college textbook, was the "more mature" woman to do about it?

"Diana, I... Oh, why do you just sit there looking at me like that? I'm not going to pop an engagement ring out of my pocket. You and I, we... Well, we haven't up to now lived by convention, and I don't think you're waiting for me to propose to you conventionally. I just think we ought to get married, that's all."

And fear had risen within her, at the thought of spending all her life beside Ralph, with the paintings that would grow even more famous as time went on, and the youthful, beatnik rebelliousness that she would find more and more ridiculous as she watched their child grow into a person and as she probed ever deeper into her consciousness, beyond rebellion and beyond Ralph's defiant beard, searching out the truth of poetry. Ralph had found a haven behind his beard and within the sacredly still coffee houses. But Diana knew, as surely as she knew anything in this life, that what Ralph called "Beatnikville," was for her but a stop along the way.

She was no happier now in the close community of the Bohemians than she had been in that of the Park Avenue debutantes. If one day she found herself as a poet, she would do so alone, in a deathly silent solitude of the spirit. She had never intended to chain herself to Ralph, and to go through a marriage ceremony with him when she knew that one day she would leave him would be to lie to herself. Through that false action she knew she would be debased. And she could not risk debasement, not now when she was striving forever upward, when even as she chiselled out the anguishingly imperfect verses of her days, she knew that nothing was final and certain in life save that she would change and grow and grope forever closer to that vision of a final and immutable poem.

"Ralph," she had said finally, ringing the rim of her coffee cup with one thoughtful and trembling finger, "I am very fond of you, Ralph, but it is not only as a woman that I have to decide my fate."

"I understand that," he had said, "but you have even told me that it's only in living with me that you've been able to give yourself to poetry. You know that far from standing in your way, I will always help you to..."

"But, no, no," she had said with anguish in her immense eyes. "No one can ever help me, that's just the trouble. You can draw inspiration from the other painters in the café, you watch how they handle things and you really profit from their example and go on to do the same thing far better than they ever could. But it's not that way with me, Ralph, at least not now. I have to be free, Ralph, I..."

"Free! You're always saying that! What do you mean?"

She had had to stop and think. "Free" was a word that she had associated with herself as closely as her name. To be free was to be herself, not bound to anybody or anything but her vision of poetry.

"I...I suppose that by free, I mean alone."

His face had fallen and she had been sorry that her words Were so brutal.

"I didn't mean that I want to leave you, Ralph; I don't... at least not now. Please don't be hurt when I say that. I'm...growing all the time, Ralph, I'm changing; today I want to be with you, but by tomorrow I may not. I... Oh!"

She had risen quickly and walked over to him; he was staring out into space and not a muscle on his face moved. She had leaned down and put her cool cheek against his tousled head, then she had found herself kneeling beside him, holding his hands in hers and looking up at him with compassion and regret, silently imploring his face to change, into sorrow, anger, anything but this expressionlessness that bespoke such suffering. But he had not moved and he had not spoken; she could not have expected him to. His safe and sure universe, built around his Lady Diana, had suddenly become a thing of gossamer, ready to blow away at the first inclement breath from her lips.

"I...I don't want us to get married, Ralph. But please understand..."

"Understand!" He had spun around in his chair, "There's something I want you to understand, Diana. This..." His voice had choked. "This baby isn't just yours, it's yours and mine, Diana, the way... the way I thought our love was yours and mine, an equal part of both of us. Diana, I... Oh, all these things you've been saying, Diana, I don't believe them! You hear me? I—don't—believe—them!"

She had reared back on her heels and stared at him. In his face she had seen that it was true: he was incapable of believing that she did not love him as he loved her, that all she could truly give herself to in this life was poetry. Poetry was aborn under her breast like this new life, this infant unnamed, and to them alone could she be true.

"I don't believe you, Diana," he had repeated, Looking down upon her with his life hanging on her eyes. "I know that there's only one thing that's ever stood between us, and...and it's the baby!"

She had said nothing, he was so nearly right. His eyes had fixed desperately on hers for another instant, then he had turned away and buried his head in his hands, as close to weeping as she had ever seen him.

It all came back to her now as vividly as she saw his easel in the morning sunlight. She stared out towards the living-room and the light of dawn, and Ralph's slumped shoulders and broken spirit were spread before her; she was guilty all over again.

Diana stared up at the ceiling. Under the nightshirt, she put her hand on her stomach, and imagined that she could feel a stirring, a new pulse, although as yet there was none. She glanced over at Ralph, slumbering peacefully with his mouth a little open like a boy, and idly she caressed his leg sprawled across her thighs. He did not awaken. She studied his face, and murmured to herself that she loved him as much as she would ever love anyone.

But that was not enough, not even for him. Who was she to make him suffer so, all in the name of poetry, when she knew she was still a groper in the wilderness of images and not yet a poet? Who was she, this audacious one: was she sure that she was worthy of becoming a poet, or worthy even of becoming a mother? She was Ralph's love, that much she knew, and that she had betrayed. One word from her would suffice to make him whole again, one proof that she cared for him, as she did, would restore him. That proof was so much to ask! But she had never in her life made a sacrifice, and poetry was nothing if not sacrifice and denial and the yielding up of every sacred image to the blasphemy of words. One word from her... After all, there was only one thing sacred to her, and that was her liberty. This one word would not threaten her liberty. What then, was there to keep her from uttering it? Nothing, she answered herself in anguish.

In the same moment, as though even in his sleep perceiving her sorrow, Ralph stirred, put out a hand in clumsy, drowsy caress, and then woke up.

"Diana? Oh, Diana!" He was fully awake now and he saw the tears on her immaculate white cheeks; he kissed them away. "Diana, what's wrong?"

She pulled him close to her and buried her face in his shoulder. "Nothing's wrong, Ralph. I was...just thinking everything over, and I... arrived at a decision." Surreptitiously she dried her eyes against the pillow behind him. "You've been saying that only one thing has come between us ever, and that's... the baby..."

He stroked her hair and held her tightly. His Lady Diana! He knew she would come to realize it sooner or later, she was so courageous and wise; he had said nothing about it, but he knew that she would come to see that there were only two ways to restore the happiness they bad known, either to marry or...

"For you, Ralph," she murmured into the hollow of his shoulder, "I... Ralph, I won't have the baby. We'll get rid of it."

THE HORSY SET

CHAPTER 1

I don't know how I'll ever get up the nerve to begin this book because I've never written anything really, unless I count that senior term paper called "Training the Horse Trains the Rider" about sportsmanship and guts and all on which I got my one and only A in the Westchester Country Classes which made me absolutely flip. When I jumped into the car and showed Mother that A she couldn't believe her eyes and put on her glasses, dark glasses because, even though she's so nearsighted that all the world is a blur, she thinks men don't make passes unless you wear dark glasses like a movie star. She stared at the A through those butterfly dark glasses while the chauffeur drove us away from school and I looked out the window at the buds on the elm trees along the Scarsdale Park Lane and made out I couldn't care less about my mark, but finally I couldn't wait any longer and I said, "Only two kids in the class got A's!" Mother slung one leg over the other in that cocky way she has in boots and breeches and said, "It was nice of your teacher to let you write about riding, because that's all you know."

Mother always gets her way and, even though Palmer wanted me to go to Vassar next fall, I'm not going to college at all because Mother says I'm not college material and would only clutter up the campus and there's a professor shortage in this country. So I'm giving the professors a break. But I don't want to be just a stable bum because Palmer's right when he says riding horses is a stupid way to spend a life unless it's your business the way it is Guy's. And I wouldn't want Guy's life anyway because he's so busy running his stable that he hardly even has time to get on a horse. So what could I do, I decided to write a book. I'm keeping it a secret from Mother and Palmer because they'd laugh in my face, but I can put down here all the things I'd tell them if only they wouldn't laugh. I'm really a person in my own right even though the parents don't know it, because I'm seventeen after all and an awful lot of eighteen-year-old girls are writing books these days so why not seventeen? I've read those girls' books and I don't think they're anymore precocious than me or really any different from me, except that, honestly, I don't have the experience they do. I'd better come right out and say it even though it embarrasses me—I'm a virgin.

I mean there's a whole area of life that's muddy to me no matter how much I hear or read about it. So sometimes I listen to people and I don't understand them and I know they're talking from that mud; they're talking about how it feels and tastes and smells, and I get dizzy thinking I'd know just what was going on if only I took one little step and sank into that sea of mud with them because they're all in it together. All the parents in Scarsdale, and I guess in Westchester and I guess in the whole world, are up to their hips in that mud and waving to each other talking about how it feels. And I just watch them and listen with my mouth open like an idiot, standing on the edge and leaning out to that slippery, sucking muck of a sea, wishing I could look through the mud and see the bottom they're standing on because the way it looks to me the world doesn't have any bottom where people could plant their feet like the roots of a scarred old tree.

And Mother and Palmer are floating in the mud like all the rest of them. The morning after I brought home my first and last *A*, Saturday it was, I was feeling pretty good what with the *A* and Palmer showing up at home for a change. I never understood just what it was that kept him in New York all week for the past couple of years, since he never succeeded in explaining to me what his investment banking house does. I guess the business is in his blood because he inherited it from his father, but his blood isn't my blood anyhow and finance just makes my head spin. So he was home and I was hanging around the garden, behind the hedge of boxwoods that leads down to the bloody serpentine of roses, and the grass had just been mown and everything smelled juicy, young and bruised.

I wanted to catch Palmer on his way out to the garage and tell him I wouldn't go to the stable that day if only he'd stay around, and maybe we'd take a little drive since the chauffeur had the car all ready to take him back to New York. With my shirt sticking to my back and my legs steaming in the riding breeches, I drifted towards the cool sound of the swishing hose as the gardener, his Italian face already olived by the sun, watered the boxwoods. I couldn't have talked with Speletto even if I'd wanted to because he hardly knows a word of English, so I settled myself in the shade and out of sight behind the hedge, looking at the drops of water caught on the budding flat tops where the sun dazzled as though it were later than May. Through the French doors open to the living room, I heard voices droning like fat summer bees over nodding, ready blossoms. Half dozing in the sweet smells, I was jolted by Palmer's voice which rose so harsh and angry it made me sit up at attention.

"And what about the house?" Palmer boomed in such a commanding tone I thought he must be firing a servant. Even Speletto turned his face of a wrinkled olive to the house, with startled eyes like two black pits. But the hose swished on and the sun shone down and only I could understand the words.

"Do you want the house, too?"

In spite of myself I listened hard, and heard mother answer in a bitter voice:

"No! I hate this house, Palmer, as much as you do."

At first I thought I was hearing things, but no the parents were talking all right, about my house! So maybe it was theirs too, but they couldn't mean they hated it because they didn't—they'd lived in it and shaped it ever since I could remember, they planted this garden rose by rose and the hedge grew up with me. So the hedge was always my size and hid me now as it used to when Mother brought me here saying, "This is your home and this man is your father now." It was like saying they hated me! I got scared as if I were still a little kid expecting to be kicked out for reasons as mysterious as had brought me here to a man I never learned to call Father.

Through the hedge I saw Palmer come to the open doorway, where the sun glinted off his bald head and profiled stomach. His suits were so well-tailored that only in profile did I see how fat he had gotten. After all, he didn't ride horses like Mother and me. He didn't have time or interest, and when Mother and I talked horses and she praised me for my guts—that was all she ever praised me for—Palmer'd look at us with his dignified disdain. We never had much in common, maybe that's why I never called him Father though he wanted me to. He was a fixture like the house, at least till the past couple of years. Poor old Palmer didn't look so good now, flabby and slumping as if he'd been through a hard time. Living in New York didn't agree with him but he told me he had to because of business. I swear I didn't know he hated the house. Maybe I was just stupid. But a lot of things had been going on lately that I didn't understand, arguments, like now.

I watched old Palmer's chins double as he seemed to be looking someone up and down. Peering, I could just see by the side of the door my mother's knees with the dressing gown slipped up to show off her calves, as skinny and muscled as mine from her years as a chorus girl. Palmer just looked over his chins at her legs until she broke the silence.

"So you see," Mother said, "we agree perfectly, and we'll be able to settle this thing in a civilized way. I know that's what you want, you're such a goddam gentleman that you're not going to fight me! You've never had to fight for anything in your life."

I could hear the sneer in her voice. Mother thinks Palmer is a coward because he always backs out of these arguments and I hoped he would now;

I didn't like to listen. Fighting your wife isn't like battling a horse, after all; it doesn't take guts and in my opinion it's pretty disgusting. That's why I never fight Mother out loud so she always gets her way over Palmer and me. When she shouted like now I got the creepy feeling that the house would fall to pieces, as if she was too loud to belong in it and I didn't either.

"No," Palmer said in this very quiet deep way he has and I was glad he had his dignity. "No." I heard his voice rise. "I'm not going to crawl down on your level and fight for you with your riding master! Ten years ago I thought I could pick you out of the gutter and make something of you. Now I don't care in what manure heap you choose to lay that chorus-girl body of yours!"

That was a pretty disgusting thing to say about my mother! It wasn't true what the ladies at the stable gossiped about her and Guy, just because she was his favorite in the Ladies' Class. She's the only one with guts and Guy's tough, that's all he respects, just like Mother, and me too for that matter. Didn't Palmer know better? I saw Mother's legs cross and recross nervously and I wished she'd cover her knees at least. I wanted her to fight this but she only shifted her legs under Palmer's eyes and mine through the hedge, and Palmer said:

"You've finally ended up on your own level, Marcy, and this time I'm going to leave you there, with that cowboy! You can dye your hair orange again the way it was in the chorus line. You should have married him to begin with except that you were a slum urchin and he likes rich women."

"He loves me!" Mother screamed it and Palmer actually flinched and I wanted to shut my ears—it wasn't true what everybody said about my mother! But I heard her go on. "And I love him, and I'm going to get him the way I got you when I was hungry and now I'm hungry in a different way, Palmer, a way that you've never been able to fill my belly! He's a man, Palmer! You don't even know the meaning of the word."

"Man!" Palmer's voice trembled. I'd never seen him in such a rage. "He's a whore like you! Take him if you can get him! But you won't have my money to buy him with, remember that!"

"Keep your money! Keep it in bed with you because that's all you'll have!"

"Just remember, Marcy, this divorce was your idea, your madness, I'll let you go on getting what you want but in the end it will be your ruin. I only feel sorry for your daughter. Because you'll end up in the gutter where I found you!"

I heard his footsteps thud on the terrace and pause as he said, "My lawyers will be in touch with you. I shall leave it to you to explain to Brenda. Though I expect she knows the explanation."

I just crouched dizzy and stupid as if it were someone else whose mother was getting divorced. I couldn't make myself understand in that moment that my whole world, Palmer who'd been the only father I ever knew, and the house where I'd grown up, all were spinning around and standing on its head. Palmer passed by the boxwoods so close to me that I could have reached out, caught at his trouser cuff and stopped him, but I just lay there. With feet a-clatter on the flagstone path he strode on toward the garage and I looked into the sun because it made my eyes hurt and at least that felt real. In the stillness then I heard my mother's voice low in the living room.

"Silver Birch Stables? May I speak to Guy, please? He's expecting my call."

There was no getting away from it so I might as well get in it and ask Palmer all I'd wanted to while he was talking, so I climbed to my feet, a little dizzy, and ran down the flagstones, the thud of my boots banging in my head, down between the green boxwoods like soldiers at attention, past the olive head of Speletto that nodded to me and watched me with an old man's unsurprise, until I saw that Palmer had heard me and halted against the blood red of the serpentine roses. I slowed to a proper walk and he waited, composing his face, because at first it was still full of anger and pain and now it became dignified, the pink and gray mask of a square-jawed banker with stern mouth but kindly eyes, the mask of a banker considering a loan to an addle-brained but appealing youth, the disguise he felt it proper to assume for my sake. For my sake! the sentimental bastard! But there was a crack in the disguise this time where his gray eyes showed through wide and uneasy and shifted away as I came up, stupidly letting me know he'd seen me a run from the boxwoods by the French doors, because sometimes the parents aren't any better at outwitting me than I am at outwitting them.

"What have you been up to?" Palmer's stern mouth smiled to put the client at her ease with the friendly fatherly question as if I'd been building sand castles and was bursting to tell him all about it, but, knowing I'm not a child, he really wanted an answer and his searching eyes put a hard question mark at the end. I looked into his eyes.

"Nothing," I said on principle. "Are you going back to New York?"

"Yes," Palmer said, looking down at me, and his chins sagged.

"Just like that?" I hooked my thumbs into the belt of my riding breeches and self-consciously thought it was just what my mother did to look cocky, but I didn't know what to do with my hands.

His throat bobbed as he swallowed, poor old Palmer, and he lifted one hand as if to put it on my shoulder but stopped halfway and took the handkerchief out of his pocket. "Would you like me to give you a lift? I see you're going to the stable."

"I don't know whether I will or not," I said, feeling sorry for him because he should have been able to pat my shoulder if he felt like it—I wouldn't have minded, I even wanted him to but he freezes all the time as if a bell rings in his head that reminds him he's not my real father. We stood there looking at each other, breathing, me in my sweaty shirt and him in the suit that hides his belly, and I wanted to shout because there wasn't anything I could say in a civilized way. How could I put it, my mother's not a whore!

"Have you had lunch?" he asked in his gruff banker's voice.

"Yes," I lied, on principle again because I didn't know what he wanted from me.

"Oh." I couldn't tell if he was disappointed or relieved. "I thought I might take you out to lunch."

We breathed at each other again in a stupid silence while I said in my head that he could have had lunch with me yesterday and today and tomorrow if only he'd live home and not in New York, and maybe little by little I'd get it out of him and he'd get it out of me whether he and his stepdaughter had to get divorced.

"How is Larry these days?" Palmer finally asked. He must have felt, too, that this divorce was between us because he got out of it by bringing up Larry and planting him at my side, Larry with the thin Ivy-cut blond hair and scrubbed face like Palmer's when he'd married mother, only in the snapshots, Palmer's hair was plastered, parted down the middle like a choirboy's of the 1920s. Palmer really didn't look different now except older and hurt and stiff, and bald with his skull shining cruelly in the spring sun. Looking at his skull I felt guilty for being young with a young Palmer of a Larry planted at my side, and I wanted to be very kind to Palmer only I didn't know how, because seventeen hasn't much kindness in it.

"I didn't see Larry this week," I said. "He's up in Cambridge cramming for his finals. But he wrote me he'll be down next weekend to put his boat in commission."

"He's a better sailor than I was at his age, Palmer said, and proved I was right about his thoughts. "You ought to try to crew for him in the races this summer."

I looked down at my boots and said, though knowing I shouldn't have, "I've got to keep at my riding, if I'm going to make the Team at the Olympic Trials."

Palmer gazed at me sadly and said, "Do you want to have a talk with me Brenda? Was there something you wanted to talk to me about? Why don't you drive with me to the stable and we can talk."

"Palmer...Palmer, are you coming home next weekend?"

His chins sagged and his gray eyes slackened like his jowls and he said, strangled, "Yes."

And I thought he was a coward for lying. "So next weekend we can take a drive and talk," I said in revenge. He didn't want to talk to my mother and he didn't want to talk to me and I, scared to talk to him, was glad he bore the blame.

"Good." His voice choked and his eyelids fluttered on gray eyes misty in the sun, behind the horn-rimmed glasses of his banker's disguise.

"I'll see you next weekend...and Larry, too." I let him leave me then, a portly figure in the smooth-cut suit; I watched him wend his way through the crazy serpentine of roses, gray suit and shining skull against the blood red of a flower maze planned for formal delight but now only a puzzle and a bar to his ponderous circling, tortuous flight.

I heard the muffled roar of the motor from beyond the roses, where at the end of the maze lay the gleaming silver roof of the garage. A few minutes later a solid mass of black slipped humming through the frame of red flower and green boxwood, the square Rolls-Royce that always looked to me like a hearse bore Palmer off safely from the silent, sunlit formal garden. And I wondered why, with a taste so funereal in cars as in flowers, he had taken a chorus girl to wed and divorce.

Mother had told me all about it so often that I felt I had lived through it in her skin and not my own. Now I felt closer to her then than to myself, for she was seventeen when I was born. Yet she doesn't talk about that marriage but only about the other when she was twenty-four and I already seven. I ought to remember my life then—most people recall something from the age of seven, but not I; either it was not real or it was all too real. Whatever was the smell of the furnished room? Cabbage, I guess, and corned beef when we had it, for those Irish staples once were served to Mother at a dinner on St. Patrick's Day at the stable, and I can still see her turning green and hear her say, "No, my God, no. You go right ahead and eat but I'll just get myself another martini. Please don't mind me."

That winter I guess there wasn't any corned beef with the cabbage because, on a certain morning in windy January, Mother had come hungry to the theater, ready to claw like a tigress for the job because she hardly had enough to feed me, much less herself, standing in line and hating the leggy young females who waited with her and might replace her after the tryout. With all her strength she had danced, as one night after too many martinis years ago, she had gaily danced for Palmer and me; one-two-three, split on four, up on six, seven-eight-nine, kick on ten, kick on eleven… Split on twelve, and she hadn't gotten up, her spread legs refusing to answer her; she had pushed herself up like a groggy boxer and the choreographer had said, "Thank you. Next please." And in tears of exhaustion she had run off to the wings.

A few minutes later, knock on the door of the chorus girls' dressing room and there appears the attendant whose face I have always imagined to be Speletto's, olive-wrinkled with all the troubles he has seen, summoning "the redhead in the black net tights." Not one but two jump up and the Speletto-attendant points out Marcy. "It's one of the backers!" he whispers excitedly. And the other redhead turns spiteful eyes on Marcy the chosen muttering, "And she couldn't even get out of a split!"

"Do you want me?" Her face creamed free of grease paint and a demure sweater over the bare shoulders, she presents herself to the backer, a sun-tanned, thirtyish young man with hair anachronistically parted down the middle and gray flannels worn square like the uniform he'd been in for the past two years, athletic, not like a muddy soldier, but a country-clubber, because the war was air-conditioned in Washington.

"I don't want to get your hopes up," the young man says with soft gray eyes of a banker but a young banker who can't refuse a loan, "because the rest of them out there don't think you're right for the part. But I think you'd do wonderfully as a dinner date."

Though wary of stage-door Johnnies, she thinks of the hefty meal and her stomach wins over her head which tells her that Johnnies don't advance a girl's career, not on the stage anyhow, where a poor girl's head and stomach are always battling for her virtue. It makes about as much sense to me as Palmer's explanations of finance when Mother says to me that virtue gets the highest reward in the market place. Mother tries to give me these lessons because she says she doesn't want me to learn the hard way as she did, but I don't have an empty belly and market value isn't what I think of when Larry and I are lying under the sun in the well of his Star, because I'm not on the Street after all—Wall Street, I mean.

But it seems Mother kept the lesson in her head — maybe she'd learned it from her shanty Irish mother—anyway, she remembered it through the dinners that followed every night that week, after which she would make Palmer leave her at the door, like a virgin, only of course seven-year-old me was sleeping behind that door. That weekend old Palmer took her on his yacht and they sailed around the tip of Long Island, rocky in the moonlight, and it seems he tired of virtue; I don't know the details but I can imagine because Larry and I don't build sand castles when we go out. The punchline is Marcy theatrically squirms from Palmer's arms and leaps into moonlit Long Island Sound. Only when she hits the water does she remember she can't swim, and screams for him to save her. He leaps in fully clothed and carries her back to the boat like a real hero.

After that Palmer really falls for her because he says he's never met anyone so tempestuous and exciting, Palmer with his banking blood and his funereal tastes. He defies his father who, in the living-room portrait, looks as Palmer does now, only leaner over a stiff high collar with rimless glasses and regular New England. And Palmer takes this Irish chorus girl with red hair and big dreamy blue eyes that see the world as a nearsighted blur, he takes these sighing wild blue eyes to parties of his own set at the country club, announcing that this is the beauty he fished out of the ocean.

Come to think of it though I didn't exactly jump out of the boat myself I would have if it had gone any farther with Larry that time. I guess in a way I have lived through a little of Mother's life. But not really! I'd kill myself if I ever thought I was just doing the same things she did. Not that I don't like Mother. Sometimes, like when she's very brave on a horse taking the same high jump I do even though she's older and not so athletic, and looks back at me with a cocky grin, I love her even. Honestly, sometimes I love her as if she were my own self. But if she's really getting a divorce from Palmer I swear I hate her. I can't stand even to think of it. And after hearing what I just did it'd kill me to think I've lived even a little bit like her.

But it happened on a boat all right, because Palmer introduced me to Larry at the country club where the Harfields are friends of his. So we were sailing just as Palmer did with Mother, sailing that first time Larry kissed me soon after we met, when his tongue and his hands made me love my breasts' itching and swelling and hardening under his gyrating palms as we lay out of sight and wind in the well under the billowing sail. And after I pushed him away I was sorry, because he sat there with his face droopy as if I'd done something horrible to him instead of just protecting my virtue and all. I mean he had a face like Palmer's when Mother said she loved Guy and Guy loved her. Larry looked that bad, like a poor old man whose wife's divorcing him. I didn't know what I'd done that any girl in the world wouldn't do, even Mother when she was a girl! I didn't know Larry the way I do now—I thought he was just like any other boy. But he's an artist.

"You think it's just physical with me, don't you?" Larry threw at me.

Surprised, I said, "Yes, sure it is!' That was the whole trouble in my mind.

"What would you say if I told you that what you did today might ruin my whole life?"

I laughed, you know, sophisticated. "I'd think it was your line, that's what I'd think, and pretty silly, if you want to know."

"God, I always fall in with these empty-headed girls!" He groaned, kind of sophisticated too, I thought. "I probably shouldn't even tell you because you'll just giggle like all the others," he said, "but I'm a playwright. There's this play I want to write. But I've got to find the woman for it."

"You mean to act in it?" I didn't know anything about plays really.

"To write it about!" He said, looking miserable, with his bare knees chucked up to his chin as one hand steadied the tiller. "A real woman, who's got the guts to be a woman!"

I wanted to cry myself, not because I cared about his play which at that time I didn't, but because if anybody in the world had guts I figured I did, and I was really breathless at the idea of somebody writing a play all about me! I thought he'd just wanted me physically, because I'd never met a boy like him who came out of another world of wind and sun and sailboat whipping the lapping waves, a world without mud and manure, where nobody talked of divorce and no man called his wife a whore. I mean there isn't one person in the whole stable who'd ever think of writing a play at all, much less about me! He was really sincere, with his face so sad, and as I looked at him and thought about it a little I decided he really could have written about me; I guess we all think we're awfully interesting and anyhow, I did. I've been thinking about myself for seventeen years now and I'm still not bored with me, I'm still trying to figure me out. Because sometimes I do things that surprise me like right then, when I went and told this boy I'd just met the thoughts I'd always kept a secret till then.

"Even if it is for a play," I said, "I wouldn't dare make love with you!' It was pretty exciting even to say "make love"—I could see it affected him the way it did me because his bare knees kind of twitched. "The most important thing in the world to me is guts, that's why I love riding, because I'm always doing things that scare me, higher and higher jumps, and that's what courage is."

He wasn't interested in riding. Right away he said, "You're scared of making love, aren't you? He liked to say the words, too.

"Yes..." I knew what he meant. "But I'm not going to do *that* just because it scares me! Because...I think that's what makes everybody crazy. You don't know my riding master, he's old and hairy, but all these women are falling all over him even though they're married, and giving him presents. I've never seen anybody with so many gold cuff links and all."

He gave this wise grin; maybe he understood it even though I didn't know what they all saw in Guy. "And Mother..." Luckily I stopped myself in time before I went on and told him how Mother was kind of crazy too because she never allowed me in my whole life to see my own father or even a picture of him—he's just a name to me. It's pretty scary not to know your own father and I think this is as queer of Mother as it is for the ladies to swoon over old Guy. "I mean," I said, "it's all just mud to me and I'm scared to death to fall into it and go crazy myself!"

"What are you scared for, your soul?" He looked puzzled. "Have you got religion or something?"

"No," I admitted, "I've never been into a church in my whole life. This is just my own idea."

He got mad then, and swung the tiller around hard so I almost fell overboard.

"Then what the hell are you keeping it for," he said when I recovered my balance, "if you won't give it to me so I could write a play about it? I mean if you won't give it for art?"

"I don't know." And I really didn't. I still don't.

"You mean you're keeping it for marriage, like All these empty-headed virgins! Come on, admit it."

'No," I said. "I don't ever want to get married! Because all these married people, the parents, I mean, and everybody at the stable, they're the crazy ones!"

He shook his head with frustration and I realized, as we crept towards the sandy shore, that he'd turned the tiller to go back.

"Are you... ever going to see me again?" I asked in a voice that came out squeaky. "Are you ever going to date me in your whole life now since I ruined your life? Larry?"

That's when I saw that Larry was really different from the parents and everybody and all the other boys I'd ever known. I don't really believe that Palmer was ever like Larry except in his face and his passion for sailing—I'm sure. he never told Mother that love was an art. I've never seen anything beautiful or touching pass between Palmer and Mother, not like what Larry did at that moment.

He took pity on me for being scared he'd never see me again and he put his arms around me without breasts or shame but purity, and that's how we lay under the clean white sail, like children hugging as he told me how he thought the life his parents lead is as ugly as I think Mother's and Palmer's is, with arguments and cocktails to blot them out. He called it Philistine: Will you buy me a mink, Will you give me the house. And he promised our love, like the play he would write, would be beautiful, and he swore I wouldn't have to make love until I was ready.

But the second time we sailed together I didn't dare let him take my breasts again because I liked him too much by then to trust myself to stop. Then for the only time in our lives Larry turned ugly and said as I felt the sky crash in on me, said with cool blue eyes that he was falling in love with me and it was too bad I wouldn't let him love me, because he was getting it and would have to keep on getting it from another girl. No, he didn't love her and there was no art in it but he would still make love to her. The crashing sky of his blue eyes drove splinters of pain into me. But it's better to live with that pain. By then I couldn't believe Larry's promise that he would turn mud into art. It was almost as ugly as Palmer calling Mother a whore when Larry told me what I try to forget about, that there's another girl like me to whom he makes love, a girl in New York is all he will say.

But I've got to stop thinking of that other girl. I can't stand to. I think of his kissing her and then, and then making love, and I want to kill myself and my lousy stubborn virtue along with it. This garden where I listened to Mother and Palmer talk about Guy, that's what makes me think of the other girl. I'd better get out of here and what the hell, go to the stable.

PROPHETS WITHOUT HONOUR

by

Pamela Moore

"A prophet is not without honour, save in his own country,
and in his own house."

Matt.XIII:46

SUSAN DAVOREN

At the opening of the story, Susan is twenty. She
comes from a middle-class Connecticut family - her father is
a high-school teacher of American history - which she has left
she is now living in a Greenwich Village apartment with another girl, NATALIE BLOCH, and is studying art history at
Columbia University, on scholarship. Having refused to accept money from her family, she supports herself by selling
poetry and "literary" pieces to obscure publications. She
has astonished herself by selling a solemnly Faulknerian
novel to a small publisher. It is at the time of this sale
that the novel begins. She has fled the small-town, Catholic
society of her Irish-descended parents, only to feel equally
confined and unfulfilled among the pseudo-artistic, semi-
political intellectuals who are her friends. We meet these
people before we are introduced to Susan herself; they are
at a party in the Village, waiting for her; the party is
turning, upon a flippant suggestion of one of the boys, into an orgy, with the overtones of "intellectual" conversation about avant-garde art and writing. The young man who
is the leader of the group reveals himself, by ungracious comment, to be the lover of Susan. When a few pages later, she
enters, we are prepared for her sudden revolt against them, an

her disenchantment with the young man, as a symbol of all
that she had before espoused. At the close of this, the
first chapter, Susan is driven to a crisis of decision, for
she has revealed to her friends - knowing that their jealousy
will finally shatter the fraternity that she had once held
with them - that she has sold her novel, and received an
advance of five hundred dollars. She is freed to change her
life, and this freedom terrifies her.

GRAHAM HAMILTON

In the second chapter, it is to Hamilton, the professor who has guided Susan in her ambivalence between the academic career urged by her father and the literary career to
which she aspires, that she comes for guidance: their association has always been dispassionately intimate. Before Susan
enters, a young assistant professor is in Hamilton's office,
currying his favor, and we learn that Hamilton is a renowned
and respected art historian whose three-volume study, "The
History of Italian Art", has become, in a few years, a classic in its field, earning him a full professorship despite his
youth (he is in his early forties) and placing him next in
the succession to a coveted chair. In the academic records,
as in this conversation, his academic and personal situation
seems - except for his extraordinary success - deceptively
conventional. But from the few remarks that he makes to the

young professor, we suspect his complacency masks turbulent
discontent, which seemingly has grown with his rapid advance-
ment.

1914 Born at the outbreak of the First World War.

1934 Graduated from Harvard _Summa cum Laude_ at twenty, began
      post graduate studies at Columbia.

1937 Married to an undergraduate, Rosemarie Beckers, eighteen;
      began two years of Ph.D study at Rome with his wife.

1939 Returns to U.S. in the beginning of war in Europe; his
      wife completes her studies at Columbia.

1940 Receives Ph.D from Columbia, his wife graduates shortly
      before their first child, CECILIA, is born. He enlists,
      to broadcast anti-fascist propaganda into Italy. Spends
      the duration of the war in Europe.

1945 He is discharged; returns, to be appointed an instructor
      at Columbia.

1946 A second daughter, Patricia, is born.

1947 He is advanced to assistant professor; a son, Peter, is
      born.

1950 He becomes an associate professor.

1951 "The History of Italian Art" is published.

1953 He is made a full professor, astonishing at the age of
      thirty-nine.

      At this point (the spring of 1956) he is forty-three;
he lives near Columbia with his wife, Rosemarie, who, although
five years younger, has aged with the cares of raising their
children - Cecilia, seventeen (a freshman at Radcliffe), Patrici
eleven, and Peter, ten - virtually alone, for Hamilton spends
even his weekends in his office at the university: it is in
this way that he has maintained the easy and undemanding

affection which exists between them. The only times in his
life when he has lived with passion were his student days
during the Depression, and the years of the war. His political associations during the thirties are darkly hinted at by
his more conservative students, but his record during the war
and the cloistered, scholarly life that he has led since then
allow his student activities to be excused as youthful pecadil-
los. But when Susan comes in, we see him as he is, and we
learn that the fires kindled within him at Rome have burned
fitfully into his consciousness. As though he might send her
into his own fervent youth, he urges the girl to go to Europe.

NATALIE BLOCH

As Susan speaks with Hamilton, Natalie, her roommate,
waits with a friend, David, whom they have invited to dinner.
Both were at the party the night before, but it is only now
that they are brought into focus: before we have seen them
as members of the Village group. Natalie is a Jewish girl
of twenty-one; like Susan, she is completing her final year
as an undergraduate at Columbia, but is studying political
science, with reference to the Middle East. She, like her
parents, was born in Paris, and came with them to New York
at the beginning of the Second World War. Her father owns
a small shop, slightly poorer than the one he had in Paris,
and at their home French is always spoken. Nonetheless, her

parents have a fierce loyalty to the country which has adopte
them, which she, only a small child when they were forced to
flee, cannot share. Raised as an American, her attachment
to the country of her growth is accidental; it is her home,
and not her refuge. When in college she became associated
with the young American intellectuals of Susan's acquaintance
her parents felt that she had betrayed them: bewildered, they
berated her for questioning the way of life which they had
fervently adopted, until, two years ago, she was driven to
join Susan in this apartment in the Village. Also on a scholarship, she earns money by translations from French of academic material, and her parents, in traditional loyalty to
family, send what money they can. Her beauty is evocative
of the Middle East: her hair is long and black, her eyes dark
her features square and regular. Looking at her, one would
not be surprised that she has - as the conversation with Davi
reveals - fallen in love with a brilliant, Oxford-educated
Indian, DHAN BENARES. Her lover has returned, after a year
at the U.N., to his work in London and the Middle East with
the Indian Legation, and in his absence - as tonight - she
has been filling her hours with the son of friends of her
family, David. This evening is one of their last together
before she leaves to meet Dhan in Europe.

DAVID PACHEVSKI

As they speak of Dhan, it becomes clear that David has, since he met Natalie two years earlier at Columbia, been in love with her. But he does not let her know it, aware that if he did he would no longer be able to see her. So deep is his love that he shares her joy at the thought of rejoining her lover; he does not need to speak in bad faith to convince her that he is a close but unpossessive friend. A year older than Rahni, David is twenty-eight; his parents, too, are Jewish emigrants of the war, from Poland. Five years before the opening of the novel, he was drafted and worked with American Intelligence in Europe for two years. This represents the only variation in the life that he has led since his parents came to New York, a life spent on the fringe of the academic community. He is now a graduate student, on a teaching scholarship, in the Russian Institute; he had been taught Russian as a small child near the eastern border of Poland. It is said of him by Natalie that he is "an affirmative person, with nothing to affirm". He is deracinated, yet the poetry of his childhood forged his soul in heroic patriotism. The classic Russian novels which he read at school instilled in him the knowledge of transcendent love before he had experienced passion: as a boy in America he mocked the "dates" of his school friends and was alone until he met Natalie. He has cast his silent devotion to her in the image of Turgeniev's patient love of the famous, married

singer, Viardot, whereas Natalie has seen in him merely a
convenient companion in the enforced seapartion from the man
she loves. David is, like the one for whom he is named, a
poet, yet his life is pedestrian. It is the deep need of his
spirit for poetic experience, for the well-springs of the
culture from which he has been torn, which will lead, in the
course of the novel, to his transformation. The process by
which he will create himself as a man of conviction and action is, however, too complex and subtle to be attempted in
this outline: its coming, in the novel, is almost imperceptible
until, when it is achieved - for the change in him is greater
than that of any of the other characters - one looks back over
his development.

                    *   *   *   *

        At the end of the first part, then, Susan has
decided to accompany Natalie to Europe. Hamilton "sees
her off": the boat leaves early in the morning, but he is
restive; he cannot return to his study at Columbia. He wanders, his spirit turbulent with the memories of his own
youthful departure for the Continent, through the streets.
Finally, he forces himself to go into the Public Library,
to calm himself with reading. He succeeds in losing himself among his studies; an article that he reads suddenly
fires him with an idea for an essay on a statue in Florence:

he feels that he has overcome his discontent. The closing-
bell tears him from his work, and, refreshed, he walks out
into the rainy night. Waiting for the bus, he looks across at
the neo-classical facade of the library, which rises serene
from the glistening, empty street: above it he sees the irregular turrets of two old office buildings; he looks to the
south and his eyes are fixed by a cluster of soft blue lights
from a skyscraper almost swallowed in mist, seeming to hang
upon nothing. Entranced by the spiritual luminosity of this
point in the dull red sky, a vision of Europe surges before
him; the ethereal body of Rome appears to separate out of the
fog, and he knows that he will go back. He returns and tells
his wife of his decision, and she, convinced that he will be
disillusioned by this attempt to recapture the enthusiasm and
conviction which he had lost, gently acquiesces, and consents
to remain in New York with their children. Within a few weeks,
David succumbs to his loneliness: he surmounts the terror
which rises within him at the thought of returning to the Continent from which he had fled, and follows Natalie to Paris -
deluding himself by the literary image in which he casts his
devotion that he will be content to remain but her friend.

*   *   *   *

PHILIPPE DE VERMANDOIS

At a cafe in the Quartier Latin, Susan meets Philipp
She knows nothing about him but, in a gesture of defiance to

the middle-class caution which she had been taught, accepts
the offer that he makes on the third time that they meet,
that she accompany him on a "business trip" to Scandinavia.
The "business" that he contracts is mysterious; it is only
gradually, as she comes to know the man with whom she is living
that she learns its nature. He is the son of an aristocratic
French family: at thirty, he has lived in most of the countries
of Europe, fought - as a boy and a young man - in the Resistanc
on both fronts, supported himself in many metiers. He is a
heroic figure, of great strength and dedication - for varied
as his life has been, he has always remained consistent to
his own philosophy; he was never "searching". It is his even
brutal manliness that attracts Susan to him, and the richness
of his background and culture make him, the man of action, a
symbol of all that is best in contemporary Europe. In falling
in love with Philippe, Susan falls in love with Europe, and
creates in herself the paradox which will from this time forth
determine her life. For she is an American and in her love
the conflict between the two cultures is brought sharply,
agonizingly, to a crisis; within it lie the ambiguities which
are expressed in different ways by the other characters: she
yearns to be one with Philippe, but she cannot share his ethos;
in moments of defeat and exhaustion at this futile struggle,
she longs to return to America, where she is accepted, but her
love has alienated her from her homeland. The beliefs that
she has held, the qualities in herself which have given her
confidence, - the image which, in the twenty years of her life,
she has created of herself, is mocked, challenged and finally

shattered. She knows the anguish which will lie before
her, even greater than her present suffering, for she will
be plunged into the gulf between two civilizations, driven
from one, unable to join the other, terrifyingly isolated.
But this foreboding even intensifies her love; she submits
to being recreated by him; she contemplates suicide, she
weeps in the solitude of rooms in Scandinavia, - and then,
at the sight of him, she is bathed in awe, renewed by his
nobility, - only to be cast again into agony. He refuses
to make love with her, so that even this last refuge of
pride is taken from her: strangers, and yet intimate in their
combat, they drive further and further north. Finally, in
a gloomy, dramatic scene under the glowering sky of Lapland,
she emerges, created in his image, with a symbolic act which
reveals her dedication and the sublimation of her selfhood
in him. They turn south and, lovers, return to Paris.

Her novel has by this time been published, and a copy
of it awaits her at Paris. She reads it, in essence reading
it for the first time. She is shocked by the realization
of her failure to say what she had wanted to say, what must
be said: she knows now what she could not have admitted to herself before, that she has in this work even betrayed the ideals
which she set out to serve, because, before she met Philippe,
she had been unable to be honest with herself, and to see clearly

the society around her which had formed her. In one day, she reads her novel, terror mounting within her. In the evening, she has planned to meet Philippe. But when she sees him, the last refuge of her independence, the belief in her writing ability will be destroyed, and she will no longer be able to justify to herself her refusal to submit wholly to his intellectual domination. She stares from her hotel room out over the roofs of the Latin Quarter: she is struck with horror at the vision of herself become the tool of this passionate, overpowering man. In this crisis, she even asks herself whether her abdication will make her lose his love, because he scorns and casts aside those that are weak. And yet, she cannot live in bad faith, she cannot pretend to herself that, without him, her writing will be anything but mediocre. Finally, she is driven in her anguish and fear to avoid the decision: she determines to flee before Philippe comes to the hotel to meet her. Frantically, she packs her clothing and takes a taxi to the station, leaving a hasty and evasive note for her lover. She will go to Rome, to seek the help of Hamilton, the man who has been her intimate counselor, hoping that he will offer her a path of compromise, without which she fears she will be destroyed.

DHAN BENARES

When Natalie arranges to meet her lover in Paris, just as Susan leaves for Scandinavia with Philippe - conveniently

vacating the small apartment which they had rented together -
she is filled with apprehension. She has deified him in his
absence; he has become a symbol of religious charity for
which she had sought in vain among political groups in New
York. In him, the metaphysical lore of her people is incarnate:
even the erotic moments of their love are touched with the
Eastern mysticism which he embodies. His London-tailored
suits, his precise English, his activity in the Oxford Union
seem to mark him as a westernized man of modern India. But
the gentleness and love of his Brahmin heritage, which have
made of him a socialist, have set him apart from his European
political colleagues. When Natalie meets him he is, as she has
feared, profoundly changed, and she learns from him the events
which, by revealing this paradox, have effected his transformation. That, during his travels as an emmisary in the Middle
East during the tension which preceded the nationalization of
the Suez Canal, he was frequently jailed for meeting with underground socialist leaders, bewilders him. It would not occur
to him to pretend that he is not a socialist, or to conduct his
work in secret: socialism, he believes, is a moral order; why
should he be penalized for his devotion to the poor? And so,
among alien nations, he resolutely continues his peaceful work,
becoming involved with a young Arab socialist in whom he recognizes an other-worldly dedication like his own. But he is mistaken: the young political leader with whom he had identified
himself makes a temporary and pragmatic alliance with the Com-
munists, whom he loathes.

He returns to London, betrayed now by both camps, so bitterly disillusioned that he comes to the conclusion that there is no place in westernized society for a political man of uncorruptible morality. And so, subtly he begins to corrupt himself: he seems to be an innocent, apostolic figure, but it becomes clear that in this refusal to act, he betrays his ideals and the love of Natalie. A young British girl, Beth, has fallen in love with him. In sincere magnanimity, because the girl bores him, he has agreed to let her accompany him to the Middle East, after her tearful threat that unless he let her live with him, her young life would be shattered and she would commit suicide. The generosity, the fear of inflicting pain which dominate his morality led him to consent to her entreaty, writing a letter to Natalie (since he would never be dishonest with her), telling her of his decision, but assuring her that it would not affect his love for her. Natalie, too, believed that is she were unselfish and did not protest, it would rather strengthen the bond between them.

Upon their return to London, Beth tells Dhan that she has become pregnant. He knows that this is deliberate. A month earlier, the strength of his commitment to society would have given him the manliness to say that, although he would support the child, he could not let himself become enmeshed in family cares by remaining with her. Now, in a gesture of defiance to the belief that has failed him, mocking the political celibacy which he had sworn, and mocking at the same time the

East-End morality of the girl, he marries her, in a Protestant
service, and greets Natalie - in whom his conscience is embodied -
with his pregnant young wife. Natalie, hurt and bewildered,
turns for brief solace to David Pachevski, who had followed
her to Paris. But she is unaware of the transformation which
is taking place in him upon European soil, which will lead him,
first, to spurn her, as he seeks in solitude his salvation, and,
later, when the change that he is effecting in himself is com-
pleted, to be her source of strength.

COUNTESS D'ALAGNO

Hamilton, before coming to Europe, had corresponded
with the Countess D'Alagno, an unmarried woman in her early
forties, of elegance and culture, about paintings in the possession
of her family. The life of this woman has been dominated by the
memory, enshrined in their home, of her mother's great love affair with Gabriel D'Annunzio; it was in the atmosphere of the
clandestine lovers' meetings that the child was brought up, and
the few personal encounters with this noble yet pathetic ad-
venturer and tragically talented poet, as well as her mother's
intimate accounts of their union, formed in her the image of
her future lover. She fell deeply in love with a young aristocrat, who was killed as a pilot during the Abyssinian war.
Unable to bring herself, as her mother had upon D'Annunzio's
death, to commit suicide, she has lived in lofty seclusion and

and self-cultivation, and, through her correspondence with Hamilton about her family's paintings, she has come to feel that this man whom she has never met is a part of the sequestered world which she has created around her.

The night of Hamilton's arrival, he declines her invitation by letter to call upon her, wishing to prolong the moment of his mystical return in which the essence of Rome is feminized by his anticipation of seeing her, and his awareness of the temptation of the seductive sensuality of the city. He is enraptured as he walks through the streets; he pauses before a fountain in a piazza, drinking of the centuries he sees spilling over it, changing its shape subtly to bring it to this moment of perfection, of pure and unchanging being, in which he shares. All sense is lost of the America from which he has come, the family and studies which he has left behind, and he is one with the shadowed, sculptured, eternal fountain. He looks up as an obviously cultured, well-dressed Roman walks leisurely toward him, and asks the Italian, with an exalted smugness, the origin of the fountain. The man shrugs and admits that he does not know. Confirmed in his joyous conviction that he is united with the culture of Rome, and is as much a part of the city as its fountains, - a custodian, like them, of its history - he has overcome his hesitation, and calls upon the countess.

He falls in love with her, and ceases to write the study on contemporary Roman art which he had given himself as

his reason for being in Rome, and which represented the renun-
ciation of his purely academic pursuits for an involvement in
the present moment. He had come to Italy in search of the
engagement in society which he had known as a student, determined to write a book which would study art not from an aesthetic
but from a social point of view. But he takes an apartment in
Rome, he collects antiques with the countess, becomes fastidious
in his dress, and loses all preoccupation with time - almost
as though he were, himself, a creation of art.

Many weeks later, the countess tells him of an invitation that she has received from members of her family in Spain.
On the day of her departure, he packs his luggage, leaving it
discreetly in his apartment, and goes to her home. Certain that
he will accompany her, he begins to speak of an essay which he
will write while they are in Spain: he comments on the change
which she has wrought in him - once a historian of art, having
before he met her decided to become a social critic of contemporary art, he is now going to write an essay as an aesthetician.
He has removed himself almost entirely from the flow of society
and the involvement in the moment which he had once thought to
be the fullest form of life. She has elevated him to a Grecian
ecstasy; he has violated the sanctions of society, he has
shattered his own ethos: he feels himself to be one with the
gods, eternal and contemptuous, jealous only of her noble love.

But finally, having listened to him in silence, she
tells him that he cannot accompany her to the estate of her

family; she tries to explain to him that even his culture
will not admit him into this sanctuary of European aristocracy.
In his shock, as though plunging the blade that she has offered
into his soul, his speech becomes raw, almost crude. He is
hurtled from the sublimity of their love upon the tumbled
shores of desperate abandon: wildly, he declares that he will
divorce his wife, leave his children, relinquish his academic
career; he begs her to marry him. She is apalled by his sudden
vulgarity; abruptly, she recognizes what she had only sensed
before, the contradiction between this man and her aristocratic
lover who perished in arrogant flight above Abyssinia; in the
home which her mother has dedicated to momentos of D'Annunzio,
who both expressed and created the epoch by which her dreams
were formed, Hamilton is ludicrous: she asks him to leave.

He wanders brokenly through the streets, coming, in
the early morning, to the piazza where he had first felt one
with Rome. It is deserted, and autumnal. Behind him in the
street he sees a small, American-style bar, garish in chrome
and neon, with two low sports cars in front - looking to him
like broken pillars before a full, glass-enclosed flame. Drawn
by what is almost a hallucination of his homeland, he enters
the bar, a gate of return. But he cannot go back: cast from
one civilization, he still cannot stand what is a caricature
of the worst in another. He finds himself again on the narrow
street, wandering among the broken images of twenty years of
dreams. Alone in his apartment amid the luggage which he cannot bring himself to unpack, around him the antiques which he

had bought and the notes for his aesthetic essay mocking him, he resolves to return to the work on contemporary art which he had abandoned.

Unable to sleep, through the night he pores over his old notes, but he can write nothing. He looks at these lines as might one of his students: he cannot return to the moment of faith and hope that created them. He has lost his point of view, and thus his identity. With anguishing clarity he sees that the complacent certitude with which he had been living since the war, coming from his conviction that in his soul he was European and would return to reaffirm and engage himself in the culture which was a part of him, had been bred of illusion. That which had given meaning to his life is revealed as having been bad faith, a deliberate self-delusion, just as was his jubilation on the first night of his return. False, too, his ecstasy in the months that followed in which he created himself as a work of art, freed from ethics, beyond the confinement of time and space, - his liberation from the consciousness of society finally symbolized in his essay on aesthetics.

He can no longer stay in Europe: he has been pursuing two disparate ends, salvation and happiness, as though they were made one in the seductive body of Rome, but finally it is clear to him that he has been seeking only happiness, which has denied to him his salvation. In a heroic gesture beyond bitterness or regret, he decides to return to America, to continue teaching, to measure his life by the flux of students and the growth of his children. He falls into a sleep of exhaustion, and is awakened late in the afternoon by a telephone call from Susan Davoren, who has just arrived in Rome.

On the train coming from France, Susan has freed herself from the anguish that seized her in Paris, by again deceiving herself. She knows the choice that is before her. The novel that she wrote in New York is a failure because it was a personal cry of rebellion: before she fell in love with Philippe, she had found no way of relating to society, and it was against her alienation, from her isolation, that she cried. Her book is unimportant: it is a caricature of Faulkner, esoteric, precious and perishable. She realizes that she can only write the novel which she must write if she is with Philippe, through whom she sees the larger world which her work must describe, and whose constant criticism, while causing her suffering because she feels that her love of him is not reciprocated, is what she needs to write with the precision and passion for which she strives. Yet she is terrified of losing her artistic autonomy, and submerging her identity in his, because by this act she may even drive away her lover, the last link which would bind her to society, and this loss would, with tragic irony, render her incapable of writing. And so, she has escaped the agony of decision by telling herself that she can continue her studies with Hamilton:

she even imagines herself as his assistant, she pictures an
idyllic life in which she will support herself by working with
him, writing in independence. It is to propose this to him
that she comes to his apartment, on the afternoon preceding
his departure.

When she sees him, she is shocked by his haggard
appearance, but he refuses to explain to her - for he is determined to tell no one of what has happened to him - saying only
that he is leaving that evening, to return to New York. She
is overjoyed at the proximity of her escape: she tells him,
obliquely, what she has done, and presents her plan. But she is
surprised to see this man, to whom she has a filial devotion,
become increasingly cold to her in the course of her narrative.
Hamilton has understood more than she can know, and he refuses
to let her compromise by modifying her commitment, by seeking
to lessen or avoid the anguish of decision. But he has been
the teacher, she tells him, who has brought her to the point
at which she was able to understand this European, so alien
to the way of life in which she has been brought up. Now she
wishes to return to the moderate philosophy which she thinks
Hamilton represents. She is terrified of submerging herself
in Europe, of which she can nver be a part, alienating herself
from America, condemning herself to perpetual exile. With
Hamilton she can work in the illusion that she is fulfilling

her ideals without losing her national identity.

But Hamilton refuses to let her deceive herself as he
has. He tells her that his paternal relationship to her has come
to an end; now, she has found a way of seeking her salvation
which can never be his. She rises, and says bitterly, "I
didn't know that our destinies were so divergent." She leaves
him, with the mixture of contempt and compassion that a fisherman might feel towards the noble salmon, which, having complete
the great, symbolic act of birth, struggles bravely upstream,
through quickening currents and swirling rapids, to reach, exhausted, his birthplace and his death. In the evening, as
Hamilton prepares to leave for New York, Susan returns to
Philippe at Paris.

THURMOND WORTH

Thurmond has been introduced as a hanger-on at the
Greenwich Village party in the first chapter, and appears during
the novel at moments in which he, simply by his presence, al-
lows us to see sharply the changes in the other characters. He
is a southern boy who has met Susan at Columbia; his initial
moment with Susan occurs before the opening of the book. During her freshman year, he was an occasional week-end visitor
at her home, when she was still living with her parents in
Connecticut: before they decided that she had abandoned herself to Greenwich Village, her family even spoke wistfully

of her marrying him.

His second appearance is before her departure for
Europe. He is a loyally Republican American, opposed to her
ideas and to her friends in New York; he remains on the fringe
of her group in the hope that he may rescue her for better
things. Although he knows that she is going to Europe to
affirm the very ideals which he combats, he struggles with
his conscience when it seems doubtful that she will receive
a passport without lengthy investigation of her companions,
and she asks him to help her, through his uncle who is an
admiral in the U.S. Navy.

Finally Thurmond meets his uncle on board a destroyer
near New Jersey, before it embarks on maneuvours. His uncle
thinks that he has finally made the decision to which he has
been urging the boy; disappointed when he chose Columbia instead of Annapolis, he thinks that now his nephew is coming
to ask him for a commission in the navy upon graduation. But
instead, after a silent tour of the massive armed ship, the
boy presents his request. The admiral is horrified, but his
nephew's impassioned defense of the right of every citizen
to his beliefs finally persuades the older man to help Susan.
Thurmond thus represents what is best in conservative, traditional American democracy.

His final scene in the novel is a decisive one. At
the bidding of Susan's parents, he follows her to Europe in
the fall, as an ambassador, the voice of her homeland, in an

attempt to retrieve her. He meets her in a cafe in Paris
after she has returned to Philippe from Rome: the struggle within
her between these two cultures is personified in these two men..

       The autumnal Paris evening is soft; an Arab boy walks
among the tables selling nuts; a man calls out the headline
from the papers that he is selling. The Latin Quarter is seductive and yet strange to Suan; she is reassured by Thurmond's quiet
southern drawl, and, after the crises through which she has
passed, she is drawn to him. He is telling her of the sorrow
of her parents; her mother is distraught with grief. Susan
is half-listening; it is not his words but the familiarity of
his voice which attracts her. A wasp of late summer lights
upon the table. As she has done countless times, Thurmond
picks up a glass to kill it. She is suddenly reminded of the
night, shortly after her arrival in Europe, when she killed
a flea, and Philippe, who had seemed to her a man devoid of
tenderness, said sharply "Don't do that!" The words which
had puzzled her echo in her mind: Thurmond brings down the
glass absently upon the offending insect. As the wasp is
gripped by death, she cries out, she shares its agony: hers,
the body curled with twisted inverted limbs, shoved upon the
improvised bier of an advertisement card from the table, sum-
marily, unceremoniously, disposed of in the dirt. The boy
continues speaking of the anguish that she is causing her
family. She is fascinated by her reaction to the assassina-
tion of the wasp: she had winced at its pain, and was unmoved
by her mother's. She suddenly realizes that she has been born

anew: she is no longer the child of her parents, but she is deeply and irrevocably involved with all things living. As Thurmond's voice hums over the street-noises of Paris, she understands the extent and the nature of her engagement. There is no need to listen further to the words of the ambassador: terrified at the knowledge that she is deracinated, bereft of homeland, she rises, and Thurmond, his eyes filled with compassion, watches her leave, a figure apart in the crowd on the Parisian street: well she might envy, he says to himself, Professor Hamilton.

*   *   *   *

This is not, of course, the ending of the novel: it is merely the arbitrary conclusion of my summation of the major characters. I have not traced, in this short space, the development of the love affair between David and Natalie, for, like the story of Susan and Philippe, I have left it at the beginning of their relationship. It is with the conclusion of these two stories that the final part of the book will be concerned, but, from this point on, the resolution will come swiftly in dramatic narrative which I do not want to relate here, since I wish these scenes - like many preceding them - which depend upon action and mood, to be written fresh, and not dissipated in so curt a resumé. As I have said, the approximate length will be three hundred and fifty pages:

I am making the book a fairly short one to maintain what
must be a swift, and quickening, pace. What I have described
here are - by the nature of this presentation - the few
introspective scenes in the novel, but nonetheless they
give a just - although, of course, oversimplified - presentation
of the characters, from which the novel will evolve.

Amy Issadore Bloom
THE ROSE

Ann, a first grader, came bouncing into my classroom in her pink Hello Kitty sneakers. "Happy Valentine!" she exclaimed with a slight trace of a Korean accent. She handed me a fake red cloth rose.

Ann was in my reading group for English Language Learners. She was an ideal student: eager to learn, respectful, quick to help others, and just the right amount of silly. Her parents were polite and formal in meetings. I often wondered what they thought of the young, loud, casually dressed staff that filled our school. The valentine showed her family was embracing our American traditions, and also was thankful for my role in Ann's education.

"You got the rose!" Gina, a special education teacher, announced when she came into our shared classroom. I wondered why she was so excited about a dollar store rose. I loved my work, but as a career switcher and someone who hated Valentine's Day; I struggled to match the enthusiasm and fashion accessories of my colleagues.

But that year, something shifted in me. Working in a Title I school, with more than half the students living below the poverty level, I saw how important it was for these kids not only to receive, but to give. Valentine's Day created equity—with little cards that proclaimed friendship and awesomeness.

My fifth grade students, who I may have thought too old for these celebrations, seemed to need it the most. These are boys who wake up in the middle of the night to feed baby siblings while Mom works a double shift, and girls whose hands are chapped from housework. They are eleven-year-olds who risked their lives on a journey from El Salvador to Virginia. I understood what that bag of cards and candy represented.

In our writing group, we translated sayings from colorful chalky candy hearts. They teased each other about who signed a card with "l-o-v-e." (Of course I would come to the wedding!)

When the dismissal bell rang, I felt the usual fatigue, yet refreshed by a new perspective. I couldn't wait to tell Gina how "woke" I was. I might even start shopping the seasonal section of Target for holiday flair.

I didn't have a chance. With a knowing grin, Gina picked up the rose. "Pull a petal."

I pulled one petal, and another, watching in awe as Ann's gift transformed into a lacy red thong.

We ran like middle schoolers, giggling down the hallway, to see Sandy—a fabulous first grade teacher nearing retirement. Sandy blushed a red to match her thong when she discovered it.

"Should we tell Ann's parents before they give them to her Saturday Korea school teachers?" I asked.

Her family would be mortified. We decided it was beyond our responsibility, and too awkward, especially with an interpreter. Plus, it wouldn't be right to spoil the potential happiness for Ann's future teachers.

One thing we like even more than holiday flair is a good story.

Patricia Henley
BEDS

The first one I remember is a sagging double on 20th Street in Terre Haute. Eight years old, I shared it with two sisters. There was no top sheet. We wore flannel pajamas our great-aunt Ada had sewn for us. They were rough, dried on the line in winter wind. I read library books by the bare bulb. Nancy Drew and Herman Wouk. My mother had told the librarian not to limit me to kids' books; I could read anything I wanted. My sisters fell asleep in spite of the light. A gremlin or molester lived under the bed. I didn't tell my sisters about him. He lay in wait to grab my ankle when I got up to pull the string to turn off the light at nine o'clock.

With another new baby—the next to youngest—we moved out to the country, a cinderblock house on a blacktop road five miles from town. There was a coal furnace my mother had to fire all winter to keep us warm. Her fingers split from cold and labor. My father worked away. The first year I slept on a rollaway in the living room. The black and white TV flickered until eleven. My mother drank Mogen David wine when the little kids had gone to bed. Eavesdropping on my mother and aunt (who drove out once a week and stayed for hours), I learned that our neighbor had a prolapsed uterus. Whatever that was.

After the first year at the cement-block house I was given my own room with a brass bed my grandmother donated. How was that negotiated? The bookmobile came once a week in the summer. What riches. I stepped on a black snake and screamed off and on for hours. The snake found its way into our bathtub. My mother chopped off its head with a hoe.

In the orphanage I slept on a high single bed in a dorm with other girls in the little girls' house, even though I should have been considered a big girl. I was thirteen. I still wet the bed sometimes.

We moved to Maryland when I was sixteen. We crossed the mountains I live in now. My bed was single, prim, and lumpy. I shared a room with sisters. I gave names Holden Caulfield might have invented to the wallpaper peeling in faded layers: Rotten Strawberries, Eat Crow. In the spring I moved my bed to the screened-in upstairs porch with its yellow bulb to read by. I could smoke a contraband cigarette—Lucky Strike—stolen from my mother's purse. Neither wind nor rain deterred me. But my mother liked to gather everyone into the living room when there was a thunderstorm. She unplugged all the appliances. She lit a kerosene lamp and set it on the floor. Later she had a nervous breakdown in that house. There was a picture of Jesus over the sofa. She thought his eyes were trying to tell her something. She thought my father was in the basement when, in fact, he was in Labrador, working on the DEW line. She went to Perry Point VA Hospital and didn't come home until Christmas.

What I don't recall: My father said that my mother's first nervous breakdown happened when I was six months old. He took her to the hospital. He put me to sleep in a hotel dresser drawer. For safekeeping.

Jelena Kecmanovic
PITA FROM HOME

There was a saying in Bosnia that a young woman needed to know how to make pita from scratch before she could get married. Pita is a type of Balkan savory pie, made with layers of filo pastry interspersed with a rich mixture of eggs, cream, cheese, and often spinach. Every region of the country, every family, had a special pita recipe. As a little girl in Sarajevo, I used to watch my grandma masterfully stretch a ball of dough, first with a rolling pin, then with her hands, over a large dining room table until it resembled a thin, translucent sail. How did she manage not to break it, even when she started sprinkling on the filling in a perfectly executed pattern? How did she move around so effortlessly, humming one of her favorite tunes and inviting me to join in with floured hands? As the smell of the baking pita permeated her apartment, I felt all the tension of life melt away. I felt unconditionally loved. I felt at home.

By the time I was turning twenty, Sarajevo had already been under a military siege for a few months. We were trapped and subjected to seemingly random sniper and shell fire from the hills that encircled the city. There was no fresh food, so we relied on a dwindling supply of boxes, cans, and jars. As I walked through the war-ravaged city on my birthday, my mouth salivated at the thought of the best present I could imagine: my grandma's freshly baked pita.

A patch of grass and shrubs to the side of the road was the only remnant of a beautiful park that once included many trees, now cut for firewood. And then I saw nettles. Normally an unwelcome weed, I remembered my grandma talking about using nettle instead of spinach to make pita during the WWII Nazi occupation. I knew that my hands would sting and burn more than when touched by jellyfish or poison ivy. It didn't matter. Later that evening, my emaciated grandma made pita over a makeshift woodstove. My family hovered around the fire as the sounds of shelling grew louder. There were no eggs, no cream, and just a pinch of cheese in the nettle pita. It was the best pita of my life.

Several years later, I was living and studying in the U.S., having eventually escaped the war. I got married in spite of always making pita with store-bought filo pastry. To me, making the dough from scratch would break the spell: I wanted the memories of home to remain untouched and unadulter-ated. Then one early morning I got an unexpected call from the old country. My grandma had died suddenly from a massive stroke. I couldn't travel to the funeral because I was waiting for my green card to be processed. That whole day and night, I made pitas from scratch, my tears spilling into the dough. I was home again.

Randi Gray Kristensen
MISS PEACHES

Hungry for the old familiar ways... —Claude McKay

Every two weeks I'm in the vicinity of a Jamaican restaurant weh name Peaches. Now you know seh is a true Jamaican restaurant car when yu go in, di board weh smaddy write out di menu a lean up pon di wall, sideways, and di nice plastic menu weh di people dem did print have too much ting pon it. Yu know seh fi ignore alla dat, and wait til yu reach di counter, and di counter lady seh, "Lemme tell yu wha we have today."

So dis a di second time mi was to pick up dinner fi carry home from Peaches. And mi tell di counter lady, "the jerk chicken dinner, please, with rice an' peas, and do you have any food?" And she look at mi kinda blank, so mi seh, "any green banana, breadfruit, yam?" And she light up at "yam" and seh, "yes, we have yam." So mi seh, please to give me lickle yam, and di collard greens, too. And she seh, di greens is a extra side, and mi seh, mi know, but mi want i anyway.

Yu don' know happy like di way mi happy fi know seh me a go taste a piece a yam in mi no know how much time. Dem box up di dinner inna di back, dem put di greens dem inna one lickle box, dem put di two a dem inna one plastic bag, mi pay, and mi leave wid a big smile. In di Uber fi di half hour ride home, mi hold mi dinner pon mi lap, car mi no wan' di greens fi tun ovah and di juice fi mash up di dinner. Mi know seh when me finish eat mi chicken and rice an' peas and vegetable and yam, mi a go feel like Usain Bolt.

Mi reach home. Mi put di bag pon di counter. Mi open di bag wit care. Mi puddown di box wid di vegetable. Mi open di box wid di dinna. Mi eye stop pon some yellow sinting inna di cahna a di box. Inna di spot weh di yam supposed to occupy. And mi feel mi heart a split as mi realize seh a no yam dis, a di odda yam, di one weh mi know as sweet potato, di one mi will eat if mi have to, but mi no really love it, even when it dress up fi holiday dinna.

Water come a yu eye yet? Me too, same way. Mi siddung an' eat mi jerk chicken and rice an' peas and vegetable and sweet potato, wit some extra seasoning from di saltwater weh did pour outta mi eye dem. Still, every day, in every way, a so Diaspora stay, nuh true? All a we is one, but a different yam we nyam.

Stephanie Leow

ALICE'S ADVENTURES IN WONDERLAND: A COMING-OF-RAGE STORY

Pure, passive, pleasant: these were the ideal characteristics for a Victorian woman to possess. In *Alice's Adventures in Wonderland*, Lewis Carroll flips these gender roles, while creating contrasts between girlhood and womanhood, boyhood and manhood, and the genders themselves. Through his characterization of male and female characters, along with his portrayal of Alice's journey to adulthood, Carroll condemns the transformation of girls into women, ultimately revealing his preference for Victorian values embodied in young girls.

The clearest example of what a Victorian woman should not be is Mrs. "Off with his head!" herself—the Red Queen. The Queen exudes malice in all of her actions and dialogue; besides constantly demanding that her subjects' heads be cut off, most of her actions involve stomping, shouting, or shrieking. Carroll exemplifies the Queen's temper when Alice talks back to her, causing her to "[turn] crimson with fury" then, "after glaring at her for a moment... [begin] screaming, 'Off with her head!'" (72).[1] Additionally, the Queen is described to be "in a furious passion," "stamping about" during her croquet game (74). The Queen attempts to gain dominance, still in her incessant tantrum, when she demands Alice to "'hold [her] tongue!'" while "turning purple" (107). Though the Queen exhibits a reversal of Victorian gender roles, she represents an extreme that is unfavorable to Victorians (along with any other audience). Her atypical position of power leads to a bossy and frenzied characterization; one could consider her character a warning against the dangers of powerful women. Carroll applies this extremity specifically to the adult females of *Alice's Adventures*, as further shown by the characterization of the Red Queen's counterpart, the King.

The King, portrayed as kinder and calmer, contrasts greatly with the Queen. After the Queen threatens Alice, the King lays "his hand upon her

---

[1] Numbers in parentheses refer to page numbers in *Alice's Adventures In Wonderland and Through the Looking Glass*, Penguin Classics, 2003.

arm, and timidly says, 'Consider my dear: she is only a child,'" which immediately distinguishes him as more sympathetic (72). In addition, the King
shows geniality as he invites the Cheshire-Cat to "kiss [his] hand, if it likes,"
despite that he doesn't "like the look of it at all" (75). Compared to the Queen,
the King demonstrates more indifference: he dismisses the cook's disappearance "with an air of great relief" during the trial (101). Carroll juxtaposes
the Queen's temperament with the King's insouciance in order to intensify
the adverse view of women who deviate from Victorian standards.

   Carroll portrays the male characters consistently as more favorable than
their female counterparts. This juxtaposed portrayal does not solely apply
to the King and Queen: concerning the three other grown non-animals, the
Mad Hatter is also characterized more favorably than the Duchess and the
Cook. Even though the Hatter's remarks are nonsensical, he never indicates
an intention to harm others. During the trial, Carroll depicts the Mad Hatter
as anxious through his turning pale and fidgeting, then later the Hatter refers
to himself as "a poor man" (98). Because of the Hatter's nervous tendencies,
the audience sympathizes with him, ultimately favoring him. On the other
hand, the Duchess and the Cook are violent and malevolent. While the Cook
is "throwing everything in reach at the Duchess and the baby," the Duchess
keeps "violently throwing the baby up and down" (53–54). Again, Carroll
reverses domestic gender roles of the Victorian mother, but he illustrates
this reversal extremely and negatively. Like the Queen, these females are
wicked; they thrive on physical abuse. However, unlike the Queen, these
women do not hold positions of power, meaning that Carroll attributes these
anti-Victorian values to all women, at least to adult women.

   Of course, a rather important female character has not been discussed
yet—our heroine, Alice. At first glance, it would seem preposterous to group
Alice with the previously mentioned females, or would it? *Alice's Adventures*
presents two Alices: the first, a proper middle-class Victorian girl; the second,
a woman whose temper resembles the Queen's. The second Alice reflects
Alice as a product of a coming-of-age story; in other words, Carroll identifies
adult Alice using spiteful remarks and aggression. The second half of this
argument solidifies Carroll's preference for Victorian girls over Victorian
women, as he splits his protagonist in half to contrast the pulchritude of a
benevolent young girl against the foulness of that girl becoming a woman.

   Alice One, little girl Alice, represents the naïveté and goodwill of childhood. Carroll portrays this Alice as endearingly silly, such as when "she
[tries] to curtsey...falling through the air," a cute and senseless gesture for a

situation that could end in death (11). Furthermore, Alice fulfills Victorian standards when she is cordial and obedient, as she acts in the presence of the Caterpillar when she complies with his orders, speaking "very politely" (41). Finally, Carroll highlights Alice's goodwill after she knocks over the jury box and begins "picking them up again as quickly as she could" for fear that "they would die" (103). The assignment of these positive characteristics to Alice mirrors Carroll's perceptions of young girls; he values the sweet innocence of them. Alice's pleasantness and passiveness demonstrate childish qualities, although they are also the qualities valued in all women in the Victorian era. These characteristics could be prescribed to children in general; however, Carroll does not regard young boys in the same way. If Alice had been Alfred, Carroll's characterization would switch, since he considers the transition from boyhood to manhood favorable, yet judges the transition from girlhood to womanhood as unfavorable.

Since all the previous adult females have been compared to a male counterpart, it is necessary that the same is done for young Alice. There exists only one little boy in *Alice's Adventures*, though the child is not a human boy: he is a pig. Contrasting to the description of Alice, the baby is a nuisance, "snorting" and "doubling itself up," making it difficult for Alice to control him (55). The Duchess perceives the child as naughty, claiming that he "sneezes/... to annoy/Because he knows it teases," and, consequently, punishes him by shaking him (54). The gender of the pig baby may appear to be incidental, yet Carroll was particular about not gendering any of the other animals. To label the pig as a boy is a singular happening in *Alice's Adventures*—one that reflects Carroll's bias. The dichotomy between Carroll's representation of girls and boys in this scene is enormous: he manifests female Alice as motherlike, while degrading a male baby to a grunting pig. Even when the text pities the baby, it is done through Alice's lens, primarily to characterize her as sympathetic. Ultimately, Carroll discounts the apparent abuse of the baby through Alice's realization that he is "neither more nor less than a pig" (55). Carroll judges that little boys are wild and mischievous in comparison to little girls, a judgment that opposes his belief about adult men and women. In this case, young Alice is favorable to the young boy, which reveals that Carroll does not solely praise males, as he values the character of a little girl above any other combination of age and gender.

Finally, Alice Two, or "adult" Alice, has attributes similar to those of Wonderland's other females. Alice Two attempts to gain dominance through her quick temper and threats of violence, and her successes are equated to her independence as she grows out of childhood. Contrasting her sweet passivity, Alice "inadvertently" threatens the group of animals around her when she proclaims that her cat Dinah is "a capital one for catching mice" and that "she'll eat a little bird as soon as look at it" (29). Alice regards her statements as regretful; however, soon thereafter, she overtly threatens that she'll "set Dinah at" the Rabbit (36). Also, she snatches and kicks at the Rabbit and Bill so that she feels less scared of the Rabbit. In this scene, Alice considers herself "grown up now," since she is physically large, and her sense of being an adult leads her to control the situation through violence, much like the Queen (33). In addition to violence, Alice resorts to rudeness. When she is "losing her temper" with the Caterpillar, she takes a jab, remarking that "three inches is such a wretched height to be" (46). Replicating the trend of Wonderland females, Alice easily loses her temper, then becomes spiteful, thus losing the characteristics that make her the optimal Victorian girl.

Alice reaches her coming of age during the court scene, "grown to her full size" (108). At this point, Alice is equivalent to the Queen: she has grown to womanhood and now matches the Queen's temper. Even though this is Alice's climax moment, she does nothing beyond yelling and threatening with her size; as a fully grown adult, she only becomes the negative extremities showcased in the other female characters. Then, waking up from her dream, Alice Two reverts back to Alice One, for she subserviently takes an order from her sister. Her sister then pictures Alice as a grown woman who "would keep...the simple and loving heart of her childhood," again attributing feminine Victorian morals to a child (110).

Alice's Adventures in Wonderland evinces that a reversal of gender roles does not necessarily correspond to a feminist agenda. In fact, Carroll does just the opposite. He exaggerates the negative opposite qualities of the ideal Victorian woman to highlight his preference for pureness, passivity, and pleasantness. Carroll displays these negative characteristics within all the adult female characters of Wonderland and within the grown version of his protagonist. He views the transition from girlhood to womanhood as unfavorable, while he favors the growth of young boys. Carroll cherishes the common values of his time, which he determines to be perfectly embodied in young girls. Perhaps this explains why his friends and photography subjects are primarily little girls: they are what he believes Victorian women should be.

Christopher Linforth
ISLAND BOY

The boy spends much of his childhood studying islands. At his rolltop desk, he hunches over a full-color atlas, his index finger scanning the slivers of land in the Atlantic and the remote towers of rock dotted in the Outer Hebrides. His hometown sits in the center of England, landlocked, the coast hundreds of miles away in every direction. At his suggestion, he and his parents visit Scotland, the three of them secluded in a cottage near Fort William. The boy stands alone at the bedroom window: he sees the shimmer of a slate-gray loch and a speedboat violently sluicing through the water. He wants to go farther north, out to the peninsulaed studs of volcanic rock. There exists solitude, an imagined place where he can leave his parents behind.

Now a gangly teen, the boy spends all his time in his room slouched beneath his bookshelf. He flips through his encyclopedias and collections of maps. Part of him craves to be Atlas: a castaway burdened with geography. One of his books says Atlas held the celestial sphere, not the Earth, on his hollowed back. The boy discovers Gerardus Mercator engraved the title page of his assemblage of maps with a white-bearded Atlas carrying a globe. During dinner, he argues with his father over the historical misconception of the myth. Even when his father hits him, bruises his shoulder and chest, the boy refuses to admit he read the book incorrectly.

In the quiet moments of high school the boy dreams of sailing to Easter Island, where large stone bodies poke out of the ground. The statues once bore red coral eyes, which scanned the inner landscape to guard their progeny. Locals believed the backs of the *moai* face the spirit world in the sea. In the school library, away from his arguing parents, he learns of a brigantine that departs New Zealand and visits the Cook Islands, Vanuatu, and Easter Island. It takes weeks to sail across the South Pacific, where the virginal waters glisten beneath azure skies.

After the boy turns eighteen, he leaves home for a studio apartment on the other side of the city. He takes the first job he can: a frontline worker at a government benefits office. His job is to help people, but he cannot even help himself. He fills his refrigerator with cheap beer and strong cider but drinks the alcohol before it is cold. Hangovers blur his days. When his parents split up, he barely notices. He watches television documentaries on remote parts of the world—places so far away he fears he will never visit them. Then telephone calls interrupt his nights, a male voice shouts at him down the line: *What kind of son are you?*

Flakes of papery skin brush easily off the boy's sunburned shoulders. He lets his hands drop to his side, and he steps to the edge of the stone beach, where whitecaps rush to the shore. Foam wets the boy's feet, his girlfriend already out in the sea, cajoling him to join her. She swims out to the gray rocks, an energetic front crawl taking her around the outcrop. She's born of this part of Dalmatia: the islands and the limestone cliffs and the olive groves. An island girl who understands. She shouts for him. He wades in, pushing aside strands of seaweed, until he loses his footing; he dives forward, head submerged beneath the water.

On the train to Paris, an escape from a parental visit to his university, the boy watches the curve of the tunnel wall, a slope of gray starred with emergency light. The Channel Tunnel seems to go on forever, a twin-tube shot through chalk marl, the dark waters above. Contrarians, like his father, celebrate Britain's lost status. They argue with bloodied fists—the undersea land bridge between the Continent and the eastern shore of the U.K. enough to declare this island no longer an island.

From the air, the boy's home country soon vanishes from his view. He fiddles with the map of the Atlantic on the TV screen, checking the plane's position, astonished by the great sweep of water ahead. The route curves over the last of the Scottish isles and across to Iceland, onward to a Midwest state, a conversion cure of sorts. Zinged on white wine, the boy writes an apology letter to his ex-girlfriend and plans a generic *Wish You Were Here!* postcard for his stepmother. He breathes in the wash of frigid conditioned air and saves it for the fuck-you note he will write his father.

A silver Jaguar speeds toward the Washington coast carrying the boy and his friends. They talk of the beach, the razor clams in the shallows of the Pacific. Questions arise about his life back in Britain, about his parents, his past girlfriends. He demurs, obfuscates, switches subjects. He points to the bank of white cloud, the threat of a snow squall. Faces press against the cold glass, take in the expanse of land and sky, the strange patches of hoarfrost. The boy shields his eyes from the winter light. He pulls his hood over the top of his head and tucks his knees up to his chest. His friends fade to the hum of the car radio and the flurries of snow whipping past the window. On his cell phone he searches for remote islands, the ones farthest from any other person. He zooms in on a Pacific atoll, a circle of coral rendered thin by a glittering lagoon. A strange dot lurks on the sandy spar. All afternoon the boy traces a fingertip over a blurred body, trying to smooth out the pixelated edge of a lone man.

Trish MacEnulty

THE TRUMP SUPPORTER WHO PEED ON MY MATTRESS

No, she wasn't a Russian prostitute. She was a fire-plug blonde from New York state with vocal cords sandpapered by years of smoke but also with excellent references as a caregiver.

I was desperate. I'd already gone through two caregivers for my ex-husband, whom I'd been caring for since his stroke five months earlier. (Why? you ask. Because there was no one else to do it.) I'd tried the online caregivers resources, but the price tag would be a minimum five hundred dollars for twenty-four hours of care; the vortex of despair known as Craigslist seemed my only option. Still my hopes were high.

The first caregiver I hired wanted to know if her boyfriend—a ne'er-do-well who didn't have a place or a car or much of anything to his name—could spend the night, and when we said no, she began vanishing each night and then during the day, all the while wheedling to be paid but not showing up; the second one ran off on the second day to buy a bottle of gin to handle the "stress"; but the third one would make the first two look like Florence Nightingale.

She drove in from a neighboring state for the interview with us. I was determined to love her no matter what. She'd been doing caregiving for twenty years. She was older and had a place of her own to go back to on weekends. She'd worked with Alzheimer's patients. Surely she could handle a man who'd had a stroke but still had most of his cognitive facilities. Also, she was a grandma. Who doesn't love a grandma?

She was an hour late getting in, but it was raining and traffic between our cities is generally a nightmare. Finally the doorbell rang. I opened the door and was smacked in the face by a tsunami of flowery aroma. Perfume? Lotion? My smile faltered. Don't worry, I thought. This is your perfect care-giver. I could explain to her that he had allergies to strong scents, and she would surely agree to tone it down.

We talked to her for about thirty or forty minutes. She was quite knowl-edgable about such things as Hoyer lifts and seemed to have no problem with the fact that she would be changing a grown man's diaper. She was an affable sort with lots of advice for handling his various issues of neuropathy, thrush, and lack of appetite. She seemed to fit that mold of tough cookie with a tender heart. At the end of the interview she asked, apropos of nothing, "You aren't Trump supporters, are you?"

"Oh God no," I said, the very thought sending a shiver over my shoulders. "And he didn't vote in the last election, though before that he was a Republican," I continued with a nod toward my ex, who was reclined in his new lift chair.

"Yeah, don't talk to her about politics," he said, pointing at me. "She'll read you the riot act."

"Actually, it's best not to discuss politics around here," I said. My ex's politics were one of the things that led to the demise of our marriage. I hated his disdain of the poor, his rote recitation of the latest Fox News inanity, and his contempt for any sort of feminist ideology. Of course, all that had changed now that he was on the way to being poor himself. Fox News fell off the radar shortly after our divorce. And after dealing with an intractable health care system, he was suddenly an advocate for "choice." All those years of sneering about the dependent poor, and here he was, getting a megadose of dependency himself. His not voting in the 2016 election allowed us to maintain a friendship in the two years before his stroke.

In spite of my avowal not to talk politics, I couldn't help asking, "Are you a Trump supporter?"

"No," she said, somewhat hesitantly. "But I'm not sure about the wall."

Something about the expression on her face told me that she thought the wall might be a pretty good idea. Then she mentioned her daughters—one of them a graduate from Berkeley Law and the other one on her way to getting a master's in social work, not to mention the son-in-law, a PhD candidate (in English, no less!) at Stanford. So in my mind, she achieved grace by association. Whatever she felt about the wall was immaterial. The only thing that mattered was could she and would she take care of my ex so that I could go back to work and actually regain a little bit of my misplaced life?

I mentioned that strong odors bothered him—perfumes and such.

"I dare not cook any Brussels sprouts," I said with a laugh.

"Oh," she said. "Well there's one thing that could be a problem. I smoke."

It was a bump, for sure, but I'd lived with a smoker before. It didn't seem to be an insurmountable issue. Did I mention I was desperate?

So a few days later she arrived with a week's worth of clothes and some toiletries. And her cigarettes. And her perfume. Within hours, the entire downstairs reeked.

But she was pleasant enough. She said she'd get up early to help him move over to his chair because he got so tired of being in the bed all night. She even offered to do it at three a.m., which did not seem like a great idea, but I figured the two of them would try a few different options before finding a routine that worked best.

It turned out she did *not* like getting up at three a.m. or being called down the next night at one thirty because he'd dropped his remote control. Suddenly, she had an attitude—not a good one. She found the Hoyer lift difficult to maneuver. She didn't like the hours of not having anything to do. And it was obvious that the two of them were never going to become lifelong friends.

Caregiving is not easy work, but we were paying the price she asked. We were also providing a nice place to live and some meals. Part of the requirement for this job is that once in a while you're going to get wakened. It's a job best done by those who can easily fall back to sleep. She wasn't one of those.

There was also the matter of the smoking. Before she would get him up out of his bed she had to go have a smoke. Afterward, another smoke. A little breakfast, maybe start some laundry, another smoke. And another. And another. Great clouds of stink followed her in the house from each of these breaks. But the perfume was worse.

I was dealing with aggravated sinuses to begin with, so I asked her please not to wear the perfume. She said she was sorry, washed it off her, and that was settled. Or so it seemed.

The day Michael Cohen testified before Congress, she was on the back deck with her phone and her cigarettes. I was upstairs, working on my taxes. (I couldn't *wait* for the big refund I was sure to get thanks to Trump's tax cuts.)

She was loud and her voice carried right up to my room.

"Rush Limbaugh says the Democrats must be so scared. America doesn't care what Trump does. We elected him. We want him. Rush Limbaugh said the whole thing was outrageous. Let's just see them try to impeach."

It was all said with a certain smug satisfaction that sounded very much like the great orator himself. I felt a little sick to my stomach but I had no idea what to do. Go down and say, "Really? You think the Democrats are scared. Have you even seen Alexandria Ocasio-Cortez or Nancy Pelosi? You think they're scared?"

But it wasn't the politics that got her fired.

"You've got to get rid of her," my ex said. "She's incompetent. She can't make the Hoyer work. Her hands are always shaking. She has no mechanical intelligence whatsoever. Plus I can't stand the smell any longer. The whole house is getting permeated." Then the kicker: "I don't feel safe."

I waited till Friday morning, handed her the cash she'd asked for (that should have been a red flag), and told her that she was right, the smoking was a problem for us. We were going to have to make other arrangements.

"It wasn't a good fit for me either," she said.

I understood. We weren't always the easiest people to be around. He could be demanding and unappreciative and while it's sometimes difficult to see one's own faults, I'm sure I leaked a disapproving look here and there. Then there was the dynamic of ex-spouses with years of history and the bickering that passes as communication. She thought it would be easier when I started work again and wouldn't be around as much, and that was surely true. But he'd decided that he couldn't stand her, and so the issue of my presence was moot.

I paid her for five days though she only worked four. I told her how much I appreciated what she had done while she was here. The laundry, cleaning, getting him out of bed in the mornings. I figured she was as glad to get rid of us as we were to get rid of her.

"Good luck to you," she said.

"Same to you," I said, and I was sincere. I wished her well. She got in her car and drove away.

Then I went upstairs. She'd made the bed. That was nice, I thought, though of course, I'd need to wash the sheets, and the sooner the better. I pulled the covers off and the sheets. Then I saw a cloth bed pad under the sheet. That was odd.

I lifted the bed pad and there was big wet spot. It couldn't be pee, I thought. Maybe coffee? It was on the upper edge of the bed, not the middle of the bed where one might normally pee. I took the sheets and the pad down to the washing machine. The odor was unmistakable. Definitely urine. How? Why? It made no sense to me.

Eventually it became clear. She had deliberately peed on my bed (or poured pee on it) and then covered it up so I wouldn't find it until I got around to washing the sheets. If I'd waited a week or so, the mattress would have been ruined.

At first, it was almost funny. What a bizarre thing to do! But as time went on and I thought about how carefully she'd made up the bed, I realized how malicious and premeditated the act had been. It wasn't funny at all. It was mean and cowardly. Her hero, Donald Trump, would be proud of her.

Of course, I had a few revenge fantasies. I could find out where she lived. I could break in and use *her* bed for a toilet though I wouldn't stop at a little urine. Or maybe her white car would look good with a spray-painted windshield.

In a way, it seemed irresponsible to let her get away with what she'd done, but I would never enact my fantasies. I couldn't bring myself to dip into that cesspool of hate. Instead, I would let karma do what it does. The cigarettes weren't the only toxic thing in her life—that kind of gleeful hatred that prompts people to laugh at the disabled, to scorn victims of sexual assault, and to cheer at the vindictive lies of an amoral leader surely is as lethal to the soul as arsenic is to the body.

So I scrubbed the mattress and aired it out for weeks. When the smell was gone, I bought a thick mattress cover, put on clean sheets, and made the bed. I thought about my revenge fantasies once more. Payback would come another way. Eventually progress and integrity will win in this country, and when it does her team of death-eaters loses. Then we'll all have some scrubbing and airing to do.

Daniel Mueller
THE WAY THEY DO IN MOVIES

In anticipation of astronauts stepping from their lunar module onto the Sea of Tranquility and ground that might, some thought, swallow them whole, Dr. Hidalgo, an OB-GYN like my father but, unlike him, a bachelor who drove a Byzantine blue 1963 Porsche 911, set up his RV-8 Dynascope in his front yard. It was manufactured by Criterion Corporation in Hartford, Connecticut, the ad for the RV-6 in the backs of my Classics Illustrated comic books—*The War of the Worlds* by H.G. Wells, *20,000 Leagues Under the Sea* by Jules Verne, *The Man in the Iron Mask* by Alexandre Dumas—I'd often pondered over, wondering how anybody could afford its $194.95 price tag.

Dr. Hidalgo's telescope was even stronger, and more expensive, its solid white optical tube as thick as a kettledrum affixed by ring clamps to a counterweighted dual axis motor mounted on an expandable aluminum tripod. It was state of the art, an amateur stargazer's dream, and as Dr. Hidalgo alternated between fiddling with the azimuth adjustment knobs and peering through the finderscope, adults and children alike congregated around him for the chance to look through the eyepiece at the crescent moon just appearing in the twilit sky.

To celebrate the Apollo 11 moon landing, our neighborhood on Fort Hood Army Base had thrown a block party, and beside me, our elbows touching, stood Virginia Nettle, her sun-streaked hair falling to the shoulder straps of her orange shift. She'd been in the same second grade class as me, and that morning after church I'd pedaled my gold Stingray, a five-speed with a stick shift between the banana seat and handlebars, the mile and a half from our olive green duplex on Marshall Street to her brown one on Fisher Avenue, crossing Tank Destroyer Boulevard on the way. What would happen when I got there I hadn't a clue, but I'd biked past her house enough times hoping vainly for a glimpse of her to know I had to do something, even if disrespecting the geographical parameters my parents had set for me could result in a spanking across my father's knee.

The carport was empty when I arrived, but I waited across the street until her parents and she returned in their church clothes and I greeted them on the drive. "Mr. and Mrs. Nettle," I said, having recited the words I would say to them in my head on the way there, "Virginia and I were both in Mrs.

McIntyre's second grade class last year, and I'm here to invite her to a block party my neighborhood is throwing to celebrate the Apollo 11 moon landing."

With the hair-trigger temper of one used to quashing irritations, Virginia's father spun on wingtips that glinted in the sun. "That's Sergeant First Class to you," he replied, a corner of a mouth not given to mirth rising in wry jest only once I'd saluted him. Next to him, Virginia's mother's effusiveness disarmed me. "Well, aren't you just the sweetest thing," she said, and with the hand not holding the bakery container drew my face to her mounded torso. Though my mother had been pregnant most of the previous year, I didn't know until then how firm the stretched flesh could become, but as my nose pressed against her dress, tulip patterned and smelling of bergamot, I worried she'd break it and I'd have to tell my parents yet another story they wouldn't believe however fast I clung to it.

Inside, grace was said, our "Amens" in perfect unison. Then Virginia reached for a glazed cruller and her mother swatted her wrist. "Guests first," Mrs. Nettle said, and though I would've liked the cruller myself, I chose a long john with maple frosting. The house was identical to ours, with a dining room and living room off the kitchen, and I found it strange that for a meal consisting of donuts and coffee we sat at the dining room table, each of us with a plate, utensils, and coffee cup and saucer, when we could as easily have eaten at the smaller table in the kitchen. But I made sure to lay my napkin across my lap, and when I did Mrs. Nettle complimented me on my manners.

Sergeant Nettle wanted to know in which village our neighborhood was, and when I told him Chaffee, he asked, "Your dad medical?"

Chaffee was where most of Darnall Army Hospital's medical personnel were housed. I nodded. "He's an OB-GYN."

Mrs. Nettle perked up. "What did you say your name was, sweetie?" When I told her, she swooned. "Your father's my doctor." Sergeant Nettle rolled his eyes. "Oh, come on, Ray, don't be a sourpuss," she said, slapping the back of his shaved head with her open palm, but when she turned to me, her eyes were shiny and wet. "He's just so, so wonderful, you know? Your father?" She dabbed them with her napkin, and in her set jaw I saw Virginia's likeness. "I mean, it's hard to find a doctor...one specializing in women's health concerns...who both knows what he's doing and how to make a patient feel good about herself. OB-GYNs like your father are as rare as hens' teeth."

This wasn't the first time I'd heard this—Mrs. Burnett, my first grade teacher, who lived in the other half of our duplex and whose own baby had been born a month before my brother, had told me that I had to be the luckiest boy alive to have a father who understood women so well—nor would it be the last. But as awkward as it was to hear his virtues extolled in an area I knew next to nothing about, I was smart enough to accept accolades on his behalf, aware that I could only profit from them.

"Why thank you, ma'am," I said. "I'm sure he'll be thrilled to know you think so highly of him."

"Oh no, you can't tell him," Mrs. Nettle replied. "That would be...too weird."

"OK then," I said. "I won't tell him. But I'm sure he'd be thrilled if I did."

"Oh I don't know," she said. "You decide. I'm big as a barn. I don't know what I think anymore." She took a bite of a bismarck, and cherry filling spewed from it in a glob across her bosom. "Look at me, I'm a mess."

"Ginny?" said Sergeant Nettle, commandeering the conversation. "Would you like to go to your friend's block party?"

Virginia nodded, and my heart rose in triumph. I was Sir Lancelot and she my Queen Guinevere. I was Wilfred of Ivanhoe and she my Lady Rowena. As Virginia changed out of her Mary Janes and into her Keds, I was David Balfour and she my Catriona MacGregor Drummond. At Sergeant Nettle's request I wrote down my address and phone number on a sheet of paper and handed it to him. "You take good care of her, you hear?" he said, and I told him I would, glad these many years later I didn't kneel.

"Come on!" Virginia hollered from the street, already on her bike. "Let's go!" As I caught up to her on mine, her dress fanned out into tailfins as her hair streamed behind her. Soon we were riding side by side, and I told her about Dr. Hidalgo, his blue 1963 Porsche 911, how parked in his drive it made everything around it spin, and how he'd agreed to set up his RV-8 so that everyone in the neighborhood could look through it at the Sea of Tranquility where the Apollo 11 lunar module would shortly land and Neil Armstrong and Buzz Aldrin would later set foot.

"Dr. Hidalgo's cool," I told her. "He and my dad are both OB-GYNs at Darnall, both majors, but somehow he gets away with wearing his hair a little longer—I don't know how—and when he comes over for dinner, he always brings a date and never the same one twice. Mostly they're nurses, but once he brought a teacher."

"So he's a playboy," Virginia said.

"Funny, that's exactly what my mom called him one night when I overheard my parents talking."

"And you think he's cool?"

From the dimple that cupped the upturned corner of her mouth, I gathered she did not. "Cooler than my dad," I said. "But not cooler than yours."

"The man you met," she said, "back at the house, isn't my dad. My dad, my real dad, is dead."

I told her I was sorry for her loss. "How did he die," I asked, "if you don't mind my asking?"

"On the ground," she replied, "fighting."

When I returned to the house with Virginia in tow, my mother and father stood in front of our new color Magnavox with Lieutenant Colonel Hall and his wife who, with their six kids, lived at the top of the crumbling hill of dirt that linked our two backyards. On the screen flickered a black and white still of craters against a backdrop of infinite space. The Eagle had landed, according to Walter Cronkite's voice. On the dining room floor, my five-year-old sister Karen sat cross-legged before my diapered brother Kurt, not yet one, trying to interest him in blocks that had been mine before either of theirs. She'd place one in the willowy stubs that were his fingers—"That's the letter A. The color red. The number one."—where his dull blue eyes would examine it before he launched it a foot like something he'd coughed up. She'd hand him another—"That's the letter F. The color green. The number six."—Karen's assiduity even then that of Sisyphus. Beyond the sliding-glass doors, flames soared from the three-legged Martian otherwise known as our barbecue grill, and on the sideboard my parents had erected a cityscape of liquors, liqueurs, and mixers, my favorite the towering yellow spire of Galliano.

So transfixed were the adults by the Apollo 11 moon landing news coverage, Virginia and I were, for all intents and purposes, invisible. I led her through the living room and down the hall into the bedroom I shared with my sister, and no one said a word to us. There I showed her my collections of Matchbox cars, placing in her palm an exact replica of Dr. Hidalgo's blue Porsche 911, G.I. Joes, Classics Illustrated comic books. At the time, I owned about twenty, all but one of which had come in the mail, and rustled through *Kidnapped* by Robert Louis Stevenson to the page at the back with the order form listing the titles by volume number. Having saved the best for last, I produced from my closet the box containing my Thingmaker oven, bottles of Plastigoop, and metal molds. I loved that toy. When I lifted the lid and unveiled the components, each custom fitted to an indenture in the block of Styrofoam, Virginia's eyes widened.

"Creepy Crawlers," she said as if what had been revealed were the answer to all her dreams, as they had been to mine on Christmas morning.

"And look," I said, "glow-in-the-dark Plastigoop." On the floor was a braided rug on which we sat Indian-style before my prized possession. I plugged the metal oven's electrical cord into a wall socket, and while we waited for the Thingmaker to heat to 390 degrees, which was just one of the reasons the toy was unpopular with parents and consumer groups, we squeezed Nite Glo liquid from plastic dispensers into cavities shaped like spiders, centipedes, worms, scorpions, lizards, beetles, and snakes. When waves of heat undulated over the Thingmaker, we set the metal mold into the recess on the top of it, using the safety tongs as specified in the instructions.

"God, I love the smell of Creepy Crawlers when they're cooking," Virginia said, closed her eyelids, and inhaled the vapors, her face that of one waiting to be kissed.

My mother worried that the fumes were toxic. "Are you sure you don't want me to open a window?" I said. My mother would not have even asked.

"No," Virginia said, her voice dreamy, "I love the fumes."

"I love them, too," I said, and breathed until my nostrils tingled with the greasy redolence of oxidizing polyvinyl. For us it was an elixir that only improved our productivity, for no sooner had I pried baked Creepy Crawlers from their mold with the included stickpin than Virginia had refilled it with squirts of Plastigoop, and as soon as I took one mold out of the Thingmaker, Virginia put another one in.

"God, we're good," she said, and when all the Plastigoop was spent, and the products of our labor in column formation by specie on the rug, we lay on our backs in euphoric exhaustion. "Have you ever smoked a cigarette?" she asked.

"Apparently when I was two I ate cigarette butts out of an ashtray," I replied, "and had to have my stomach pumped. But in answer to your question, no, I've never actually smoked a cigarette. Have you?"

"No," she said. "But I'd sort of like to now. We could pass it back and forth, the way they do in movies."

I was intrigued by the idea—my father smoked Viceroys—but said, "Come on," and sat upright. "I have an idea." This wasn't something I had planned, but only seemed natural considering that all the Creepy Crawlers we'd made glowed in the dark. "We'll scatter our creations all over the backyard. They'll charge in the sunlight, and when the sun goes down, they'll glow so brightly the astronauts will see them from space."

"You think so?" she asked.

"It's worth a try," I said, and we took our Creepy Crawlers out the back door stuffed in our pockets and dribbling from our clutches.

By then the block party was in full swing, and men from the neighborhood, all holding cans of Schlitz or Hamm's, huddled around my father as he flipped and basted chicken, while the women, most in floppy hats and sunglasses, sat together in lawn chairs, each with a Mai Tai, Harvey Wallbanger, or Old-Fashioned. One thing I could say about my neighborhood: though most of the men had been drafted from private practice or straight from medical school, and none of them relished spending two years in Fort Hood, Texas, none complained about it publicly. That was reserved for the privacy of the home, and if at times I'd wondered what held my own family together through it all, the atmosphere had improved now that my father's service commitment was nearly over and we were moving to Minnesota by summer's end.

The strange thing was, though my mother had stopped cursing and crying during the day and my father no longer came home in the evenings incensed by the incompetence and pomposity of medical officers higher ranking than himself, I already missed Fort Hood, the tarantulas that pranced like blind spots across the parched lawns, the fluorescent millipedes as wide as combs that squeezed up through the bathtub drains, the pair of coral snakes I'd found entangled in a discarded Burger Chef bag, and the diamondback that moved so mirage-like through the brush in which I played I doubted my own eyes until they fell upon the rattle dragged behind it like an awkward piece of luggage, the reticulated segment rows of baby teeth already tobacco stained.

As Virginia and I covered my family's own parched lawn as methodically as planters sowing seed, dropping a spider here, a beetle there, I already missed her, too. When we were through, I asked her if she was hungry, and she said, "Starved," so we went across the street to the Winfreys for helpings of Mrs. Winfrey's Frito pie, then zigzagged up and down the block, dining as we went. Every home was open to us, and because I'd eaten supper at least once in most of them, I could recommend what was best at each, whether it was Mrs. DeBusk's lime Jell-O with quartered canned pears suspended in it or Mrs. Spurlock's peach cobbler with its crisp lard crust or Mrs. Trickey's meatloaf, which she made with A-1 Steak Sauce instead of ketchup. Fed and full, we played kick-the-can with some of the neighborhood kids, all of whom Virginia knew from school and who flashed each other impressed, if quizzical, glances when she punched me in the arm or booted me in the shin. These, we all knew, were displays of affection, as clear to everyone as a French kiss, and I was thrilled that she never left my side, even when we were hiding from It, which was what we were doing when Dr. Hidalgo emerged from his house with his magnificent telescope.

In Bermuda shorts and paisley knee socks, he looked as if he were carrying a sousaphone, with the mount resting on his shoulder and the dew cap the bell from which a counter-march might grumble. "Game over!" I called to everyone from our cover behind the Grandlunds' oleander bush, and when they saw what we saw they materialized from their havens like creatures entranced. Adults, too, were drawn to the spectacle, some with kids' arms wrapped around their foreheads and transistor radios glued to their ears, for by then the moon had appeared as a wisp of itself, barely there, but astronauts were on it, and the truth seemed impossible to grasp.

As we joined the crowd, Virginia was laughing. When I asked her why, she whispered in my ear, "Dr. Hidalgo isn't a playboy."

"No?" I whispered back.

"He's with a different woman every time he comes to your house for dinner because no woman will date him more than once."

Though I knew what she said was true, I pointed between the assembled at his Porsche. "What about his car?" I asked, but even it seemed duller than it had the last time I'd looked at it, as if the sun had seared some of the luster from it.

"Eh," she said. "I stand with my mom. Your dad's cooler."

"But how do you know? You didn't even meet him."

"I saw him with the other men. When we were in your backyard. They were all listening to him with bated breath."

"And what was he talking about?" I asked.

"A patient, a golf ball. That's all I heard, but it was enough to totally convince me."

"There," Dr. Hidalgo proclaimed, "she's all lined up and ready for public viewing," as if the moon were an actress or model and he somehow responsible for how she looked that evening. He'd been born and raised in Argentina, and affectations I'd once thought women had to find charming struck me in Virginia's presence as unfortunate, if forgivable. Clearly, he was enjoying the attention, and taking joy in the anticipation each of us felt as we awaited our turns to peer through the eyepiece at a moon that would appear, he kept telling us, sixty times closer to Earth than it really was.

"Do you know what a telescope is?" he'd ask each mother and, before she could answer, say, "Nothing but a scientific means of connecting two heavenly bodies. The moon is a heavenly body and so, my dear, are you."

When it was our turn, I said to Virginia, "You go first," praying he'd refrain from the smarm for as long as it took her to see the moon in the aperture, and he did.

"Wow," she said. "That was amazing. Have a look."

As I put my eye to the lens, Virginia placed her hand on the small of my back, and what appeared in the night sky as a slender crescent flat as a clipped fingernail appeared in the Dynascope as an orb, a sphere. You could see its curves, its craters, its lit *and* shaded edges. I'd looked through Dr. Hidalgo's telescope before and seen the moon when it was full, but on those occasions it hadn't had people on it, and as I looked at it, now I kept thinking that although it was in space, it was also in Virginia's mind—she had, after all, just looked at it—and I imagined what else I might find if I dared to venture even further into the darkness.

I didn't want our day to end, though soon my mother would be calling me to come inside and get ready for bed. I asked Virginia if her mother and stepfather were expecting her shortly. It was too dark for her to ride all the way back to her house alone, and I'd expected all along that Sergeant Nettle would eventually come to get her, her bicycle fitting easily into the back of his Country Squire. It was why, I thought, I'd written down my address and phone number for him.

So I was surprised when Virginia replied with absolute certainty, "No one's coming to get me."

I didn't understand. "Do your mom and stepdad think you're sleeping over?" I asked.

"They aren't thinking about me at all," she replied. "They have too many other worries."

"My parents can drive you home," I said. "I'll go inside and explain the situation to them. It'll be easy."

"Please," she pleaded, "don't ask your parents to drive me home." She clung to my arm, and even as we walked down my street past windows lit by televisions, in every home someone I knew, the drag was tremendous and unexpected, and I wanted the day to end.

But I didn't know how to end it, so for a time we sat at the picnic table in my backyard. All the neighbors had returned to their homes, and the Creepy Crawlers we'd sown pulsed in tiers of greenish light, faint as the bioluminescent plankton that made the oceans sparkle at night, and in my mind we were already much, much older.

K.P. Taylor

GARDEN OF WEEDS

My mother loved her garden: the Lily of the Nile, the roses, the lemon tree...the hydrangea at her bedroom window. Hydrangeas flower blue or pink depending on your soil—hers were always blue. The weeds she did not love. "A weed is just a flower growing in the wrong place," she would say as she ripped out a dandelion. I felt sorry for the dandelion—it was almost pretty enough for her garden. There were other, less pretty weeds with less pretty names: pigweed, beggar tick, cruel vine... The cruel vine was a frequent visitor to our garden. Unchecked, it would quickly strangle host plants—we lost a rambling rose to it. Unless you cut the cruel vine off at the root, it would continue to grow and develop grotesque seedpods that looked like wrinkled pears. The pods would burst, and the silky-haired seeds would scatter to the wind like so much cotton candy, like asbestos.

When we weren't battling the weeds, we fought the early morning frost that covered the plants in a thin skin of ice. Occasionally, if it got cold enough, there would be a black frost. The moisture inside the plants would freeze, and the plants would appear fine until their leaves and stems suddenly atrophied, turned black, and withered away. We killed the weeds, endured the frost, and planted flowers. "I could never be a farmer," my mother said one day as she was turning the soil with her trowel. "To plant things and to wait, to put all your faith in the earth. To just hope and wait, hope and wait." She shook her head. "I could never be a farmer." My mother grew a magnolia. She watched it for years, but it never flowered.

My mother's illness began as a subtle madness. She would say things that made no sense. She would talk to the television. The disease manifested in other ways as well. She would become rigid. If she were standing, she would need to sit. "Eat something!" my brother would yell, convinced that she had low blood sugar. We knew better, though.

We couldn't get anyone to see her—we lived in South Africa, and we had no medical aid. This was how people died. My sister and I took her to the local public hospital, Tambo Memorial (named for the resistance fighter). There, in a dimly lit corridor with benches on either side, we waited. We waited with people in wheelchairs, people with bandaged heads, people who moaned and shook and cried out. There was an old man in a wheelchair ahead of us. He was so thin and so dark and his hair was so white and his eyes were so large and milky that he looked more like a spectral shape than a corporeal being. He had almost made it to the front of the line when there was a sudden shout of surprise. The people on the benches leaned forward and then receded like waves. The man was wheeled away. He wouldn't have to wait anymore. He had died. My mother looked at me. "I wonder... If you could see ghosts, how many would there be at this hospital?"

The doctor was young, Indian. He didn't smile. "What's wrong, Mrs. Taylor?"

My sister and I began to list all of my mother's symptoms: her strange patterns of speech, her spells where she would drift off...

"I'm not asking you. I'm asking your mother."

"I'm fine, Doctor."

He looked her over for a few minutes. My mother was sixty years old. She was in good shape, and she was strong. There was something unseen, though. Something dark and deadly and spreading like a black frost.

"Your mother is fine. Go home."

We tried another hospital, Johannesburg General. It was much farther away. There was a brusque woman at the reception desk. "You can only come here if you live in the area. Do you live in the area?" We lied and said we did—we didn't want to go back to Tambo Memorial, back to the Indian doctor who didn't smile. Again we had to wait, with people with eye patches and broken people who smelled of urine and vomit. We spent so much time waiting. Every brief appointment would have a follow-up that would be scheduled for weeks ahead. No one took us seriously. A CT scan! We wanted a CT scan. We wanted proof that we weren't crazy and that our mother was. We were shunted from pillar to post, but at last they acquiesced. They admitted my mother for observation and finally scheduled a CT scan. Now we would hope and wait some more.

Her bed was near the window. She smiled and told us that it wasn't so bad— she was sleeping well, and the food was better than she had expected. "How wonderful," she exclaimed, "to look outside and see the elephants!" My sister and I smiled and indulged my mother's madness. We kissed her and left and were almost at the elevator when my mother called to us from down the hall. She had sprung out of bed to remind us to bring her radio. "It gets a little boring here," she said with a laugh. We brought the radio the next day, but my mother would never have a chance to listen to it. She had slipped into a coma. Her eyes were shut, her mouth was open, and her breathing was labored and ragged.

A doctor took us aside. "I'm not sure if you know this, but your mother is a very sick woman." We were struck dumb. They were telling us now what we had tried to tell them all along. A few days later the phone rang while we were sleeping. No good news at this hour. "Your mother has died." We drove to the hospital in the still, dark quiet of early morning. They had moved her body to a small room with a pale light. We peeled back the sheet and held the hand that was no longer my mother's hand and kissed the forehead that was no longer her forehead.

The doctor told us later that they had found lesions on my mother's brain—cancer. It had started somewhere else, her stomach maybe. It had grown in silence and inched its way toward her brain, like a root pressing the earth. Like a weed.

We went to her old room and picked up her radio and her purse with its little scribbled notes and yellow money. I stood at the window. The sun was just coming up. This once grand part of the city was in decay, but from here you could see all the jacaranda trees that the settlers had planted. So many purple flowers scattered along the streets. The entire city was a walled garden. Beyond the purple canopies, I recognized the Johannesburg Zoo, and my chest tightened when I saw a pair of elephants roaming their enclosure.

Mark Terrill
THE DIRECTOR

We're sitting in a restaurant in downtown Hamburg going over the script when his nose begins to bleed. The script is his work, written in German, which I've translated into English. Sometimes his way of articulating his visions and ideas is so vague and abstruse that it hardly makes sense. In the process of translation I try to clear up the ambiguities and bring some clarity to what he's written. Usually I'm successful, although this is seldom acknowledged. Occasionally he even takes affront at the changes that I've made, insisting that I've lost or twisted the original meaning of what he wanted to say. Sometimes I'm not so sure he even knows what it is that he wants to say, much less how. But it's a job, it pays well, and the money is welcome.

I don't think he conjures up the nosebleeds on command or on purpose, but there does seem to be some sort of psychosomatic connection, an ulterior motive of sorts, the intention being to garner some sympathy for his situation. It often happens when we're having one of our disagreements over the way I've translated one of his texts, when he's feeling as though his artistic integrity is being questioned or even challenged. So the nosebleeds are like his way of saying, *Back off, look how much this is stressing me out!*

It's then that I always have to remind myself that he is an experienced and perhaps even gifted director, well versed in actors, acting, interpersonal psychology, and the almost imperceptible nuances of manipulation, and that he, if anyone, knows best how to play his role. And so I watch him playing the whole thing down, saying it just happens spontaneously now and then, no big thing, no need to worry, rolling up two paper napkins and stuffing them in each nostril and leaning over the script and going back to work in order to show his undaunted commitment and determination to continue with our work.

I watch him hastily cross out an entire paragraph and quickly scribble some lines at the bottom of the page, which he then passes over to me for my approval. I read what he's written and do not approve, fully aware that if I were to let stand what he's written it would be my own artistic integrity that would be on the line, while out of the corner of my eye I see him tipping his head back to help stifle the bleeding, readjusting the two rolled-up napkins, now both bright pink, protruding from his nose and now drawing the attention of other patrons of the restaurant at some nearby tables.

Also at the bottom of the page are two bright red drops of blood, staring up at me like a pair of beady red eyes, waiting for me to make the next move.

Amy Alfier
AMELIA'S ULTIMATUM

Then:

She was a perfect faux-wife.
Made him a blueberry buckle—
took first place in the work potluck,
the recipe from a woman with couch arms
and double chins screaming *it's to die for!*
from the cover of a once-glossy magazine.
She'd torn off the address, stolen it from
some doctor's office, well worth it.

But critical and self-entitled...
not a good combination. Just two short bottles
of shitty red wine and he'll sneer
at the length of her dress. Mere moments
and he'll flip it over her head, take her
from behind, still watching the game.
How to explain a broken back tooth,
shattered against the weight of his frustration
at a fumble close to the end zone.
He claims he drinks for taste—she drinks
to get drunk. He is a liar.

Now:

There is a between hour
that rolls in like mist on the river.
She likes this hour, how it passes—
men are disoriented, she is strong.

The pull so subtle, it comes every day
like the tides; they don't even know.
She lights a Kool Blue,
listens to the phone summon, he can wait.

She may be his by day, many are hers by night.
She likes these men dark, like her,
slightly canted, sails awry.
No discussion of ring sizes, just a kiss,

cash on the bureau, get out. She's made her stand,
doesn't give a damn what anyone says, is always
a lady. Wears pearls before 5 p.m., diamonds she didn't buy
after, and never wears white after Labor Day.

JC Alfier

MORGAN CITY FRAGMENT

The bus from Central Catholic
drops them at the corner.
They cross the lot
to my liquor mart & deli,
just off the levee road.
Faces caked with makeup
bluff a claim to drinking age,
their forged IDs as shaky
as they come.
They eye the bottles
shelved behind me,
ask for Sazerac Rye
and Jim Beam Black,
just to hear the names roll off
their tongues, knowing damn well
they're out of their league.
Though I swear I won't,
I cave to their entreaties,
grab a red-eye cherry gin—
vow it's loved
by movie stars. I make the sale
to the tall one with ox-blood nails,
her ID the most convincing.
She tucks the bottle
in her bookbag, quickens off
with the imperative of a fire drill,
the glance over her shoulder
touching me once.

IN WABBASEKA

The shuttered Texaco
out on US 63
is a meth lab now
behind its soaped-out
windows. I know
who cooks it up,
know users' names,
though they're unaware I do.
I can name binge drinkers
leaving the corner market,
bags tucked tight under arms
like runaway toddlers.
None of that loser's life is for me.

Six days a week
I paint cars in Pine Bluff.
Never missed a day.
I swear by quiet weekends
home with mom and dad.
Some evenings we hunt
feral pigs rooting
fields near the swamp.
I bagged one once
down Hartley Dump way,
its teeth full of wildflowers,
the moon so intense
it could've burned the grass.

Tobi Alfier
MAN AS BROKEN LEVEE

Stars tattooed over
the scar on his neck,
phoenix wrapped around
his broken femur.
Lord, this body has
so many stories...
       Like a breached levee.
Trash flooding downstream
leaving in its wake:
ruined houses, wrecked
opportunities
for a life that's good,
with love and laughter,
the same fine woman
for more than a month.
He is an honest
man, just loves his drink.
Ain't no place for booze
with a missus who
craves a family.
You can't be a dad
if you ain't at home,
your place at the bar
isn't the dinner
table. What is right...
       Twenty feet of mud
wrecking a stunning
house, with two babies
bawlin' and the wash
pinned up in the sun,
or an ice-cold brew,
a catch of sea bass,
buddies with nicknames

you can't even say.
You gotta decide
on priorities
before that levee
bursts, and once again
you ain't got nothin'
but a cloud of stars,
stories to keep warm
with on winter nights,
no woman, no kids,
no plans, no nothin'.

Linette Marie Allen
THE BRIDGE BY PENN

You are Rubik's cube nailing American iron
ore, the grandest parade I've ever seen; you

draw lines & circles under hexagons, kite pussy
willows from Quebec-floating oceans; you

stage English dramas in summer, at midnight, street
lamps like monkeys in the trees; you

get a little rum in you & damn the caesars; ghosts
claiming Poe lift glasses, nod, read a little something

& cause accidents, prattle on forever about orange
being too close a cousin to yellow, about the tree that survived

the fire, how she was slighted & should have netted a medal
for nearly saving that clown found fisted in her hair, why *pellicle*

is classier than *film* & then fade
from Vincent to Gustav on Charles. You

sit there, say nothing, let morning sirens
morph into famished horseshoe bats; mourning

for the sake of mourning never suited, never lined up. You
rise, peel square labels, abstain from color, claim power

from Jupiter at Olympia, read a little something
& do no harm, say how much you love

shades of gray, those little foxes in the city, that thing
he does aplomb

—with lightning.

CASTING CROWNS AT MEMPHIS

Po

Said imperial yellow to topaz: I love
your land, your jutting dew, your wingspan—
the way it spans like natron over trains.

Bashō

Said delicate vine to thatch roof: I love
your cherries, your drive to sojourn seas, be
sound, sycamore fruit, lute of the limestoned.

Rumi

Said thin asparagus to tangerine: beloved,
I love your songs—your contraltos climbed
trees; they were but sweet, but stoves of delight.

Elephantis

Said rose freeze to semi-gloss: you candle
short breaths, new breaths, long breaths—breaths that carry
ejections, grape-seeds under strong tongues, I love!

Virgil

Said fetching pink to botany beige: loving laws
I learned from your lap; Balsamic moons have nothing
on you. This crown is made of age—salute!

Fontaine

Said ivory peach to montrose: your script
gave me doors & windows & stairs to lasso the
world in red, white, and blue—stars, castles, too.

Shakespeare

Said translucence to gray dignity: verbs
that topple empires & those who dare wear purple:
kings? why I praise thee, lip thy rubied ring!

Whitman

Said tangy green to spring grass: how massive
your earth-gifts: the -metry, the -gia, the -ism, -angle
-logy, the -scient! Big leaves die paying.

Nancy Allen
MEXICO

We are roaming rows of blue agave,
standing in line to buy tamales,

fiddling with strange coins in our palms.
Our feet are dusty in sandals

and all the sounds around us are words
we barely know. They could be poems.

We have no right to expect kindness
in Mexico and yet the people

are kind, "Don't worry; we've had asshole
presidents too. It's not your fault."

They are patient when we mangle
expressions, order food, ask directions.

We vow to study the language, travel
in South America despite fears,

re-read Neruda, Paz, Lorca.
In my mind we are driving south

with a copy of *Twenty Love Poems
And A Song of Despair*, *en español*.

KING OF THE DOGS

Tucked in with parked cars, food stands, and piles
of trash and coconut shells are homes

made of discarded wooden boats and tarps.
Stray dogs snooze in the sun, barely move when

tourists sidle past en route to the beach.
Local kids know to leave the dogs alone;

they're neighbors, not pets. That Rotti stud
swinging away despite your calling him back?

He's not your property. You would like to
rescue him, neuter, worm, and confine him

to your house, walk him on a braided leash.
A story to tell! You imagine that big dog

curled at the foot of your bed thinking grateful
thoughts. In your mind, he's not dreaming soft sand,

the shush of surf and shade of sea grape trees.
He's not remembering all the bitches

who loved him, called him *rey de los perros.*

RESORT

Seaweed from southern storms rolls in and in
with the surf, is piled waist high the length
of this resort beach. Skinny Mexican men
with ropy arms are hard at work with rakes
and shovels loading it into a pickup
to haul away where it will decompose,
stink, and attract flies far from paying guests
whose deluxe cabanas line the beach. The men
commute from miles inland, are drenched in surf
then the rain that starts pelting buckets while we
shield our umbrella drinks and run for cover.

David Alpaugh
ROO–ZUH–VELT/HISTORY

ROO–ZUH–VELT

Only 9, when Mr. Uhlich, the old man who gave
me 38 pigeons—did me the honor of sharing his
bitterness. I'd seen his shell-shocked son, eyes
cast down, mutter his way about town. 3 sticks of
dynamite exploded from old Mr. Uhlich's mouth:

Roo-Zuh-Velt! "Damn liar promised no mother's
son would die on foreign soil—then let the JAPS
come to get us into war!" I'd yet to get to Honest
Abe. FDR, an utter mystery. But old Mr. Uhlich
& his ruined son were my first brush with *living*

HISTORY

Rose Mary Boehm
SUMMERFEST

We sheltered from that
sudden summer drencher.
For a moment we imagined
a green Mediterranean world
instead of the gray August shroud
covering sunflower fields, olive trees,
shrubs, and tufts of grass.

The rain drummed wildly
on the corrugated iron roof
and the earth smelled freshly broken.

A black sky cut
by zigzagging lightning strokes.
The horizon a gigantic smelter
extracting green sheen
from magic ore.
Trees bent, giving in
to the force of the storm.

Abruptly the drumming stopped,
the last bars left to the brushes.

A Spanish summer sky pretended
nothing had happened,
and the sun fell on us
with a drunken spell.

Ace Boggess

ADVICE FOR KILLING A SPIDER

angle your weathered tennis shoe to skip & drag
like the tail of a biplane
bouncing down for a rough landing
let it scrape the carpet so at worst it wounds &
the enemy can't sprint beneath a door

hairspray handles the black spot on a low ceiling
only (a) don't stand directly under lest it parachute &
(b) never set the stream ablaze—
warfare should not be a suicide pact

emptiness = vacuum

watch out! while you focus on the bullseye in front of you
don't overlook its partner at your feet

leave your house
drive to a motel room in another state

unlike in a game you win
the levels get harder & go on forever
until your walls are a graveyard of ugly stains

Paula Bonnell
KNOWING

It isn't the ladykillers
(though they think they are)
who are God's gift to women
No, it's the guys no one
would pick out of those
sitting quietly in the seats
of the airplane rows. But
sometimes you sit next
to one, and you know.
He's courteous, he
makes you laugh, he's
married (of course) and
he lets you know, but
then you both look away
and you know he knows
you're happier that way
(and so is he) and you
know that he knows
you understand where
he's at, but there's that little
knot as you both swallow
your way past these
understandings and the
necessary pause in the conversation, and then you
talk afterwards and you wish
it were as good as talking
afterwards.

INSTRUMENTS OF PURPOSE, CONSIDERED

What is the difference between a nail and a screw?
A nail wouldn't have worked for red-headed Frances,
    the skinniest waitress in the Majestic Steakhouse,
who plucked a screw from the floor and
shocked me by saying, "You could give it
    to your boyfriend and say, 'Wanna screw?'"

A nail can be hammered in first
    to show a screw the way.
When it's pulled out, its threadless shaft
    may be corkscrewed a bit,
Then the screw makes an easier fit.

Guys who work in the trades would say,
"Both are male"
And in pop music, both are verbs
    that attach you
        to him
    or the wall
        or both

But in walls or furniture, think
how quiet and friendly and ongoing
this attachment is, the metal
patiently   quietly   enduringly
holding the wood together.   Nail or screw,
    either can do it

What is the difference between *fuck* and *love*?
Just recently I thought to look up
    fuck in my dictionary (now that
    times have changed and it's likely
        to be in there...)

Here's what I learned from the fat red one:
Fuck comes from a very old word meaning to strike—
     fokken or something like that
The sexual use is simply by extension
It's a kind of sex that is a form of striking
What does it strike?
                  you or sparks
     or both

Shirley J. Brewer
ACCOUNTING

2 days in a row
I aced a movie trivia quiz
over lattes at the Leaf & Bean.
Forgive my braggadocio.
No one else could recall

Pacino's best line from *Serpico*—
*If you love the garden, you gotta
love the man*. I saw the film 8 times,
those words blazing in my brain
like a Sicilian volcano.
I'm a sucker for incidentals:

20,000 pounds of ostrich feathers,
16,000 lemons
lost on the *Titanic*.
I picture all that fluff and fruit
carpeting the floor of the sea.
12 newly married couples
honeymooned on the ship. Every bride
survived. Only 1 groom.

In 6th grade I wore a red plaid skirt
the night my brother sank
at the county spelling bee.
He made it to the final 4.
Commentary, the word he missed.

Now, I'm adding up how long
my cousin lived with Parkinson's.
It stole her speech, her sparkle,
the last ounce of air from her lungs.
16 years—my commentary reveals.
That's 5,840 days.
Numbers startle my tongue.

MARILYN SPEAKS

I made her up,
that hot goddess babe.

My career took shape
in Bed Bath & Blonde.

Men used my hourglass
body to keep time.

Reporters always said
I gave up diamonds

for Lent. In my jeweled
clutch: red lipstick, pink pills.

Makeup concealed
the real Norma Jeane.

Tell me, what more
did you want to see?

My star burned,
set fire to the gold lamé.

Fame killed me, honey.
Before I went down

even my pubic hair
glowed in the dark.

Joan Colby

FLOATING

A floating world of guys and dolls,
Crapshoot enterprise of thrown dice.
Woodcuts of tsunamis and Kabuki
Villains. Three beauties and Nathan Detroit
Smoke opium in dreamy pipes.
The fat woman floats in the pool.
Her rich flesh defies gravity.
A hawk floats over the moorland.
Voices float from adjoining tables
Where gossip lures luminescent
As will-o'-the-wisps. The earth floats
Toward the oblivion
Of its generous star. Time floats
Complicated fingers on the harps
Of galaxies. The water lilies
Seem to float upon Monet's pond
Yet are anchored with a mass of roots,
The subterranean otherworld he imagined
Over and over and over.

DIA DE LOS MUERTOS

It is the Day of the Dead
And I have no sugar skulls to offer,
No tequila, no red flowers,
Only the memory of your rictus,
Mouth open as if to curse.
I thought you were still living,
Small intestinal whispers,
But Gabriella said no, closing your eyes
With her palms. I would rather
Remember you, young in an apron
And your maroon sweater, making Welsh rarebit
For Friday supper. The cheese edged brown
On the toasted bread.

Today a raw drizzle and the oak leaves
Falling in a slow mournful chorus.
All Souls Day is what we called it,
This time of recollection. You had
Green eyes, black hair. I know now
You were pretty though as a child
I saw you as worried, a cigarette
In your stained fingers or a rosary.

On the Day of the Dead, the Madonna
Is honored. Or Santa Muerte
Who loves the assassinated.
The piñata of recollection
Breaks open and everything falls
Randomly. How eagerly we grasp
What we can. Mother, I can't believe
What you believed. The better place
With your family gathered; someone about
To carve the turkey, your sister's famous
Lemon meringue pie.

None of this matters on the
Day of the Dead. It is finished.
They carried you out on a gurney
Like a parcel. I wept with sorrow
And relief. It was over, your life that had
Diminished to a chair and a bed.
You were content, you said.
I was not. Shamed that I hated
This transformation. How you
Perpetually saluted the
Empty air.

On the Day of the Dead, the dead
Rise in my dream: Mother,
Father in the '41 Dodge singing off-key
As we drive through the Big Horns
Where years earlier the radiator
Of the Model-T boiled over.
They filled paper cups from a
Mountain creek laughing.
I wasn't born then. I was still
Where the dead are.

Gail Braune Comorat
IN THIS DREAM OF ENDLESS AISLES

You and I are racing rickety carts
down rows of a colossal liquor store
built in a future
you never saw

we're filling our baskets with spirits
laughing at the absurdity of their names

It is years before you'll begin
your chase for Wild Turkey
Red Stag anything that tastes
like rotgut like moonshit

we're laughing oh my god we are laughing
and the aisles are unending

You're seizing bottles
with abandon Toasted Head
Gnarly Head Plungerhead
Black Dirt bourbon Heaven Hill

we're racing each other wheels unbalanced
careening acquiring and spreeing

You're undecided
Fat Ass tequila or Bong Spirit vodka
Monkey Shoulder or Donkey Piss
Crystal Head or Frozen Ghost

we're wasting hours taking time we don't have
but you're laughing just look at you

You target craft beers
their crafty names delighting you
Hop Ness Monster Pandora's Bock
Hoppy Ending

we're running this marathon together
down aisles stretching before us like eternity

You say *So many choices*
the words catch me off guard
and in this dream
I'm no longer charmed

we're stuck in this dream we'll keep roaming
no time thankgod to uncork to decant to slow sluice

You lean your weight
on your wobbly cart
where bottles clank and
glow with savage beauty

I can see we're heading toward the final stretch
nearing the place where we'll pay for it all

Your cart's bounty will grow
until it can hold no more
my cart's wheels will groan
from the weight it carries

still I dream we'll go home and stand these bottles high on a shelf
before the transom where the sun will illuminate them

like a new city a glittering skyline of distant glass

Robert Cooperman
WORSE

I did psychedelics four times: each trip
worse than the one before; well, I was young
and stupid, and it was the sixties,
our civic duty to try as many drugs as possible.
The last time, that night in a sprawling house
in the Catskills; perfect, we thought, for peyote,
and downed the dried mushrooms with lemonade,
to kill the taste of the psychotropic poison.

We waited and waited, and were about to snort,
"Fuhgeddabout that," when those savage little
buttons kicked in like the hard boots of biker gangs.

Marti still won't talk about what she saw,
but for me, two giant ball bearings smashing
against each other, the universe tearing itself apart,
and above that crashing, a voice commanding me
to abandon all hope, for I was truly in Hell.
Hours and hours for the thunder and terror
to subside, and I could breathe again.

But Marti couldn't. Nothing in the house
to calm her, so we sat in a diner and I poured tea
into her, tea even hotter than her tears
that streamed acid gullies down her face.

Finally we staggered into an emergency room,
the resident, Marti swore, a three-foot green
homunculus who'd just waddled off a UFO,
so she grabbed my hand and we ran out.

When at last both of us were calm and seeing
and hearing nothing but New York City traffic,
I swore reality was strange and terrible enough:
war a demon that might swallow the world.

MELVIN DICKSON, THE GIRL SCOUTS, AND POT SHOPS

The Girl Scouts of Colorado have decided it's now cool to
peddle their baked goods outside marijuana dispensaries.
—The Denver Post

The little dolls wear Cheshire Cat smiles:
drug dealers in training, sirening how perfect
a combo weed, Thin Mints, Lemonades, or Trios
would make: the instant munchie cure.

But now it's legal, not as much fun
as scoring from a neighborhood dealer,
his kitchen delicious with weed-stink,
then on the lookout for cops dying to bust
a guy trying to take the edge off his week.

I remember once, when I brought a lid
to a friend in need, I wore my sports jacket,
and carried the dope in a satchel
when I walked past a black-and-white.
Afterwards, a rush like the best grass.

Now, smiling preteen angels offer me
boxes of cookies. I dart inside, stroll out
with a paper bag full of stuff guaranteed
to blow away the top of my skull,
and all of it legal as sitting at a hotel bar.

So why do I feel like a pusher contributing
to the delinquency of minors? Though,
more likely, they're the Lorelei tempting me.

Barbara Crooker
CROW MISCHIEF

Out beyond the ideas of wrong doing
and right doing, there is a field.
I'll meet you there. —Rumi

There's some crow mischief going on
in the cottonwoods; listen to their muffled
harrumphs and squawks. In a world
inured to suicide bombings,
school shootings, random stabbings,
this little murder is elevator music.
Rumi writes that there's a field
where we can move beyond
the great divide, lie down together.
The grass is sharp beneath
our thin shirts. Its hot breath
rises, the essence of summer.
The wind washes over us, a baptism
of dust. And we are specks, next
to nothing, in the eyes
of the crows.

MOON

Nestle the ample moon
of your husband.
—"Is There Lightning on Venus?," Marilyn Kallet

The ample moon of my husband is rising softly
as he breathes through his CPAP hose. He looks
like a baby elephant, the elongated crinkled tube
attached to his nose. Everything has softened now,
in both our bodies, and we ache in places
we never knew we had. Moonlight frosts
his hair, which is no longer old pewter
nor the luster of silver. Instead, it's the garden
in January, after a storm. Drifts piled
against the window.

So let me nestle against you, O my beloved,
your full moon riding high. Together, we can
make our own mournful music. The night is cold,
but our bed isn't empty. Let us ride in this small
boat on the incoming tide.

BLACK AND PURPLE PETUNIAS

after a painting by Georgia O'Keeffe

She sat at my table, hands restless,
fiddling with the chipped tea cup.
She flicked at her hair, twisted it
up with a clip, then let it loose,
falling over her collar, the white
blouse hiding the marks where
he gripped her, tight. She knew
they would bloom, black
and purple, a handful of night.

Mark Danowsky
GRACE

Crows remember our faces
though we can't tell them apart

Some crows know water better than a child
but don't care how much of it we have

Elephants hear me as you see me—generic
rank among the broken
who rampage, who trample

All elephants learn touch soothes—
one places its trunk in another's mouth
taking in the silence

BIRD IN A BOX

Before I worked there
I saw a bird in the Walmart rafters
While browsing seed
For my feeders

I went to the hardware aisle
Retrieved a 28 cent box-cutter
And slit a cross

Subtle
I motioned to the bird

See how I try

Heather L. Davis
BECAUSE OF POETRY

Before you won that big-ass prize, this was the year
without a summer vacation. Now, I blame the judge,

Mr. Billy Collins, for the beach heat trapping us
like a blast furnace until we are wavery

and indistinct, curse him for the freckles blooming
across my nose and cheeks and the way our knees twist

as we cross dunes to the water's edge for a hard-earned
kiss of coolness. It's his fault that our son won't leave

Zelky's arcade, which booms like Godzilla pummeling
Manhattan. Collins has caused our daughter to wield

her phone like a mirror, finding new ways to be beautiful
by the sea, peering into the screen as if it is both riddle

and solution. Here, in sunny Rehoboth, I hold Billy
responsible for making us consume too much craft

beer and weird ice cream, as if Dogfishhead, ghost
peppers, and cardamom could save us from dying. Thanks

to this poet laureate and his prize-giving, we shut down
Funland every night, collecting bruises on the bumper cars,

going dizzy on the carousel, feeding ball drop games
with shiny coins, frantic as addicts. But more than anyone

and more than luck, I blame you, Jose Felix Padua, husband
of twenty years, for this predicament. Your terrible habits—

staying up until all hours, noticing every small thing, twisting
language into odd new shapes—brought us to this. In

other words, I blame poetry. Thanks to verse, this morning,
it's all I can do to rise at dawn in this busy coast town—

groggy-eyed and achy—for a little peace and quiet
before you and the kids wake. It's enough to make me

weep—so much time to read the ocean, to walk, to breathe,
before stopping to pick up coffee, fresh pastries, and nectarines.

Robin Dellabough
OZ REDUX

I'm Dorothy drowsy in the crimson poppies
or the witch muttering *what a world, what a world*.
I have some courage, much heart, and too many brains.
I'm a wise charlatan behind a scrim
of smiles and secrets, making outlandish promises
to myself: to be content with a raggedy dog
in a rain of animals, thundersnow, diamond dust,
stray souls knocking at the red door,
my home an open book.

ALL OUR STORIES

Stored like acorns too tannic to eat—
buried in beds of hay, wood chips, tattered cotton pallets—
they wait to break open:
Once upon a time a child kissed a goat.
Once upon a time a woman wept for her lost words.
Once upon a time a hummingbird siphoned her heart.
Once upon a time, all our stories were told
in a single lyricless song we could hear
between a shaking aspen or a river's rush.
Once upon a time, we listened.

Margaret Diehl
WOMEN REMEMBER

being girls, naked at thirteen
in bath or bed, the secret thoughts
still secret but frail as old silk.

Another world, the 1960s, Greenwich Village,
where I lived then and now,
though not continuously
since. Not like him, big-city provincial
for whom I pine

as a dog pines, mute
except for the whine. Nothing elegant
slides off my tongue, no precise
viper-dunked dart. "Love me!"
He says he does, it's just

that he loves her more, whom he barely knows,
who was born too late—
She can't remember the '60s,
or interpret the old silk.
I never expected

him to. He doesn't understand
this: I loved his ignorance.
It gave me freedom.
It's like the box
inside the bigger box under the bed
if you never vacuumed and the dust

furred and feathered,
if the Eleusinian
Mysteries and Agatha Christie
infected each other
if the dream and the real had sex
only once and got stuck together
nobody could separate them

so we accepted
that ungainly beast with its immense
cathedral shadow
where we would meet & kiss.

WHY I WRITE NOVELS

So the dead can live in them
returned to their young beauty,
their demonic cleverness
contained by the glue of bindings.

There is order here, like a neighborhood
in which all are careful
that the tips of the grass do not encroach
on the sky's hem.

And there's a party, perhaps
a family celebration. Ripe figs
for the thin uncle with the New York eyebrows,
who never speaks

and a whole pig roasting slowly
on a spit, in a plaster of aromatic leaves
the youngest daughter made before she began
the day's drinking.

The dead take tiny bites
of anything red
and sigh. No one notices.

*

To gather readers. Sex
is always effective, afternoons in bed,
my grandmother's satin quilt, lowered blinds.

A big man sits uneasily,
post-pleasure, in the feminine room,
half in love with one who sleeps

her espresso-colored dress
like a peeled skin on the floor
in and out of the bars of sun.

Her bare shoulders tremble
like unset custard.
She is in the cradle of wanting
that keeps rocking whatever is found.

*

To punish the dead.
To make worlds they never knew
and can't take over. This severed head
for example, may not be his;
I let the dog carry it off to the mazy wood.

Alex McRae Dimsdale
DIPLODOCUS

Beloved of children, who recognize
the power in your size, who memorize
your name and love you for being improbable,
extinct, and gentle as a Great Dane—
you were my companion.

It wasn't always easy to cling on,
to ride the stately wave of vertebrae
as you browsed the treeline,
your contemplative head
droopily mustached with weeds.

Sun warmed our backs,
you basked as lesser beasts dozed
in the garden of your shade. Up there,
I saw young weather roll towards us,
huge glowing clouds of dust,

the thrum of feathers as a blur of raptors
thundered across the humid plain;
and when storms cracked open, I hid
under your massive haunches,
tried to avoid the lash of whiplike tail.

You slept curled like a cat,
small head tucked to tail. Your belly
was soft and waxy smooth, your shedding
left empty palaces of onion skin
tumbling through the brush.

We were happy among the patient herd,
and the world was so quiet—
the forest stretched for miles,
green and cool, and hornets' nests
swung in the dusk like papier-mâché lamps,

humming electrically. You turned
and turned, then settled in your nest.
I tried to make myself invisible,
as the moon shut her eyelid,
and other, avid eyes flicked on.

KIWI

The hedgehog of the bird world—
bushy, bustling, pursued into tunnels
by rats. Its furry feathers mildly earthy,
like the smell of leaves mulching
on the forest floor, the damp soil printed
by footsteps. All the black night
of the Southern Hemisphere is bright
with squeaks and shuffles,
insects that glint like jet beads,
a string of invisible errands,
secret assignations,
hurried sex and fights—

and I live my small life too, briskly
as everyone else in the dark street
with shopping bags and door keys,
our phones snug in the pockets
of puffy coats, glowing as they relay
messages back and forth
in a sheer dense thicket of signals,
responsibility and desire fluffed out
from ourselves like downy feathers,
warm and well designed to camouflage,
floating from our bodies
into a kind of flight.

Catherine Fahey
SEAL EYES

I. WATER

Fishermen lie. The ones
that get away are bigger,
faster, tastier than regulated
catches. The girl you didn't
marry is prettier, sweeter,
skinnier than your wife, and
a better cook. The catch
is low because of Congress
and limits, those damn seagulls,
thieving seals, because of foreign
boats. There's always
a reason.

The sea teaches
cycles, ebb and flow.
Selkies come back
to their skins. Once you get
a selkie's skin, they never
leave you. Selkies, like tides,
come back.

Fishermen know this, like
they know cod,
lobster, and missing
fingers. Steal a sealskin,
gain a wife. A selkie wife
will stay with her
skin, not complain
about days at sea, the smell
of fish, the waiting.

II. SKIN

A selkie wife
is trapped. She has
no choice, really. He takes
her skin, takes her
to church. The preacher says
the words, all fire and brimstone,
nothing at all like life, cold and wet,
on this Atlantic rock. The fisherman
husband holds her sealskin, her
passport in a lockbox, keeps her
on a cash allowance. Monitors
her visitors, moves her
inland. Away from the sea, isolated
from her people. Her days empty,
she stares at the TV. Stares at the stove,
the laundry. She stares at her flat,
human face in the dull, static
mirror. Crooked nose, bruised,
shadowed eyes.

The selkie saves her
pennies, establishes good
behavior, just enough.
Enough to buy whiskey and cold
medicine. Enough to ensure
he's asleep.

She steals her skin, slips away from the fisherman, swims into the sea.

III. FUR

The fisherman wakes.
An empty bed, yesterday's
coffee cold in the pot. He smells
old shellfish, low tide. He
swears and slams, cursing
his no-good-stupid-bitch-runaway wife.

He goes to his boat, where his crew believe him.

A storm comes up, as storms do.

A wave, a faulty engine, a failing pump. The boat takes on water, as boats do.

He cries out
to his selkie wife, begging
her to save him, take
him back. He'll do anything, he'll
change, really he will. This time
will be different.

Harbor seals swim
by, a local pod, fish
stealers, catch botherers.
He scans for his wife. He
knows her by her skin,
though it's been years since he's
seen her wear it. He knows
the spots, the intimate curve
of her head. There.
Surrounded by her people. Playing
in the storm. She wasn't looking
until he called out. She turns

> her black eyes, merciless, inhuman as the sea.

She stares as he slips beneath the waves, seal eyes unblinking.

Gary Fincke
MIRACLE FISH, LOS ANGELES

Thin red cellophane, the miracle fish
Swimming within it, curls into *fickle*,
Flops into *false*, lies still for *trustworthy*,
My granddaughters placing them on their palms
To watch my gifts of cheap fortune telling
Declare their futures as unsurprising
As their Disney collection DVDs.

So predictable, our fortunes, though once,
In a Toronto high-rise, a lawyer
Wanted to make every touring student
Consider the rewards of his practice,
Insufficient to stand and sweep one hand
Across the skyline, not if he needed
To make clear the privilege of leaning
Into the twenty-fourth-story view, fear
So impossible he slammed his shoulder
Against his spotless window and tumbled
Into the news, proving there is always
Reason to cross-examine the future.

Those girls, turned back to television, want,
For now, the fantastic, their feet fitted
Perfectly into glass, their hair let down
For the hand-over-hand of princely love.
Me? I'm working at faith, learning, lately,
That a star must be three billion years old
In order for complex life to evolve
On one of its planets, and even then,
Need the luck of the Goldilocks Effect,
The neither too hot nor too cold porridge
Of atmosphere stirred with water and age.

Those girls, for now, must live in the city
In which their father has abandoned them.
In the morning, I will hug them goodbye
And tell them how, before *Voyager II*
Left gravity behind to spread the news
Of us to aliens, Carl Sagan
Added his lover's pulse and breath onto
That capsule's golden record, recording
Her brain waves while she concentrated on
What it's like to fall in love: Happiness
And heartbeat. Kiss and laughter. Closeness. Touch.
I will fly two thousand miles to winter,
And they will audition another fish
For its brief fantasies of the future.

I will not tell them, not yet, about how,
When *Voyager* left the solar system,
Sagan was years dead, how, while unhooking
Her lace-trimmed bra or sliding off a slip,
His lover recollected how Sagan
Imagined the lingerie of planets
Unreachable for centuries, and how,
An eternity from us, those others
Undress and embrace into ecstasy.

Soon enough, they will discover desire
And need the fingertips and parted lips
Of the ordinary. And possibly,
That disc will be played, proving to others
We are capable of dreaming beyond
Ourselves, longing to be entered for love.
And those girls, two resilient orphans,
Will become citizens of happiness,
Noisy with dreams, welcoming each morning
Because possibility's as vast as
The distance longing and love will travel.

Michael J. Galko

THE PROTECTIVE EYE

How does the torturer
see the drain on the floor?

In short, he does not—
unless it is solely for function—

where the blood goes, the piss,
the fingernails, the burnt

hair. But in truth the
drain is the devil's eye—

and he waits down there,
sharpening his tools,

seeing.

Kathleen Gillespie
THE BALLAD OF LOVECRAFT COUNTY

Each time I told someone I was going to Kim's crypt, I would get a funny look.

She was neglected long enough to harbor maggots.

It's always inherently life threatening, more dangerous than suffocation.

People who live in Hibernation don't really exist anymore in the same sense.

My firm recommendation is that you try to go.

Around the city, the ghost ship fire has been an issue.
Patrons enter alone and navigate dark despair.
You get a story told by two undead mermaids, with well-rehearsed roles,
after being shaken around in a morgue cabinet.
It is obvious that the entities are still working out things among
themselves. Because they find our work compelling, radical, and urgent, it
goes without saying that the city has numerous problems.

Dominus has proved to be a cancer.

So while it was a trek to venture out to the newest location, we finally
came up on the floodlights of the next Haunting.

This was a dark ride, groggily eyed, glow-in-the-dark.

Our bones begin to ache, being an adult life in this world will twist your
arm completely around.

When the man failed to put his gun down and started pointing, I had just
an instant of doubt.

You don't come this far in a battle and give up.

He jerked a thumb at a slit of light on the ground.

My dad was killed, heading inside without an agenda.

His song fades off in the casual howl.

James Grabill
IN A SLEEP-DIVE SWOON

A few hell-hound whines out of Kerouac's astronomical
meat-wheel, and everyone's turned inside out, beyond
hot and cold, under revolutions of the more shamanic
stars in the dead of night, where rhythmic runic healing

can be hard to find in shadow canyons gone translucent
after 100-year downpours on the public plants of speech
twisted from close exotic torque of indigenous extractions
under a black umbrella, days before the end of the reign

of Western identity from accelerations of unprecedented
simplicity holding large families hostage under cloaked
surgical-strike capability with its quick bird-swallowing
and brother-gutting, mantle-fracturing, and big oil-drilling

business raking in untold hauls of spontaneous ice-cold
dogma moldering on Alpine mountain tops of microbial
sleep at work on what we've found when a sleep-dive swoon
spawns a fresh unseeable scripture of lying that cheats up

to reach future highs in an instant backslide at greater costs
to the present than what slips back in a generalized truck
borne of the harkened refineries in a tick-clock bison-flash
of Western supremacy denying sense exists for green-headed

mallards when unburdening the mother root of large money
around what might or might not survive archaic exposures
to temporal reddening which summons those who were born
for a long-term organic retrofit before half-buried inaccuracies

appear at the thunderhead edges in East European banks
of rain where the beginnings of Klee feather back into seas,
while global leaves comb power out of time, until it splits
into urgent public information uncountable eons from now.

OUT OF UNFATHOMABLE TIME

So the beauty of Venus has its wildfires
spreading now through geomagnetic
pulse that resounds in the small breasts
of songbirds and rooting down-dug possums.

So Blake gazed, in the glow of genetic indivisibility,
at classical shoulders and the elegant torsos
of translucent mammalian thermal conversions,
while the immense gas giants were luxuriating

in primal x-rays that have never stopped nursing
on cataclysmic creation. The concentric instant
jets ahead on squid-shot sea-depths packed
with waking and sleeping, and fresh remains

still awaiting word, longing to hear, with light
rising as it turns even when it's almost nothing
but grocery aisles and carbonic 6:30 traffic
making the place smaller. Where craving fills

its pea pods with a viable version of the future,
with arboreal rhizome sweetening in elastic time,
it takes sharp curves melting and unfolding
in the unfathomable pollination of Tuesday

for breath heating up to reach theater prep rooms
as lamp-quick bulk reflected off the Himalayas
at the top of thought, which must answer
to the mother of humanity in the sensorium.

James Gross
VIBE-BRANDED

if Bill Evans played it—
& Monk
            hit his strange
dissonant 2nds with hypnotic ease
between ebony keys

then the pianos at
Village Gate,
Village Vanguard,
and THE TOWN HALL

are vibe-branded with genius;
mellifluous, polyphonic,
            omniscient finger marks

fire-pressed—
into ivory flanks

Hedy Habra

ALLEGRO MA NON TROPPO

After Wadada Leo Smith's Four Symphonies (# III)

Think of a boy lost in midst
    of a rippling sound wave still
        hanging from his umbilical cord
    he lands on a tipsy summer moon
who tries to chase away the shadows
    from last night's hangover
        the boy wants to catch
his own shadow with a fisherman's
    pole that is really
        a violinist's bow.

        A page has been turned   there's a gap
    in the   symphony

The boy waves his bow around
    a dragonfly and a pink-lipped orchid
        he wants to become
           The Little Prince
    get closer to the orchid's heart
but she is only pursing her lips for a kiss
        he envies the dragonfly's dance

        Another page   turned   another gap

    Spiritual fires rise out of darkness
in the moon's secret landscapes
    the dragonfly hides under its shadows
        the orchid sleeps awaiting a kiss
the boy knows he needs to keep in touch
    with his own shadow and will only
        hear its music with eyes closed
to find out where he came from
    and what he wants to become

Chloe Hanson
YOUR BODY, THE AFTERLIFE

After Clarice Lispector fell asleep, cigarette in hand,
she no longer resembled Marlene Dietrich.
She could not paint her full red lips, eyebrows
that no longer arched over black eyes, so like yours,
I think, like a cat's eyes,
that same wildness.
Some things can be reconstructed. Skin,
for instance, grows like climbing vines,
plant it over hurt and it will knit you back together.
Memory is more difficult.
The woman tells another story. In her late years,
Lispector hired a mortician's beautician
to apply her face like a sarcophagus lid while she slept
so she'd always rise beautiful.
I think of you, always embalmed in perfume
and wonder if they sprayed it in your coffin
for the resurrection. Some churches now claim bodies
resurrect whole, despite being burned down to bones.

Donald Illich
SUCCESS AS THE RAIN

First, you must drench the grass,
even if tells you you must die.

It'll be worth it when old shoots
renew, new ones sprout upward.

You have to turn concrete porches
into shimmering pools the children

will dive into, crack their heads.
If possible, flood roads, carry away

vehicles, leave the drowned on shore.
You must be summoned by the gods

as a punishment. Watch evildoers
and innocent alike die in your swirl.

The clouds can then stop. They
can refuse to call out your name.

CRABGRASS

He couldn't spell "happiness."
Or "festive" and "holiday."
His language lacked these words.
Trudging over his lawn,
he thought "crabgrass, crabgrass."
pacing his job's hallways,
he whispered, "deadline, deadline."
You might try to get him out of his funk.
You might stop him outside,
the sunlight off your shoulder,
thrust words "dinner," "lovely night" at him.
He couldn't bear it, though.
"Yes" wasn't possible in circumstances
like these. Imagining missiles above him,
a mushroom cloud dissolving the city,
he had to appease "worry" at home,
serve "anxiety" tea in his living room.
You cease asking, leave for work.
He was free to contemplate "drought"
for his grass, dream of "seed,"
falling everywhere but his yard.

Mike James
GHAZAL 1

Noah gathered animals two by two. Desire works the same way.
Not one person, alone. Like our hands, desire is a coupling.

Both is my favorite. That's a problem. Give me the cherry
Pie along with the apple. Give me the cheerleader and the pool boy.

My favorite place to go is inside my head. Pleasures and damnation
Swim along as old friends. Sometimes, it's like ice skating in hell.

Sartre said hell is other people. My father said hell is where I'm going.
Thankfully, Sartre is not my father. I live, helpless, among ambiguities.

The only thing I miss is what I leave out. For instance, there's no you
In these lines. I know... Cue violins. Maybe brass trumpets. A kazoo.

GHAZAL 2

When the rattlesnake lies on asphalt at night, her body
Stretched to exclamation, all she's looking for is warmth.

Even a dying star gives off light. You remember that fact from
Tenth grade science class, but you forget the formula for warmth.

Prophets in the desert bathed in ashes, wore unpainted sackcloth,
Ate locusts, and still gave hosannas. All in a longing for warmth.

Moses, when he turned his eyes away from the desert's flaming bush,
Was frightened not by the sight or by the voice, but by the warmth.

At day's end, what do you fear? Not snakes. Not that night dream of
Being lost in the desert. Only a final darkness, past any ring of warmth.

Brad Johnson

WORLD FORGETTING BY WORLD FORGOT

After explaining how Sofia's hair was orange
not red, my three-year-old son begins to lecture
Sofia's mother on the differences between
dragons and dinosaurs while I share a beer
with Syed as he grills onions, vegan burgers,
and kosher hotdogs in his backyard.
He tries to explain how the Women's March poster
of the woman wearing the American flag hijab
can be considered both liberal and conservative.
I listen closely because I want it to make sense
but Robbie interrupts with a line from Bob Kaufman.
Syed thinks Robbie's talking about Andy Kaufman
and does a lame Elvis lip and hip impersonation.
I ask if Bob Kaufman's the guy who directed
Eternal Sunshine of the Spotless Mind where
Kirsten Dunst quotes Alexander Pope but calls him
Pope Alexander. Robbie gives us the finger
before leaving to join Jamie and Lucy's discussion
about the new James Baldwin documentary
I Am Not Your Negro. Jamie claims Baldwin's
Sonny Liston article floats like a butterfly
while Norman Mailer's stings like a bee.
Melissa shows my wife a picture of her brother
when he was four years old, insisting
Tell me that doesn't look exactly like my son
while my preteen daughter lies on a lounge chair
ignoring us all, her legs extended like the necks
of excavators. She's busy converting the final scene
of *Full Metal Jacket* into a gif on her iPhone,
clipping it where American soldiers march
through burning rubble, their dirty faces lit by the sweat
of fire, singing *The Mickey Mouse Club* theme,
spelling out "Mickey Mouse" letter by single letter.
I hear my son tell Sofia's mother he doesn't have
ten fingers. I watch him lift his palms to her face.
I only have eight, he says. These two are thumbs.

NORTHERN AGGRESSION

Like a rainbow trout caught in overfished waters,
for the good of the habitat and fishermen
who may come after, we let it off the hook.
We've been hearing the same arguments since Appomattox.
Words are only light; what's needed now is fire
to finally end the Civil War and rid ourselves
of anti-federalist, state's rights fundamentalists.
The older generation won't like it
but this older generation is the problem
we will solve by federalizing New York state's tuition-free
college proposal so kids can stay in state
and get a university education or travel
to New York, California, Michigan and get
an out-of-state education for the same cost.
Kids will leave the South and the country will blend,
diversify as kids from Brooklyn, Bloomfield Hills,
and Brentwood, happy to get away from home,
will spend four years in South Carolina,
Mississippi, or Arkansas before getting the hell out.
And when native Southerners graduate from Northern schools
they'll never go back to thinking the planet's 10,000 years old,
or that climate change is liberal propaganda,
or that Jesus rode a pterodactyl,
or that corporations are people who deserve voting rights
or that the Deist rhetoric of the Founding Fathers presupposes they intended
the United States to be a Christian nation in perpetuity,
or that economic segregation is not planned segregation,
or that a free market will regulate itself,
or that there's no need for Black Entertainment Television since there's
no White Entertainment Television as though ABC, CBS, Fox, and NBC
are not a monopolized White Entertainment Television conglomerate
where sitcoms set in New York City lack any black actors much less characters,
or that one's sexual history dictates one's sexual identity,
or that the NRA isn't a business front for a terrorist organization,
or that feminism is an encroachment on male sovereignty,
or that the Confederate flag is suitable to present anywhere
other than in a Rebel museum or a Dixie Land cemetery.

George Kalamaras
SO WE CAN TEACH OURSELVES NOT TO BLEED

—for Sandy Denny

I don't know if I ever walk
down a narrow stair without thinking
of you, Sandy, or paper-cut myself, mildly,
and watch my finger almost bleed.

Your voice is great and awful
and gifts us. To be *full of awe*
when I turn to wash a fork, a glass,
run my fear along the rim, the warm

edge of the knife, and calibrate
your less-than-half-a-life. Thirty-one years
is younger than some bars of soap, younger,
even, than a middle-aged tortoise by a decade or two.

Your songs held something of your pain, an ancient
sway—your British folk voice voicing a past
when we could easily step into a pile of fifteenth-century
manure and die of staph. You sat with a candle

by your breast, burning centuries back in the dripping wax
so we could hear our years in what we hoped
one day not to bleed. How the death of a horse
from four centuries before might be lodged there

in our nerve endings, then stir one morning, unexpectedly,
when the car refuses to start, when we take a moment
to hear a nickering as we caress a tube of glue,
mistakenly step on a pump-house ant

and beg forgiveness for the blind depths of our step.
But I am no Jain monk, Sandy, sweeping insects free
from unsuspecting dirt, no Lancashire abbot-scribe,
no Privy Counsel mending the candle's wax.

Let's "Meet on the Ledge," as you say,
eat bowls of cold stone soup at the table
of Shakespeare's *Timon of Athens*, fierce it out
with Lear, with an insolent handmaiden, and feel

the scruff of our past so we can teach ourselves
how not to bleed. Inside, Sandy. Where the how and why
and in what way of your voice is there gathering
the night—gathered by the night—and all it bleeds.

ARTHUR WALEY'S DEATHBED PHOTO

For years I'd wanted to hang it on the wall
of my meditation room. To say to the world,
This is your mirror. The inside howl of the wind's guts.
Highgate, 27 June 1966 is not only then but 846 C.E.
Po Chü-i left the body and his years of suffering.
The corpse he saw, that night alone at the Hsien-yu Temple.
"Golden Bells." "Remembering Golden Bells." "Fishing in the Wei River."
These and more, Waley, you gave us,
with "The Chrysanthemums in the Eastern Garden."
Now I wonder why you lay in bed facing east,
a floral wreath fogging your bookshelf
but no hound dog to lick the salt that likely left
through the pores of your fever. Someone placed a book
in your hands. I want to think it was Tu Fu, still wandering.
We are all in exile from the things that love us.
We think we love, that we want the world. That we ache
more than constant wind sorrow. We "Winter Night."
We "Dragon of the Black Pool." We "The Beginning of Summer."

There is much confusion. No action words to describe our inaction.
Words of love linger our lips. Even as a corpse,
you move. Someone has opened curtains toward the garden.
Light bathes your chin, prominent nose, prods remnants of breath
to join the rest of you. Wang Wei is playing the lute,
chanting, *You brought us, brother, again unto the world.*
Now you are dead or continuing
to die. No one to Lazarus this corpse of a man in Highgate.
If you had a hound, pieces of you
would be alive in the dog's broken heart.
There is no one among men, Po Chü-i said,
that has not a special failing. One of my many
is for this photo. For years, I wanted to hang it round my neck.
To say to the mirror each morning, *We will all one day have no day.*
No night. To peer into your shelf and count the books
you left behind. I imagine the cotton-felt tongue
of your pajamas and how much more rough they are
than the dog's possible pleading. Impossible
you had no dog. That you had nothing warm to stroke
the final breath release. You, no longer "Madly Singing in the Mountains."
I that was once a man of the North am now an exile here.
So said Po Chü-i when he bought the wild goose at market
just to set it free. Your words, Arthur, flutter backwards
and forwards at once, uncaged and streaming.
Now, it is fifty years since the birth of your death.
For years I wanted to hang this photo on a boat
traveling the Yangtze. To let it move through the ghost
of Li Po, as he tries, still, to hold the moon,
floating away.

(June 24, 2016)

Rodger Kamenetz
HOMER AND PENELOPE

—Master I wrote a love poem and now I'm in love.
Homer nodded a vast silence that held the idea of space.
—Master how do I find the words?
The landscape spread below us a peopled valley. Light streamed from a hidden center in each person's chest. Then the rays joined together as a second sun a vanishing point where all light returns until it can come again. Yet each and all go about their day connecting only sparsely. That was the tragedy of the lack of vision that leads to war.

Blind Homer knew all about it. People stumbled past each other in the daylight dark. But a little girl lit a candle in the name of love and all the names were lit by it even *death*. She turned to me with a diamond eye. The word she spoke then I am still trying to remember. It was the perfect word all poets seek the perfect rhyme. Instead of Homer I now longed for Penelope, for home.

NEKIYA

—Odyssey Book 11

Sprinkle blood into the dug pit and thirsty ancestors rise up to drink. Hold back on tipping the jug of blood until they answer your cruel questions. You need to know how you got here lost. Wanderer with so many questions stirring up hard scrabble with your wrinkled hand. You too will go under you are already thirsty. You too will have answers no one needs until they are lost.

Here comes my mother with her last breath. Here comes my father stepping into thorns. There goes the sky a torn envelope. Here is the son who never heard his name. Down tips the gray cloud pouring dim rain. There is the child never born. The stick makes a crease in the broken ground. The blood stains the walls of the hole. The thirsty tongues of ghosts turn red in the poured blood. They speak: beholding and beheld.

Lilah Katcher

INVASION

After H.D.

You loom older than memory   graystone rising to white-covered heads
troops of giant   climb slow   wooden tread
plant deep footholds   steadily devour
your rocky sides   grassy meadows   aster and lupine
until you drown   in pools of fir

WINTER LANDSCAPE WITH ICE SKATERS

On the painting by Hendrick Avercamp, known as the Mute of Kampen

Admire the life in this painting:
So many bodies, busy with movement,
vivid against the dull winter sky that shows all the colors
of no color. The lake holds a muted upside-down world, not the world
of the artist, whose brush transformed a cacophony of detail
into living warmth spread across the ice.

Here, a couple skates hand in hand, and there, a boy readies his hockey stick.
Another boy points, laughing, at a man lying flat on his face.

How the painter controls your gaze:
Pulls it to the right, to the distance, and back again,
but never toward death. You must be told: follow the birds to the leftmost tree,
then look down to where its roots are buried under snow.
In that corner, a dog and bird eat
what used to be a horse.

Sandra Kolankiewicz
SNOW ON THE MOUNTAIN

We used a machete to hack the stems
off at the bottom so the cuttings would
be tall, tower over the vase on the
porch, the petals fluttering down with our
laughter: snow on the mountain. Imagine
our surprise to find in the morning we
were covered with sores from where the milk had
touched our hands and arms, hives on our necks and
chests, blisters on our arms from carrying
the branches as we crossed the lawn in our
rubber boots, the path we made from garden
to steps strewn with leaves and blooms we lost on
the way. For weeks the welts lingered on our
bodies in the summer heat, keeping us
from contact with others. We swallowed draughts
of antihistamine and scratched ourselves.

Kathleen Kraft
CUMULATIVE RAINFALL

The rain is cooler, drearier today as August draws
to a close and Houston floods continuously,
and we sink lower into climate grief. I click on
a heroic story: Cowboy Chance Ward and son Rowdy
swimming their horses through the heavy waters
of Liberty County to corral lost cows.
Excitable tourists now, they gallop toward land with the Wards.

There's more, of course, from across the globe—
but today's high card: the First Model clicking
down the Texas tarmac in sky-high snakeskin stilettos
and mirrored aviators...to help people?
And someone and a thousand people on Facebook say,
Who cares. But what should we care about now?

My partner's mother who lives downstairs and has Alzheimer's,
has a refrain: *August is almost over, soon the kids will be back in school.*
She's rushing things along—apparently a lifelong habit
but she's also making conversation, being social—
screens are of no interest to her, just the past
and the confusing future.

I've had enough of August, too—the clips, the streams,
the march of white hate—What stage of dementia
are we living in now? Will September's clarity arrive,
diffusing memory and reflection? Will it cool us
as the flood recedes and returns with more posts to cling to?

How should I share *today?*

I refill Agnes's stash of Red Rose, slice a juicy peach for us—
Some days the tea is so good, she says with a smile,
not rushing anything for a change.
I feel inspired and make a cup, and we chat a bit,
then she looks towards the window and says,
August is almost over, soon the kids will be back in school.

Andrew Lafleche
FORGET THE REST

he didn't resist when we took him from his daughters
he didn't resist when we used zip ties to bind his wrists

we paraded him from his village, all the neighbors aware
we were kids; this man had a family. had a family.

unprepared, we stacked sandbags. wrapped the five by
five cell in barbs, fashioned a door in razors and wire;
set guards around the clock

I've never been to war, but I was there this day.
his religion demanded prayer five times daily

I took the fifth watch, the mosque sounded, he stared
betray my country or betray my brother, remember humanity

I spoke to him in broken Pashtu, he knew English
my rifle readied, I opened the door, removed his restraints
secured the door again, as he faced West, bowed, and prayed

Susan Lewis
DUMB LUCKS

—after "What we didn't know then" by Dawn Lundy Martin

What we didn't know then was the submissive nature of truth when belief was mandatory as water or air. The ease with which it could be hoisted & tossed, as if you were Mr. & Mrs. Universe. Every image having to do with an attitude of arrival, a slim European cigar tapped & balanced. A fury warming your explanations, daring us not to demur. What we didn't know then was the puny feeling at the core. One might say, perhaps, that there were a man & a woman with different if like things to prove. That we were a captive audience, flickering in & out of view like a convenience, an after-thought, a weak signal. What we didn't know then was the interlock of tall tales & the slow-burning emergency of survival. Incongruities pricking the bubble of belief like splinters threatening to fester. The intuition of hazard buried & unearthed, surfacing to commandeer our breath. In the yard there were other dumb lucks, like the anxious animal punished & pampered as a weapon of revenge. What we didn't know then was how an observer—one of you, perhaps, or someone else entirely—might have noticed a child's sorrow & reconsidered that elegant cigar, how it made you feel both big & small, how you wanted to be convinced it belonged in your nervous, graceful fingers.

VALOR ADDED

—after "Association" by Rosmarie Waldrop

As peace crumbles
piece by cracked and

fractured piece of
rough and ready

scrapping for a fight in the
fright of the spit-storm

burning the wages
of some,

tracing the music,
facing the trajectory,

unlinking the chain
of demand.

Or disagree to agree
in this group with no members

floating in the ether
bobbing to the song of the spheres.

There were limousines.
There was war and abomination.

It was America,
caging continents.

We made placards
and childlike icons

to battle the
reign of prison,

of search and destroy,
firestorm and barricade,

self-suiting
hide the ball,

dodging off that
all may die or mouth

the break fist
of champions.

Like so much excess and
valor, value added like

scrapped recognition,
cognition re-tooled to

interrupt this broadcast.
Emergency nullification system

stopped, dropped, and sold.
Rubbing skin to skin

with the best of them,
riding the slippery slope of

fingers kind and un-,
new selves sprouting pleasure

and pain and fear and
fear of pleasure and pain and fear.

Sweet. First.
Breast. Kiss.

Technique of
comporting explanation,

wallowed holes
swallowed whole.

Cream castles afloat
on cloud mine.

Asking back
what is to be done

not what is said to
be done to say what

is done to be said when
all is said and gone.

That wan hope
for warm hands

in the coldly
burning sun.

Miles Liss
FOLDING UP NETS

Prairie grass rubs against my jeans
as I help Nico fold up nets
she uses to measure declining
bird populations.

Bobolinks, grasshopper
sparrows,
red-winged blackbirds,
meadowlarks.

Blue sky far as the eye
can see,
then endless deserts of commerce:
corn, alfalfa, and soy.

Over thin strips of sanctuary,
phalaropes, dickcissels,
eastern kingbirds, and sedge wrens
build nests in prairie grass
to hide their young.

Kristian Macaron

THE WAYS I HOLD MY FLOODS

For all the constellations I have learned, star cyphers and moonsets confuse me, unwieldy wheels of phase, but I have been entombed and unburied and the ways I know to hold my floods are mystic, even though I'm desert skinned and scaled and two halves of a moon, I know that we all have different kinds of water holding. I used to find it strange the way that quicksand murmured, but now I find it even more peculiar that I can't rush through my days without forging some soft anchor. If marshes are wide prairie sinkholes, desert lakes self-stranded, meadows wet with rain or tidal pools of salted grass—holding all and keeping so the hopes can't disappear or we are lost when the rain halts mid-laughter, no reason for swamps, their river-forest holding, passing, burying all and breathing water passages, from caverns of *Bogs, the cloying ancients,*   currents, but some is bewildered, forever, in deep arterial roots, entry to new veins,   *and in them there is sinking*;   by way of skeletons and orchids. Hidden fens, the constant quiet shallow rivers, high   *we all want to say*   waters, thin rain shells, someone calling my name and I answer, but my voice sounds   *we've never been there but*   like wildflowers in the wind. Maybe they are wind, but probably they are water too or   *we have: fallen to a blanket of unknown*   another wild whisper. I play by ocean rules, but I will never map the waves I'm made of: *earth and unculled dark*   empty orchids, crossing winds, crocodiles cooling in the night. Moons setting like flower petals fall into the mud.

Joyce Enzor Maust

MAKING A CIGARETTE RUN WITH A TRIO OF MY HOMELESS FRIENDS

The smell of unholy incense
mingles with that of alcohol.
Outside the car's open windows,
the lights of the city danse macabre.

The Vet's gnarled fingers grip a Winston.
He recites to all who will listen,
"In 'Nam, I shot a kid to stay alive."
Silence always follows.
The cross tattoo on his left arm
runs murky.

An American Spirit dangles between
the talons of the Wanderer.
Jumping trains from coast to coast,
he once stabbed a killer to death
in an L.A. park—
a karmic blemish he keeps close.

In the Boy's shaky hand,
a Lucky Strike Long burns low.
His father's fists
sheltered him from the world.
New to the street, he struggles.
He's still finding his voice—
it's in the process of changing.

Faces upturned in rapt devotion
and the radio a cantor—
"Don't Stop Believing"
becomes a doxology.
And the choir sings
with more conviction
than harmony.

Mark Melnicove

UNCLE B WOULD SAY

Uncle B would say, "The line between dreams and waking
is nonexistent. I cannot fathom how I, as a youth,
found courage to fall asleep, for each time I woke I left
undone all I had been. And so, here I am—disheveled,
unfounded—missing what I could not take
with me, and can only visit on rare nights when lost visions
spring forth—a stray cat, a hungry crow, a limping horse—
beings I can almost touch and soothe, before it is my fading
form I inhabit, waking again, shivering in starlight."

IF WEEDS MADE NOISES

If weeds made noises from within as we do, if
they sat in judgment and levied fines
when they were pulled,
if stones could be commanded to move
to make room for them,
if they became angry at being called weeds
and not their given names—*Taraxacum,
Chenopodium album, Stellaria media*—
if houses were for them and not humans,
if no one evicted them,
then Uncle E would be happy.

Nancy Mercado
CATCALLS TO MY BRAIN

No 1980s tight young ass to pounce on anymore
No smooth skin to assault anymore
No frightened little girl to follow
Down cold shitty Lower East Side streets anymore

Nowadays the boys catcall my intellect
Corner me in conference rooms
Universities
In restaurants

¡¿Oye mami cuántos libros has leído?!

¡No sabes na bruta!

Where did you graduate from *mami*?!

Your university degree means *nada nena*!

They attempt to inflict
Injuries with blank pages
To drown me out
Under piles of exclusions
To erase my existence
To whittle me down
To a stub

N o t h i n g

Silence.

These days my catcallers
Are the intelligentsia
Postmodern jeering elitists
Hyperbolic hipsters swooping in to take charge
Our modern-day land grabbers
The white settlers of the information age
Revolutionary revisionists

My cat-calling boys come with females in tow these days
Sold-out dames of trendiness
Fast-talking fools
Puking memorized conceptual hullabaloos
Living delusions

They are lost souls

Existing in their own holograms of fame
Convinced masses in the world
Know their name
Believe their immortality

Don't my catcallers understand
They have yet to be born?

Michael Milburn
STRONG SILENT

Not saying much
is my defining trait.

Even when I think I've been chatty
I hear the opposite,

as if talkative to me
is taciturn to others,

and more than that—
hostile, distant, cold.

Tight-lipped stars,
Eastwood, de Niro,

Neeson, McQueen,
smolder in a way I don't.

What they have
is what I'm after:

an enigma effect,
putting up walls

the world wants
to break through.

Liz Minette
PIANO

Only the keyboard above water,
Eric Harding is playing piano
in his flooded house somewhere
in Houston.

Over the radio, the notes sound
delicate and poignant, a weave
of survival and half-note tears.

After she died, the auctioneer's men
chopped apart Connie's piano because
they didn't want to haul it intact upstairs.

It was the piano we as kids
used to play on, plunking
the keys that looked like
wooden teeth, and that made
sounds between brass clang
and dying carousel.

It was the piano because
Connie wanted it. It was the piano
Louise the cat would caress her long,
gray Siamese tail against making
the upright wood seem softer.

The men now bring the piano,
its body, out in trash bags, lay it
amidst other articles of a whole life
displayed in the estate sale rain.

Miles David Moore
GRANDMA AND THE HURRICANE

"The Big Dipper—she's losing!"

The wind is so strong that it blows the constellations around in the sky. Never losing their shape, they are cookie cutters tumbling against each other. A spray of misty stars spills from the Big and Little Dippers, and from the jug of Aquarius. The two fish of Pisces flop helplessly, impaled on the trident of Poseidon. Aries, Taurus, and Leo charge Sagittarius, who cannot steady his bow. Canis Minor laughs to see such sport.

Earth, caught in the gale, feels unsteady under your feet. There is only one thing to do: tell Grandma.

You watch the cartoon you running into Grandma's house. The real you stands in her kitchen, warm and smelling of the chicken broth that simmers with her homemade noodles on the old-fashioned stove. She is snapping beans into her battered iron pot, as you have seen her do more times than you can count in your half-decade of life.

Grandma is calm and patient. She always is.

"What is it, honey?" she asks, not looking up from her beans.

You want to say, "GRANDMA, GRANDMA, THERE'S A HURRICANE!" You know that if you say that, everything will be all right.

But the invisible hand reaches from behind and grips your mouth. All you can say is, "Grahh, grahh, therahurrahane!"

Grandma never looks up. She never learns of the danger that only you could warn her of.

And you wake up, in your calm dark bedroom, a gentle breeze playing in the starlight outside your window.

You think of that again, waking not a half-decade but a half-century later, to a howling wind of February. Invisible hands throw fistfuls of stars at your windows. The three a.m. clouds admit no light; the streetlamps flicker in the storm. You are alone, and you can see Grandma only in your dreams.

Elisabeth Murawski
FROM THE STATION

Two margaritas.
An army of cold streets.
The Bronx sparsely lit
with Christmas tree lights.

I fight maternal images,
whack Mary
down the middle. Impatient
busy signal, she lies there

beeping in the straw,
trying on
the imagined assault,
the code blue heart.

The breakfast *Times*
crackles. Mary
must have died
on that train. No lie

is safe with me.
I walk the coals, a two-bit
fakir. My electrons
sparkle. I do not burn.

URN WITH HUMMINGBIRD

Superstitious, she never put shoes on a table
or hung things on doorknobs.

The elephants she collected
all had their trunks up.

Was it bad luck to answer my questions?
Daddy was dead, couldn't hurt us.

Unforgettable, her letter, the enclosed
clipping from *Newsweek*

on memory, kids making up touch.
And now she's grit and powder.

The urn they bought my sister
has a hummingbird on it.

Sugar water in the feeder
drew them to her window.

I hear she told her daughter
in her last days

"There are things so terrible
I'll never tell you."

I want to shake her awake
in her pretty little house.

To say "Come back
and tell me what you know!"

Jordan Pérez

WILD CACTUS

Every woman should be told she has two weeks left
to live so that she will bake a cake in moonlight
and eat it with the last of the artisan honey,
with the inherited rum saved for her wedding day.
Then she will tell things just as they are—
that pears are gallbladders and Sundays
goldfinches and even the finest beet tastes like dirt
tastes like leaning through a car window and saying
goodbye. Let her tell about being the other woman,
that it was like holding sugar beneath her tongue
that he smiled the way wild cactus tastes—
brined and viscous in a blown-glass jar
that she comes and goes as she pleases
because she is dying, and has important
things to tell about, like how cacti are fish fins
and sweet potatoes shriek in the steamer.
Let her tell that while she is sad to have forgotten
so many waving trees
that her dying will not be shut like a box.
It will be flung open, blown from the mouth

THEODORE ROOSEVELT ISLAND

When you reach the shore you will smell what you have learned
to call fish but is just sweet rot. Run your fingers
through it as you might my hair, forgetting
how many sticks you have casually broken along
the way. Sweet man, do not forget to look down. See—
pine bark has crusted off like snakeskin, leaves of sea
glass, berries with green nipples, rocks blushed like kidneys,
sticks waiting patiently for their excavation,
an elephant foot stump, stones so pocked they may be
just peach pits, a daddy long leg compound where the
leader has one very long leg like men sometimes
have in their beards. You will see my prayer carved into
the cedar where I grooved your name so deep, will long
for me to taste the wormy tree goodness with you.
Beloved, this is free for the taking. I will come
make us a home out of soft leaves.

David Romanda

BEFORE I MOVE IN

I'm patching up
The holes
Sandy's ex
Punched in the walls.
I can't fix
The door, though.
That'll have
To be replaced.
I wonder if,
Given time,
I'll punch my own holes
In these walls.
I wonder if I too
Will break down the door.

Mark Rubin
MOUSE AND FOX

Their tails gone, three blind mice,
Invisible, Irrelevant, and Alone,
felt the ground beneath their feet move.

A mouse body ends where a twig begins;
yours, at the end of a white cane
and book in a folding chair outdoors.

I left to pour a glass of iced tea.
Your back was bent like a stick of licorice,
fingertips reading the raised bumps on the poem:

> *Mouse and Fox*

> *The whiskered mouse ran quickly*
> *though the dark, a pipsqueak*
> *minding its own business, clueless*
> *a nearby fox was minding it too...*

God of touch, so untouchable,
God of the failed heart, so imminent.

Was it a blind or sighted mouse hiding
under the last leafy word on your page
its tiny breath, trembling
in the right-hand margin, a red fox
tensed with an appetite for wet mouse?

Did your heart stop one word too soon
to warn the mouse that saw the fox
that saw you spill like a sack of molecules?

God of why now, so unknowable,
God of no returns, who takes back everything,
talk to me.

Leslie M. Rupracht
WHIRLED PEAS, MAN

In Saturday's cold evening rain,
I pump gas into the tank of my aging Toyota.

One aisle over, a guy pulls up in a '69 Beetle
the color of Heinz ketchup, a peace sign

on left rear-side window, Michigan classic car
plate on back bumper. As petroleum feeds

his Volkswagen, the loud engine idles. Mentally
I plead with him to cut it off, show respect

for those breathing its exhaust. I want to tell him
it's illegal to leave the motor running in North Carolina

but have no idea if it's true. I'd really like to ask
how he dares drive the ultimate cool hippie car yet

cares nothing about his carbon footprint. It's dark.
I bite my tongue, feel unsafe to pursue environmental

preaching. My tank fills and the safety fails. Gasoline
spurts out, puddles onto pavement, sprays

my jeans and suede boots. Now I'm part of the problem,
and I'm profoundly pissed off.

Beate Sigriddaughter

EMILY WATCHES HIM SHARPEN KITCHEN KNIVES

Rust red stone, water, patience.
A thin pitched sound repeats
as steel glides to perfection.
She wishes one could sharpen love
like that to trim the dull
fat of acceptance and complacency.

ROSEMARY HONEY

A man just stomped on her
last sliver of interest
in a desperately friendly gathering
by blistering her words
with expert self-absorption.

It is not just contempt she feels,
but boredom, emptiness, as hungry
ghosts circle around the potluck spread,
picking up an olive of applause,
a grape of mild wrath, a crumb
of visibility, a boastful morsel
of consideration of the moment.

A woman looks at her with starving
eyes. She can tell they have nothing
in common. Somehow, they must
survive. *Someone said you brought
this honey*, Emily says. *Oh yes*,
the woman eagerly responds. Her eyes
relax. *It's rosemary honey. We also
brought cheeses from upstate New York.
Try some. They go together well.*

ON ICE

Every woman wants a volunteer
to love, someone who wants to give
her pleasure even as she lets him off
the hook. So Emily, for example, one
New Year's Eve at the ice rink.
They'd made a date two weeks before.
He didn't seem particularly enthusiastic,
so she told him, *If you don't want to,*
I'll go skate by myself. She never thought
he would accept and opt to sit nearby
in a café to read a magazine, while she
rented her skates and entered the rink.
The music was sweet, the lights
were magical as she skated round
and round, gliding among children
who seemed far more experienced
than she was on the rink laced with laughter.
Blue turned to pink, to purple. Though
she hardly noticed. The hope in her
kept throbbing. For an hour she expected him
to change his mind, to suddenly appear
with skates on his feet, laughing
as they cautiously held hands,
imitating professionals with attempts
at grace, then quickly grabbing a gate
or a post or a railing for balance. Once
she thought she saw his ponytail, but
she was mistaken. In the second hour
she made peace with the amazing flame
in her chest, still keeping a shrine for hope,
even for a half hour, a quarter. Then time
was up. A fanfare, a wish for a happy
new year. *Did you enjoy yourself?*
he asked. For a moment she considered
lying. Then she said no.

Noel Sloboda
PROGRESS REPORT

Last semester, the government funding came through to support our
project of cloning famous writers. We only received 60% of what we
requested, so we had to make some adjustments. We did not have a
chance to fully vet our Shakespeare DNA. As such, we produced a Gilbert
rather than a William. In another case of mistaken identity, we created
a Thomas Wolfe instead of a Virginia Woolf. But upon reflection, most
agreed that this was a blessing. The successful clones retain peculiarities
of the original authors, which we had not anticipated. Our Christopher
Marlowe insists he can only compose by the light of candles—something
(we explained to him several times) we can't allow because of safety codes.
Likewise, our Edith Wharton maintains she can only pick up a pen while
in a king bed, even though there is no space for additional furniture inside
our lab. Despite such minor challenges, we have had encouraging results,
especially during Friday evening happy hours. Our Fitzgerald makes
martinis for everyone, and after two or three drinks our Dorothy Parker
tells jokes so dirty they would make the Devil blush. Once the company
finishes adjusting to our milieu, we're pretty sure most of them will make
great literature again.

Ellen McGrath Smith

SHAKEN 19: DEVOURING TIME BLUNT THOU THE LION'S PAWS

Yes, and set it [the lion] on that rock, over there,
poking out from the side of
the mountain.

Back and forth we can stare; I'll sing to him
in such a way he tries to dance,
but being on a precarious perch, it will take the form
of furious scratching

against the rock
beneath him. If that happens and the claws
disappear,
I'll name that lion fear.

SHAKEN 22: MY GLASS SHALL NOT PERSUADE ME I AM OLD

She wobbled, held the backs of chairs,
to keep from what? She hobbled,
and I asked her if she still was doing yoga.

She said yes, then joked that meant
she would live forever.
I don't see her much,
we were at a funeral, my uncle's,
just a few years older than she.

Let me tell you about yoga.
Sometimes, I am in a contest
with a roomful of bodies
thirty years my junior.
I am thirty years her junior,
and I wonder if I came off
as condescending.

There are few things people
much younger than I can say
that I don't hear as condescending
(when did that start?). Suddenly,
I know a part of my parade
of selves is ending.

Jeff & I went up last week to Seven Springs
to visit our students at their writing retreat.
We were giving them some writing prompts,
or as he put it, *exercising the young*.

Of my fifties, I keep hearing the line
from Frost: *What to make
of a diminished thing?* The student of mine
who wrote his paper on that poem last fall
stopped by today. He complimented
my hair and asked if I was growing it out.
I can take this as condescension if I want.

Of yoga and living forever, I said to my aunt,
but would you want to? This was meant
to show I understood something important
about aging. Another kind of contest.

On Facebook, I see that L., who turned ninety
in December, is letting her gray come in.
She sits in her profile pic's powdery halo
as though beaming in from another world.

SHAKEN 25: LET THOSE WHO ARE IN FAVOR WITH THEIR STARS

The marigold souls for which we toiled
        are razed quite. Those who are in favor
with their stars buy orchids and keep them
alive all year round.

Our stars were the marigold souls, painful
        warriors warding off bees
with their peppery petulant scents.

The sun's eye oversees the frowning
stems and deadheads, unloaded pistils.

We toiled for them with the stretch
        of our chromosomes into the moment at hand.
We told ourselves no longer would we toil
as they had to
for the princes and their favorites.

We planted them as if they were princes,
and in principle, according to the lessons
the nuns taught us in school, they were.

Those who are in favor with their stars
        would raise their hand in class and blame
the labor unions for the razing. You can see
the shimmering vases that support them,

crystalline, prismatic their distortion.

J.D. Smith
MUSHROOMS

They are of the nature of brilliance:
from nowhere, or between places, until

an August rain and dark hours
raise their society.

Buttons that emerge privately
in the salons of grasses,

then draw moist encouragement
silently sipping at dew, sipping at the water table—

that springs sudden caps into light
where they cantilever, stems thickened,

flaunt veils for the world to see,
and swell, grown gregarious,

waving colors to one another
at a distance, form clumps and bunches,

gather in troupes and circles, still swelling.
A few, drunk on humus,

stoop to consuming stumps,
or scale trees toward bracket cousins.

By sunset skins of all shades split,
peeling from growth

they cannot shape or shield, releasing
flesh to its contortions in the air

as prescient gills flare, freeing spores
in soil and wind

before a clear night and dry dawn leave
the flaked ash of a humid fire.

A VANISHING

The Man in the Moon eroded to a ghost
and the mountains smoothed away.

The rest dissolved like
a ball of talc in the wind.

Then no great light ruled the night, only lesser
points in shifting leagues and alliances.

For want of tides' lullaby
many lost sleep and sickened.

Some died exhausted
from long striking the waters

as if they might be revived.
Or punished.

Maya Sonenberg
THE LOST POEM, 1978

for Merce Cunningham

New York night/outside the windows

I went to a rehearsal of an Event at Westbeth. From the risers, watched it form from separate pieces into a whole beautiful entity. The dancers would do a section. Merce would talk to them, make corrections. They would repeat it and repeat it. In silence.

The extended leg/the arched back/intertwining twigs

Feet striking, lungs struggling/to stretch the leg to the other side of the room

Dancers dark shapes/before the lights come on

New York night/outside the windows

New York night/outside the windows

Rehearsing his solo. Just walking around, moving one arm, kneeling down. Not dancing but what he was going to do, doing it almost.

The extended leg/the arched back/intertwining twigs

I had to write a prospectus for the poem in order to submit it for a prize. Like all such prospectuses, it was crap. I won't torture you with it here.

Not completely lost; drafts survive in my journal.

Rehearsing his solo. Just walking around, moving one arm, kneeling down. Not dancing but what he was going to do, doing it almost.

He puts her down gently/her hands on his shoulders/and head bent

Wind to boat to sea

Written Event

I had to write a prospectus for the poem in order to submit it for a prize. Like all such prospectuses, it was crap. I won't torture you with it here.

Wind to boat to sea

In Events, Cunningham combined dances (or parts of them) in a new order—overlapping, juxtaposing. There was no music or new music or music chosen by chance from the repertory. Costumes pulled from the closet.

Not completely lost; drafts survive in my journal.

Energy transfer/windmill, waterwheel

Written Event

I went to a rehearsal of an Event at Westbeth. From the risers, watched it form from separate pieces into a whole beautiful entity. The dancers would do a section. Merce would talk to them, make corrections. They would repeat it and repeat it. In silence.

Winter 1978. I was a high school senior, taking class at Cunningham's Westbeth studio 2 or 3 times a week.

I had to write a prospectus for the poem in order to submit it for a prize. Like all such prospectuses, it was crap. I won't torture you with it here.

After the other dancers picked up their sweaters and grapefruit peels and left, he was alone.

I went to a rehearsal of an Event at Westbeth. From the risers, watched it form from separate pieces into a whole beautiful entity. The dancers would do a section. Merce would talk to them, make corrections. They would repeat it and repeat it. In silence.

Step and push the earth behind

Wind to boat to sea

Feet striking, lungs struggling/to stretch the leg to the other side of the room

Energy transfer/windmill, waterwheel

It's not easy/making space concrete

Cunningham famously used chance operations to determine his dancers' entrances and exits and where they might meet; or to combine movements for head with movements for legs, arms, torso, etc.; or to sequence the movements he'd choreographed. As I have done here to order these lines.

Wind to boat to sea

Sometimes like lovers

It's not easy/making space concrete

Winter 1978. I was a high school senior, taking class at Cunningham's Westbeth studio 2 or 3 times a week.

Step and push the earth behind

Energy transfer/windmill, waterwheel

He was alone after the other dancers picked up their sweaters and grapefruit peels and left.

Sometimes he does such incredible things with space I gasp. Space becomes solid. Space moves around the dancer as the dancer moves through it. If those moments only went on for a fraction of a second longer, you would know....

Einstein says we curve our space.

Time.

Shenandoah Sowash

DAVE ANNOUNCES HE'S MADE PARTNER, SO I'M THINKING MAYBE I SHOULD TOO

Friends: I've made partner at the firm
of spending time badly, the firm of walking
along the muddy path, the firm of getting struck
by lightning which used to be the firm of setting
things on fire until we were acquired by
the firm of burning toast. Hell, Dave,
I've made partner for my mastery of the ordinary:
drinking water, sending in the rebate,
buying the softcover.

Said another way, if you intend to be successful
but instead find yourself alive when you thought you'd
have been dead years by now, well, that doesn't count.
There's no partial credit just because you harbored
a death drive fiercer than fame and somehow
you're still showing up each morning.

Catherine says that for people like us just staying
alive is a miracle and I want to believe her when
she tells me I'm fierce and remarkable,
when she calls me Woman, calls me tough.

They're going to throw me a party—the firm is,
and everyone's invited to dip shrimp in cocktail sauce
and talk about their kids. All the streamers will be
recycled phone books from places I used to live
and the evening's entertainment will be a storyteller

who specializes in myths about me.

Marilyn Stablein
THE BATHS

At first bell, I rise naked from sleep,
tie on a kimono in the dark. Pee, fold
a bath towel. Crooked footworn leather

sandals, lonely against the doormat.
A trail to the bathhouse passes the *dojo*.
Inside men and women sit in silence,

face a blank wall. Pillows cushion legs
folded above wood. Meditators
keep a steady breath watch.

Soaking in the steamy pool,
my limbs rise buoyant. Body half floats
in bubble spring. Shadows from tall,

fragrant weeds darken my thighs
like strokes from a bamboo brush.
Women bend and stretch: yoga, tai chi,

asanas, naked praises to a morning's sun.
One dawn I slip into an ancient pool
where Buddha soaked one full moon dawn.
Gone. Gone. Gone to the other shore
the farthest shore.

A HARD READ

A book with spikes like cactus thorns
is crammed between art books
on my library shelf. The book is a present
from a relative. We're not friendly

I should say. We haven't spoken in years.
But to acknowledge the gift
I decide to read the book.
It is not about Tibet.

I open the cover and start to read.
Immediately I vomit but bravely
keep going. Every time I turn a page
I vomit again.

Throughout the book I vomit on every page.
"Phew!" I say shutting the book
carefully to return it to the shelf.
"That's one hard book!
I don't recommend it."

Kurt Steinwand
SETTLERS

This particular citrus,
watered daily from a virgin spring,
balanced both sides of a slave.

They risk a sunny, exposed planting,
risk their Puritan ways,
venturing into savage forest.

Seedlings not yet clementine,
zipper-skin, kid-glove, the Latinate—
their taxonomy years away

on a Southern plantation
where sacrifice honors the bush
into flowery, fragrant tree.

Blood-orange ripened, blackened skins,
property like so many snuff tins,
flintlocks, livestock, pounds per bushel.

They harvest Senegambia coastal,
load up ships with nameless property.
Spoilage: percent loss of inventory.

All-out war for this single symbol,
mammon, pulp, a seed's survival
in the orgy of discovery.

RICK SUNSHINE

smelled real nice, like Hawaii.
Dated Haylie, my dream gal.
Tried out for football. Quarterback.
Ripped his ACL, had to rehab.

But he was no quitter. A mile tall,
Rick could dunk two basketballs,
throw a no-hitter. Girls dug his smile,
drawn to it like ants to a Bit-O-Honey.

Rick didn't need to study.
He leaned back, feet propped,
absorbed theorems, emitted his chemistry.
Was caught with a trunk full of pot,

laughed it off, joked about the plainclothes
approaching him in the seniors' lot.
Rick, shirtless in handcuffs. The image goes
with all the debutantes I didn't ask out.

Rick asked for me, then went with them himself.
A test drive, he called it, winking at me.
He could do that. He held a free pass, a wealth
of confidence that lined up the ladies.

I walked near him, hoped a few would drift my way.
Rick sort of floated, in Sperrys without socks.
High-fives at lockers. Freshmen carried his lunch tray.
Looked like he wore lipstick. Rick. Pretty boy. Jock.

The last time I saw him he was working overtime
on a fledgling lawn service ("Rick's"—you guessed it),
glistening like Charles Bronson bare-chested
running to tackle some molester. August of seventy-nine.

Today I look him up. Nothing. No heroic thrills.
Like Rick never existed, never got busted,
except in the movie that ratchets along in my head,
for which I edit the space he left to fill.

Marjorie Stelmach
UNJUST

Finding no traction on the slippery slant
of greenhouse glass,
a ragged gang of robins plunks
their little butts in the guttered snow and drinks
from the trough at the sky's metal edge,
                    where just
below their nodding beaks, a sheet
of mirrored clouds floats, and underneath,
it's springtime: tended rows of tender green.
Now and forever. World without end.
But not for the robin flock. Instead,
                    it's just
a world without—a plight they're long
familiar with. At intervals, a stubborn
or unworldly one is lured again,
but the slope remains too steep for grip,
the sky ungiving, and in the end
                        it's just
another promised land not meant for them.

Joseph Stern
GLOBAL REPORTS AND ANALYSIS

Line	Noun	Verb	Article	Conjunction Preposition	Adjective Adverb
1					This
2	takeover			by	
3	technology	is			
4		transforming			
5	culture	manufacturing			
6	it				
7	unit			by	
8	unit			into	
9			a		shiny
10					rust-proof
11					cost-efficient

To read the rest of this report, please register.

Global Reports and Analysis

Community driven, globally supported.
Welcome to the global community.
Robust, and open source.

Log In

Register

Inquiries

Gail White
THE AGING PROCESS

The question now is whether health or money
will give out first. I'm betting on the cash.
I've got good genes. My mother lasted, funny
as hell, to eighty-six before the flash
of blood that struck her brain. And then—no kids
to drag me bleating to the nursing home.
Here in my paid-for house, I can take bids
on all the furniture, and starve alone.

I'd like to fall asleep and be found dead
alone, my fingers eaten by my cats,
not in a hospital, but my own bed,
my last-read book face down beside me. That's
the ending I would like to choreograph.
Let others be dismayed. I'll have last laugh.

Sally Wilde
SNOW DAY

It's an old-timer's joke. When it snows, they call:
"Liberal Leave—That means liberals get to leave!"
Nature's predictable unpredictabilities, a big freak snow
(deniers say there's no such thing) springs the drones,
Federal workers, and their contractors, and their sub-contractors,
And their sub-sub-contractors from our pens in the cube farm
Before that 5 o'clock whistle blows. Down the rolling

Hills of McLean we slide in holiday mode,
And into the bar that bygone days called Charley's Place.
Halfway into the first round, and already the ends of our hair are touching.
It takes three to make a conspiracy: You're a drunk,
I'm a PR trinket; Eddie, just another glassed-up geek.
Where did you learn to make your voice sound like a man in a movie?
Is this the part where I stumble to the ladies room and everything goes black?

I don't know what brought you here, but I'll tell you what got me:
It was the smiley people on the PowerPoint, those scrawled emoticons,
There among the Getty-grab montage, the calculated ratio
Of racially ambiguous stock-photo faces and bare-faced
Helvetica, there it lay, that half-assed plan to swallow it all.
Most of them were all, yeah, OK, they saw it as a technical
Issue, more overtime, something to spin
For more gold. He saw it and turned cold.

You don't even have to be the type who's played these games
Since birth (it helps to have a dad who came home and drank and never
Came to your school or told you what he did all day in that suit) to know
A few simple hacks that can change your life! Ghost and encrypt,
Randomize, keep it all in draft form on a shared address,
A sort of cloud-based mutual masturbation; and, um, *cui bono*, what else?
Oh: Look for the glitch. Glitch first, then pattern recognition.
Your innocuousness is your greatest asset. Cultivate a single
Artisanally crafted eccentricity, as a sort of vaccine. You want to be
Overlooked. Like the Potomac. People live here for years
And never notice those rocks. That current. It's lethal.

The roads are ice and our wheels are spinning, trying to play it out,
Another million, another fiscal year, another sub-sub-sub—
(It makes a sound like going down the drain. It makes a sound
Like in a basement. Concrete. Rust-red water. A hole in the floor.)

Contract for the app that drives the device that drives the system that drives the
Payday. You come up gasping, like Jean Valjean out of the sewer
And into the snow, dented cars, salt-rimed and ice-stippled.
Slipped through their fingers again. It looks like Moscow out here.

XVI: THE TOWER: DRUNKEN JENGA NIGHT

I am only following orders to get out
More, make some new friends, get my mind off
Things. Like that. So it's margaritas in the babble
Of the bar, hours after the happy hour—it still smells
Of handbags and 5 o'clock breath, a fresh layer of powder.
I'd say that flop sweat of the cubicle still hangs
In the air like smoke, except no one is permitted
To smoke anymore. I sneak them. I sneak everything
These days; I am a master sneak, a sip, a look
At my phone, those are just the ones you catch me at,
Diversionary tactics so you won't notice the big deception.
You'd be wise to think of everything you see these days
That way. But to the task at hand (mine shake.
Are you sure you want me on your team?):
The destruction and simultaneous reconstruction of the tower.
One is the one that sets the tone. Two is the one I'll leave
Up to you. Three is the one that no one could see.
Four I perform for the man at the door,
Who couldn't bear keeping the order any more.
Five is the monster who waits at the gate
To topple the tipsy woman he hates. Six! Six! Six is success,
Writ large on the poster above the picture of a gleaming window wall.
Seven—oh, place what you have taken away
So carefully. More and more holes in the structure,
Rickety, swaying: You'll never get it back
The way it was. You know that's not the way
This game is played. Seven, seven, they all
Stop to watch what happens next.

Paula Yup
MY APARTMENT

for Betsy Sholl

feels like a museum

legacy of my husband Dean

passed after Christmas

his paintings

in the office

the living room

the kitchen

and the bedroom

a moth

mountains a waterfall

a stream

a sketch of Ansel Adams

a sketch of Leonardo's head of Mary

so even in my sadness

while the world lost a marine scientist

I lost a husband

while his handiwork

keeps me company

James Armstrong
LOCKS

Way back when we were in college, you had those long locks of beautiful golden hair. I remember how when we first met during the fall of freshman year I would watch your hair as it tumbled down over your shoulders or waved out in the wind. It occurred to me that you were the type of woman I wanted to marry one day—not you in particular—but someone like you. She would have long hair like yours, which she would wear in a braid or a ponytail in the summer, but in the winter she would let it hang down over the back of her neck, perhaps wrapping it in a scarf or—dare I hope it?—a fur-trimmed hood.

I'm not sure where I got such ideas, but they occurred to me so vividly then that I can't help but recall them now, all these years later. This beautiful ideal came into my head, a vision of precisely the kind of woman I wanted to be with—when the time came. I was in no hurry, of course. There were classes, and papers, and club meetings to attend. Someday, though, I would find a woman just like that, and I would be happy.

Perhaps that's why I was so surprised that day. You sent me an email, back in the days (unimaginable, isn't it?) when email was still new. This was the spring semester, though, so we were all pros by that point and used it constantly. The email said to meet you in your dorm if I wanted to see something crazy. You lived in Webster, the one we used to call the Nunnery, because all three floors were just women, while all the other halls were co-ed. The nickname was more than a little ironic, though, since we all knew what sort of things went on in there.

I got to your room, and written on the dry-erase board were the words "IN THE BATHROOM." I went to the bathroom, which was just two doors down, and knocked. "Come in!" you yelled.

"It's me," I said through the door. "I got your email."

"I know," you said. "Come in. You're almost too late!"

At that point, I still had some reservations about going into a women's bathroom. It was not uncommon to find men and women in the same restroom, sometimes showering together, sometimes just going in to pee because it happened to be closer. You had followed me into the men's room before, which was quite shocking the first time, less so after that. For me, though, it was different. I'd never been inside a women's room before, especially not in the Nunnery.

"Come on," you said. "It's almost over. Get in here!"

I pushed the door open a crack. "You sure you want me in there?"

"Stop being a wuss and come inside," you said. And so I did.

On the floor were whole haystacks of golden hair. You were smiling into the mirror, admiring what came to be your signature pixie haircut. Jess was behind you, still adding the finishing touches with a pair of scissors. How she learned to cut hair like that, I'll never know.

"My God," you said, "my head is so light! How did that happen?"

"You cut your hair," I said.

"Smart ass."

I wasn't actually being sarcastic. I just couldn't believe your beautiful hair was gone.

You must have seen that in my face, because after you looked at me, you immediately said, "It'll grow back." It didn't, though. You still have that same pixie cut on every Facebook photo you post. It suits you. I just had to adjust to such a drastic change from what I'd expected.

Afterward, we went back to my room so I could play you something from a new CD I'd bought. (Remember CDs?) You laughed at me because I locked my door. "No one's going to steal anything," you said.

"But my computer," I said.

"On this campus, please," you said. "I never lock my door, and I don't think anything's ever been stolen."

"You don't think...?"

"It hasn't," you said. And you were right. No one ever stole anything from your room, not even senior year, when Amy had that sketchy boyfriend from off campus who robbed half the rooms on her floor to get money for heroin. (By the way, can you believe heroin is a thing again? I thought we were the last generation stupid enough for that. I guess not...)

After I accidentally locked my roommate Alex out while he was taking a shower (and boy was he pissed) I stopped locking my door, too. We might have been idiots, but we were all idiots together, leaving our doors open and trusting each other to always do the right thing. It was just the way things were.

Sophomore year, though, you and I drifted apart for a while. There was that whole to-do with Cassie, which she always blamed on you, but given what we later learned about Cassie, it was probably her fault, anyway. Everything settled down eventually, but like everyone else, I kept my distance. It wasn't until the very end of that year that you and I became close again. I'm sorry about that.

I remember though, right before Easter, how you and I ended up in your room, talking all night. We talked about Cassie, and my crush on her, and how that had ended, and we talked about God, and having faith in the future, even when it's hard, and we talked about what we'd do after graduation, "when we grow up" we'd say, and we'd laugh about that.

I think that's when I told you I was a virgin. It wasn't like it was a secret, but I guess a lot of people assumed something happened between me and Cassie. In fact, a lot of things happened between me and Cassie, just not that.

You told me it was OK, and that you were a virgin, too, that you'd been waiting for the one God had picked for you, and you didn't care what anybody else thought, because there were lots of people in the world who waited. There were.

We talked deep into the night, and I said I didn't want to go home, and you said I didn't have to, and I said I did, and you said I could sleep over in your roommate's bed, since she lived close by and had gone home for Easter, but I couldn't sleep in her bed, so you said I could sleep on the floor, and you had a sleeping bag in the closet if I wanted it, and I said it was awfully late, and you said you thought I should stay, and that settled it. You rolled out the sleeping bag right next to your bed and I laid down on top of it. You handed me a pillow and a quilt, and you climbed into your bed. Once we were both comfortable, I turned off the light, but we kept talking. Easter was the next day, and since most of the rest of the students had gone home, campus would be quiet, and it would be nice. At some point, at who knows what hour of the morning, we drifted off to sleep.

The next day I woke up to the caress of your hand against my cheek. I looked up at you, and you brushed the hair away from my eyes. "Good morning," you said. You were lying in bed, and your right arm was dangling down off to the side. I looked up from the floor, and the light danced around your face like a halo. "Good morning," you had said, and with those two words, I think I might have fallen in love.

We spent Easter together, walking through the woods behind campus, and I can't think of a holier service we could have had. Monday morning, though, classes resumed, and I had that history paper to write, and you were afraid of failing statistics. Right after Easter was always crunch time until the end of the semester. Over the summer you met Peter, and I had Valerie to break my heart. Maybe that's why when we met up again in the fall, we were both so relieved to greet each other as friends.

You wrote postcards to me when you studied abroad for a semester in London, and we exchanged letters—not emails, but real letters—the summer before our senior year. I remember how that year was filled with anxiety, not just about what we would do after graduation, but what we would do without each other. We had grown such close friends, and the prospect of being without you frightened me almost as much as not having a job or knowing what to do with my life.

I ended up in New York City, a place that had always scared me, and you went home to Buffalo, which was supposed to be just temporary, but we all know how that can go. We kept up the correspondence for a while, but I was so busy working for the magazine back then, and you were reconnecting with friends upstate. I was pleasantly surprised, though, when you called me looking for a place to stay in the city. I was in Astoria then, but I had my own place, and there was plenty of crash space for you and your friend Damian, who had a gig to play in the East Village. Of course you could stay with me. And Damian, too. What were friends for?

Meeting the two of you at Port Authority, I realized how long it had been. For three years we hadn't seen each other, and there you were again, with the same pixie haircut, but no longer the smile I remembered. You seemed tired, and not just from the trip down from Buffalo.

Damian was a piece of work, wasn't he? He reeked of cigarettes and Greyhound bus. But while the first thing you wanted to do at my place was to take a shower, Damian asked for paper, plain white paper, and didn't even say why.

The next day was his gig, and this was back when the East Village was still the East Village, back when CBGB was more than just a T-shirt. Damian went off to have a drink before the show, and you and I went to find the manager of the venue. She was busy, but she gave us the keys to the metal gate and to the door so we could get in if we wanted to set up. Damian was the first act of the night, so we could set up his amps whenever we wanted, and she'd be along later to set up the mic. That's how it worked—bring your own amp, but they supplied the mic. We had hauled all of Damian's equipment from the bus to Astoria and now from Astoria to the Village, so I was relieved to find a place for it now.

Giuliani was mayor then, but the city hadn't yet been turned into Disneyland, at least not the East Village, so there was a padlock on the gate, and then another key to operate the gate. The metal slowly rolled up, revealing the storefront, and then there were just two more keys for the door—one for the deadbolt and another for the regular lock. You said it wasn't like this in Buffalo. I think there's a lot that's not like it is in Buffalo.

Damian showed up with a can of Pabst Blue Ribbon, which he was drinking entirely un-ironically. He just wanted to get buzzed in the cheapest way possible, and PBR did the trick. He spent a couple of minutes setting up his amp and checking the sound before heading to the backstage area with another can of beer. You and I waited out in the bar while the manager started letting people in for the night.

"Isn't he great?" you said. "I can't wait for you to hear him play. Damian has this sound that's not like anything I've ever heard before."

"So are you two dating?" I asked.

"Umm," you said, "not really." He had just broken up with his girlfriend of six months, and you weren't sure he was relationship material anyway. Still, he was cute, you said, and I had to admit that he was, in a scruffy kind of way, and almost endearing in his childlike hedonism.

I don't really remember what Damian's music was like. Do you? It was so long ago. I remember enjoying it, even though it wasn't exactly my thing, and I remember him being frustrated afterwards, because he hadn't been as good as he wanted to be. I watched the next couple of sets while you comforted him and he had another can of PBR.

The next morning, before we left with the backpacks and the amp and the guitar for Port Authority, Damian handed me a piece of paper with an ink drawing on it. The drawing was more of a doodle than a sketch of anything in particular. Several abstract designs folded in on one another, then fanned out again, filling the entire paper. He must have worked on the drawing on and off during his whole stay.

"For you," he said. I was charmed. I hadn't expected a gift from this musician I hardly knew, who had stayed in my apartment, who had allowed me to carry his amp and deal with the bar manager while he went off and got drunk. The drawing looked like something I'd seen kids do in middle school, only more studied, more practiced, as if he had spent years perfecting the art of immaturity. I couldn't help but like him for it.

I don't remember what happened to that drawing, but I remember your call a few weeks later. "Damian left me," you said.

"What do you mean left you?"

"He was staying with me after his ex kicked him out, because where was he going to go, right? So he was living with me, but now he's gone. He said he's getting back together with Tiffany, but I don't even know if that's true. He says he can't see me anymore. I know it's ridiculous, but I loved him. I really loved him, even though I knew he wasn't good for me."

"I'm sorry," I said. "God, you must feel awful."

"And you know what the worst of it is? I slept with him. All through college, I was saving myself, waiting for the one God wanted me to have, and now along comes Damian, and I sleep with him—just give it right up. And he doesn't understand, does he? He doesn't understand what it was like for us—the things we felt—we dreamed. He'll never know. I'll just be another girl to him. But you remember how it was. The way we all lived together like a family. We trusted each other. I trusted, and now he's gone. Why did I do it? And yet I know. I was tired. Tired of waiting. Of dreaming and not living. But what do I have to show for it now? I want my dreams back."

"Forget about Damian," I said. "Forget about Buffalo. Come to New York. Stay with me. It'll be just like old times. We'll figure it out. Like we used to. Even if we never figured it out then, at least we tried. And we can try. Come to New York," I said, and I half-believe I meant it.

"I don't know," you said. "Maybe I just need some time alone. I'll think about it, though."

The next month was 9/11, so that ended all talk of your coming to New York. You even asked jokingly if I wanted to move to Buffalo. That would have seemed cowardly, though. I stayed on, even after the magazine shut down and I ended up working for a string of websites. You and I carried on, separately, but in our own ways.

And every now and then, I think of visiting you up in Buffalo, where you own your own house, and rent out rooms to college students—or so it seems on Facebook—but what would I do? What would I say? There's nothing to do. Except write long letters, like this one, which I know I'll never send, which I know I'll tear up or burn, just like all the others.

But we understood each other once. We knew those secrets you just can't say. And some nights, as I'm lying next to the stranger with whom I share my life, the woman I married who will never know what it was like to walk through the trees on Easter Sunday, to know that the world is holy, and that people can be good, I get up from bed and I go to the bathroom. That way, if she asks why I got up, I can claim it was indigestion, but what I'm really doing is thinking about what it was like to sleep on your floor, and to wake up to the touch of your hand, and what it felt like to have you brush the hair from my eyes, and when I think of that, I have to close the door so my wife doesn't hear me crying, because what would I say? What could I possibly say?

I don't know if she ever hears me through the bathroom door, but I always keep it locked.

Jonah Marlow Bradenday
THE PLAYWRIGHT

The curtains shivered and the crowd settled into the steel folding chairs. Neighbors stopped chatting and began pinching their children's ears to hasten the quiet. Beatrice leaned into her mother's knees, crossing her own legs beneath her on the wooden floor. Other families sat around them on red corduroy cushions. The families with small children like Beatrice sat towards the front while the back of the room was reserved for the oldies. Mr. and Mrs. Bernard sat back-middle, surveying the town before them, while other seniors spread out to their left and right. The cushions were reddest in the back where the occupants claimed elder authority. In front of the oldies sat the newly married couples, the future of the town. Their seats were faded, but still fluffed. The Jackson boy had his arm suggestively over the shoulders of the newest Jackson girl. They were a happy couple based on their flushed cheeks and nervous chatter. Mrs. Bernard squeezed the boy's shoulder from behind and whispered something about his wedding bed. He turned from pink to maroon and stopped chattering altogether. In front of the happy couples sat the pregnant mothers and their doting husbands. Wilkons, Rackets, and Conrads waited for their babies with nervous trembles. Beatrice twisted her neck to look at their swollen bellies. They were alien compared to her mother's flat torso, tight from rigorous gardening and riding. She looked up at her mother's face and reached up, asking to be lifted. Mrs. Dulberry looked down at her and shook her head, flashing her eyes and bringing a finger to her lips. Beatrice sank back to the floor and waited. Soon the only sound was the screech and whine of folding chairs. The curtain shook again and the lights dimmed.

"Welcome," a bodiless bouncing voice addressed the silent crowd. "I'm glad you all made it." Many of the oldies chuckled amongst themselves. The happy couples smiled through tight white lips and Beatrice watched her mother's mouth crack open, revealing spotless teeth. They often lounged together in the garden, Beatrice amongst the rhubarb bushes and her mother upright in a white plastic lawn chair drinking lemonade and talking about the men who constantly pursued her.

"Bea," she would say. "You're lucky you don't have my smile. Men can be so very tiresome."

Beatrice loved listening to her mother's liquid voice as she sat beneath the large green leaves and picked at the dirt. The gymnasium voice was far too exciting and sharp.

"I bet you're all wondering why I brought you here tonight," it teased.

"Get on with it," Mr. Stevens heckled, warranting a thick pinch from Mrs. Stevens. The curtain rippled and canned banjo music blasted from the speakers. Beatrice stuck her fingers in her ears and pulsed them, reverbing the sounds as if she was under water. A bowl of chocolate peach slices rode down the aisle, passed from family to family. Mrs. Dulberry took one piece out and handed it down to Beatrice before giving the bowl to Mr. Rosson, seated next to them. Beatrice began sucking on the peach as the banjo music stopped.

The curtain shot open to reveal the slim form of Mr. Handle, wearing a tuxedo and smiling performatively. He took a slight bow and raised his hands in front of him.

"Welcome," he repeated, "to the two hundred and tenth performance of *Oomph*." He wiggled his hands through the air on either side of his face, like two gasping haddock trying to un-net themselves.

"There will be comedy," he said pulling his lips away from his teeth with his thumbs and released them to make a wet plopping sound. Beatrice and the other children laughed and imitated him, filling the room with smaller, wetter plops.

"There will be tragedy." He spun away from the audience and tilted a glass bottle onto his face. When he turned back, his face was dripping and he pulled his lips down with his thumbs and released, letting them sputter against each other, flicking water into the air. The children's giggles were joined by the oldies, who found their gummy mouths particularly good at this imitation. Beatrice looked up at her mother's still face. The corners of her lips tilted up.

"There will be intrigue." Mr. Handle made his hands into a telescope and surveyed the faces of the children, who copied his every move. Beatrice couldn't line her hands up correctly and only saw fingers through her tube. She put her hands over both eyes and opted for a more binocular approach, staring up at the playwright.

"A little bit of mystery, and even—" He paused and batted his eyes.

"Hot steamy romance." He pumped the air several times with his hips and dropped to the floor, immediately spinning back up, his shirttails flapping around him. Mrs. Dulberry chuckled along with the other parents and Beatrice smiled in imitation.

"Are you ready?" he asked and the oldies yelled back, "Yes." He cupped his hand to his ear and gyrated his hips.

"Are you ready?" he asked and the children screamed back, "Yes." He cupped both ears and squatted into a split.

"ARE—YOU—READY?" he asked and the entire room bellowed back, "We're ready."

He shot back to his feet and batted his eyes again before taking a deep bow, scraping his chin to his knees. He looked like the frog that Beatrice had found in the garden. His spindly legs bent as if he would leap away from her hand if she got too close. His feet were much larger than the frog's damp cold fingers, making him more of a frog king perhaps.

"Well then, why didn't you say so," he said and skipped offstage, his wet hair flopping across his forehead as he went. The chatter returned for a moment before dying again with the purpling lights. Beatrice felt nervous for the ceremony and leaned further into her mother's legs.

"Before there was life, there was a mother," Handle's voice returned from the speakers. Ms. Jennifer, the school teacher, emerged with a balloon beneath her blouse, holding it with both hands as she waddled across the stage.

"She was the first mother, and she was terribly lonely."

The oldies chuckled again.

"Ms. Mother Jennifer, could you please find your fellow mothers?" the voice asked and Ms. Jennifer rubbed her eyes with her fists before waddling down the steps and into the crowd. She walked past the toddlers and tweens and their parents and into the next row, where she grabbed Mrs. Wilkon's hand and waved at the others who joined hands and stood. The "March of Pregnancy" sung from the speakers as the chain of bellies made their way up the stage, the front one faking the waddles while the other's tried their best to walk normally. Beatrice rubbed her own belly, happy with its relative flatness. She reached up and felt her mother's stomach. Mrs. Dulberry stroked her fingers as they traced the long thin scar from hip to hip. She felt her own scarless belly again and closed her eyes for a moment.

"Such lovely ones this year," the voice continued. "Not like last time."

Next to Mr. Rosson, Mr. Hansom bumped his palm against Mrs. Hansom's shoulder who blushed. All the adults laughed along with Mr. Handle and the children smiled at their parents.

"The first mother and her friends were tired after a long and heavy pregnancy," he said. The four Benson boys wearing white coveralls and stethoscopes slid onto stage, pushing wheeled hospital beds and surgical trays. They bowed at the mothers and pulled back the sheets.

"What comes first?" the voice asked.

"Babies," the crowd cheered back.

"Babies is right. Give us babies," the voice sang. Following Ms. Jennifer's lead, the mothers climbed into the beds and pulled the blankets up. Ms. Jennifer pushed the balloon out of her shirt and handed it to the Benson boy before collapsing to her pillow and wiping her brow.

"Babies, babies, babies," the crowd chanted as the curtain lowered. Beatrice mouthed it quietly and stroked her knees rhythmically.

"Let's give these gals some privacy," the voice laughed and the national anthem played on the speakers as the town chanted. Beatrice closed her eyes again. It was her mother's favorite song. She sometimes set up a radio in the garden and hummed along as she drank her lemonade. Beatrice tapped her fingers on rhubarb stalks to keep time.

At the end of the third time through the song, the speakers went quiet.

"Is it time?" the Hansom girl asked.

"Is it time?" the voice repeated. The crowd asked as one, "Babies?" and the curtain opened.

The Benson boys held a balloon, a Wilkon, a Racket, and a Conrad to their bloody chests and rocked them slowly.

"And then there was life," the voice said and the fathers laughed and waited as the babies were brought to their arms. The mothers were wheeled backstage. Several of the oldies got out of their seats and cooed over the newborns before returning to their places. Beatrice stood and peered over her mother's shoulder to see their crinkled faces. They cried grating whimpers as their fathers rocked them. Beatrice looked at their strange bald heads and twisted her hair in her fingers. The room quieted once more as the stage went from purple to green.

"And then there were children," the voice said. Ms. Jennifer walked out on her knees with a lollipop in her mouth. She beckoned to the front row and smiled, showing her pink teeth. The children murmured and pipped. Some stood and climbed the stairs, while others, including Beatrice, held back, clamping their fists to their parents' clothing. Mrs. Dulberry pulled Beatrice off and pushed her away, where she tentatively made her way to the stage. She watched as the Bernard boy tumbled down the steps on the first try, but made it on the second. He stood triumphantly at the top, beaming out at the green flare. The children circled Ms. Jennifer, sitting cross-legged around her. Beatrice sat between Timmy Benson and Claire Rosson, her cheeks becoming hot.

"Our children need to work, don't they?" the voice asked.

The crowd chanted back, "Work, work, pitchfork."

"Let's give 'em jobs, I say" the voice said. Ms. Jennifer reached into her pocket and pulled out a stack of cards. She shuffled them and gave one to each child. Beatrice took hers and inspected it, anxious to understand the black markings.

"Show them to your families," Ms. Jennifer said, patting Susie Penelope on the head. Beatrice jumped up and was first off of the stage and back to her mother, where she handed the card over, gripping her mother's knees and looking up at her.

"What does it say?" she said.

"I've got a farmer," Mrs. Hutchins called.

"I've got another doctor," Mr. Benson said and the crowd laughed and Mrs. Dulberry shook her head.

"A painter over here."

"A teacher."

"Another farmer."

"Oh, this one's a playwright," said Mrs. Dulberry, not looking down at her daughter. The crowd cheered and drummed their feet.

"A playwright?" the voice asked. "Well it's about time, I say. I am getting quite old." The oldies all laughed and the parents pinched their children to quieten.

"What's a playwright?" Beatrice asked. Her mother tucked the card into her pocket before answering.

"Not now Beatrice. Be respectful."

Beatrice frowned and slumped back to the floor. Her mother only ever called her "Beatrice" when they were around other people. At home it was always "Sweet Bea" or "Bea Bear," which she liked the most. It made her think of a mouse-sized bear with little wings. One time, when they were in the garden, Mrs. Dulberry drinking lemonade and humming and Bea lying on her stomach, looking at a beetle in her palm, she asked her mother about them.

"Do bee bears make their own honey?"

Her mother chewed on an ice cube before answering, "I suppose so. Whenever they like."

The green lights turned pink and Ms. Jennifer sauntered onto the stage, wearing a toga and carrying a small bow.

"And then, there was love," the voice gushed. Ms. Jennifer slid a thigh out from the sheet and wiggled her finger at the audience. Everyone but the children laughed.

"There's only one way to show love," the voice said. "To show it, you got to make it." The oldies began pushing at the shoulders of the happy couples, chanting, "make it, make it." Again, Beatrice mouthed along and watched her mother chant.

Ms. Jennifer beckoned and shot an invisible arrow into the crowd, where the oldies swooned to catch it.

"Make it," said the voice. The oldies pushed the happy couples to their feet. They stood there for a moment sharing intimate glances before walking to the stage. The Hendrick boy walked with his chest out, swinging his arms, while others like the Jackson girl stared at the ground with rosy cheeks. She made eye contact with Beatrice and her eyes swelled for a moment saying something before flicking away. Beatrice wedged her back in deeper between her mother's knees and closed her eyes. She remembered her first time in the garden. Her mother had taken her to live in the Dowage Apartments. At first, she didn't want to leave the green house on Main Street. She loved the circle window on the third floor where she could spy on the busy city folk without them knowing. She loved the cast spiral staircase and the garage that smelled like lemons, but when her mother took her to the garden outside of the new apartment and placed her next to a rhubarb leaf the size of her head she almost forgot about all of it. She leaned into the bush to watch a pair of entwined slugs unfurl and part ways across the pink and green stalks. She opened her eyes and the couples were standing on stage, holding hands with each other and facing the crowd.

Ms. Jennifer cupped her hands to her mouth and said, "wedding beds." The Benson boys appeared again, stripped to the waist, their loose coverall straps slapping their thighs. They pulled identical wheeled beds, these with pink sheets. Ms. Jennifer pointed to the happy couples and then to the beds.

"In order to give us babies, you need to make us babies," the voice said. The couples sat on the beds and got under the sheets, propping themselves up on their elbows. Beatrice was happy that she didn't have to sleep in front of so many people.

"Should we give them privacy?" said the voice.

"Privacy," the crowd echoed.

"Make it, make it," they chanted as the curtains lowered. Mrs. Dulberry tapped along with her foot, bouncing her daughter slightly. The curtains stopped a foot above the ground and Beatrice leaned in close to see, but Mr. Handle popped his head out from beneath the curtain and shook his head.

"Tsk tsk, that's not privacy," he said and yanked the curtain down the rest of the way. The speaker played the national anthem and the crowd chanted some more.

Beatrice joined in, no longer just mouthing, "make it, make it." Halfway through the song, the room went silent, but she kept chanting in whispers.

"Are they done?" asked the Hansom girl. "Are they done?" whispered the audience. Mr. Handle knelt and stuck his head out from beneath the curtain. He stood quickly, pulling the fabric up as he went. The happy couples sat wet faced and red on their beds. Mr. Handle bowed to them deeply.

"Thank you kindly for your contribution," he said. Ms. Jennifer led the couples back to their seats before returning to the stage. Mr. Handle turned to the crowd and spread his arms. He stood more erect now, no longer a frog. Beatrice's mother had once painted a large white bird while they lounged in the garden. She had called it an egret and its black knobbly legs looked like Mr. Handle's.

"Has your night been entertaining?" he asked. The crowd nodded and Beatrice whispered to herself.

"Yes."

"Are we done yet?" he asked. The crowd shook their heads and laughter rang from the back of the room. Beatrice stood high on her toes and looked back at Mrs. Bernard kissing Mr. Bernard fully on the lips.

"Horn dog," called Mrs. Hansom and Mr. Handle chuckled before motioning for silence.

"What comes after life?" he asked. The crowd didn't move. Beatrice looked up at her mother for answers. Mrs. Dulberry looked straight ahead, unblinking, like the cherub fountain beyond the rhubarb patch.

"Ms. Jennifer, would you kindly help our oldies to the stage?"

Beatrice closed her eyes again and imagined the garden. A large white bird stood over the wide leaves, picking insects from their shade and ruffling its feathers as the wind blew louder.

Jody Lannen Brady
ANYTHING YOU NEED

In all of Dorothy's gardens, it was a summer of crisis. Rose rot. Fungus on the rhododendron and dogwoods. Japanese beetles devouring the crepe myrtle despite blasts of pesticide. The front lawn dying despite a fortune in sprinkler-induced water bills. The transplanted azaleas were losing leaves, and the straggly flowers she had tried to kill off were the only things growing in the middle terrace out back.

Instead of enjoying her trip around the yard each morning, Dorothy found herself taking inventory of all the wrongs. She had sprayed and weeded and watered, but this year she had nothing to show for her efforts. When her husband Charlie had been alive, he hadn't helped much with the gardening but he had gotten so much pleasure out of her work that there seemed to be a point to the weeding and mulching, the fertilizing and watering. Dorothy hadn't given up, but it seemed that her gardens had. It was as if the plants knew that they'd lost their best audience and they weren't interested in performing any longer.

Now, to top off Dorothy's frustration, the corkscrew willow was dying. In past years, the willow had dangled over the deck, with its twisted branches and its long, slender leaves shading Dorothy by day and rustling in the night breeze to keep her company after dark. Now she sat and looked up at bark curling off all the bare branches—there were more of them each day, it seemed.

A tree man came knocking at the door one day when Dorothy had just come in from the deck. He was young, a homely man with a dingy baseball cap pulled down almost to his eyes and he spoke with a broad, country accent. Even before she read his card—"Dearl Franklin Frazier"—she had guessed that he was one of "the boys from Culpeper," as they called the scruffy tree men who drove in from the country to knock on doors and ask to cut down trees all summer and then returned in the winter to hawk the wood from the back of their rusting pickup trucks.

"I see you got a dead tree out back," the man said when Dorothy answered the door.

"It's not dead yet," Dorothy snapped back. It annoyed her to hear the man condemn her tree.

"No, ma'am, it's not. So if you'd like, I could just cut out those dead branches and top the tree and she'll come back for you beautiful next year."

He was smarter than he looked, Dorothy thought. The sharpness in her voice had registered with him, and he had changed his tack without any hesitation.

"You think you can save my tree?" Dorothy asked. She knew he couldn't; corkscrew willows lived only fifteen to twenty years and it was going on seventeen since Dorothy and her husband had planted the tree by the edge of their first deck. Nothing was going to save a tree that had reached the end of its natural life span, but Dorothy wanted to see what the man would say.

"Oh, yes," the man said. "I seen it many times before. We could have that tree filled out by next year."

"Well, how do you explain all those dead branches?" Dorothy said.

"Let's go back and look, all right?"

Dorothy wished she hadn't said anything, and had simply sent the man on his way. But he was already walking around the side of her house. At the corner, he looked back and smiled at her, scratching his head. He was waiting for her, she realized. Dorothy followed the man around the side of her house.

"Well, look at that," the man said.

"What?" Dorothy looked up at the willow to the area the man was pointing out.

"Struck by lightning it was," the man said. "Oh, yes, we'll have to take that fork out and cut her back quite a bit."

The long split down one of the tree's largest branches was no lightning scar. Dorothy knew that it was just part of the process of dying. She'd just read about the willow in a giant gardening book at the library, and knew far more about the tree now that it was dying than she'd ever bothered to learn when they had bought it, or in all the years that they had enjoyed it together or in these last two years that she had sat under the tree's branches alone.

"Least you can be glad it didn't strike your house," the man said and grinned.

"Well, I'll think about it," Dorothy said. Now she wanted the man to leave.

"You talk it over with your husband and I'll stop back later," the man said.

"I don't—" Dorothy started to tell the man that her husband was dead, but then thought better of it. "I don't need to talk it over with him," she said. "I'm not ready to do anything just yet. But thank you for looking at it."

The man looked crestfallen. He stuck his hands in his pocket and let out a sigh.

"I'll keep your card," Dorothy said, although she already didn't know what had happened to it and, even if she did find the card, she had no intention of calling the man to come back. Clearly, he knew nothing about trees beyond how to attack them with a chainsaw.

"You got any other work?" The man hadn't made a move to leave. "I do lawns and fences, too. Anything you need."

"I don't think so," Dorothy said. She shook her head.

The man lifted his cap. "OK, you call if you change your mind, ma'am." He turned and walked around the house. Once she heard his truck pull off up the street, Dorothy walked around the house herself and went in, deadbolting the door behind. She felt shaken, but didn't understand why. The man hadn't been threatening. They hadn't argued. She felt his card in her pocket.

Under the man's name was a list of his services: *Trees for Sale. Firewood and Mulch. Spraying and Feeding Trees and Shrubbery. Lawn Work. Fence Repair & Painting, Remodeling. Lot Cleaning. Shrubbery Work. Topping, Trimming, and Taking Down. Odd Jobs.*

She walked across the room to throw the card away, but something wouldn't let her. She stood over the trashcan and read the card again. Finally, she put the card in her coupon drawer and got on with her day.

She was out spraying Daconil on a rhododendron in the front yard when something bumped into her leg. Dorothy spun around, almost knocking over a little boy taking wobbly steps into her garden.

"Get back," she said sharply and held the spray bottle away from the little boy staring up at her. She put her hand on his chest to keep him from walking further into the garden.

"I'm sorry, ma'am," came a woman's voice from behind Dorothy. "He didn't mean anything."

Dorothy turned around. "No, of course he didn't. I just don't want him near this," she said and held up the sprayer. "It's fungicide. Poisonous."

The woman bent down to take hold of the boy's hand and pull him away from Dorothy. She was a little heavy, dressed in an oversized shirt and shorts, a stumpy ponytail sticking out from the back of her head.

"He's hard to keep up with," the woman said. The little boy tried to pull away from her.

"I remember those days myself," Dorothy said and smiled.

"You have children?" The woman knelt beside her son and went to work tying the loose, frayed laces on his little sneakers.

Dorothy nodded. She had children, and she had grandchildren. Her children used to call all the time when their children were toddlers like the little boy in front of her. "Could you come over?" they would ask her, and she and her husband would sigh and roll their eyes at one another, and then Dorothy would agree to the day or weekend or, once with her daughter's children, two weeks. But the grandchildren were older now and the calls didn't come very often. Now that Dorothy wished so much that she was needed.

"He loves your flowers," the woman said. "That's why he keeps trying to run up your driveway."

"Well, let him," Dorothy said. "Let him look at the flowers."

"Oh, he won't just look. He'll run right through them and pluck the blossoms off. He's terrible that way." The woman shook her head, but she was smiling.

"Well, there's not much damage he could do." Dorothy said. "Not this year. Everything's already dying."

"Oh, no! That's not true. We love your garden," the woman said.

"See this rhododendron I was spraying?" Dorothy pointed at the bush. "Fungus. And the slugs are eating all those marigolds." She pointed down at the flowers that the little boy had managed to reach despite his mother's hold on him.

"No, William," the woman scolded and pulled the boy closer.

"Look at that tree," Dorothy said, pointing at the willow. "It's dying."

"Oh, I'm sorry," the woman said.

Dorothy felt foolish. It wasn't like her to whine, but here she was listing off her sick plants to a woman she'd never even introduced herself to. Lately, she felt as though she was losing control. She couldn't count on saying the right thing. She couldn't make things grow. She couldn't figure out what to do with herself all the long hours of the day when she couldn't bring herself to tackle the endless "To Do" list she kept tacked onto the front of her refrigerator. She had always taken care of things, taken care of herself and everyone around her—but somehow, for no reason she could pick out, it seemed that she had lost the ability to be caretaker of anything or anyone, including herself.

There was a squeal from the little boy, and Dorothy turned back around to see that he had broken away from his mother and was running up the street.

"Well, I have to get after him," the woman said. She stuck her hand out to Dorothy. "My name is Alice," the woman said. "And that was William. We're renting up the street and I guess we'll be seeing you a lot. William likes to walk."

The woman waved and then turned and jogged slowly after the boy, calling his name.

Dorothy stood and watched them disappear up the street. She'd never introduced herself.

With her second glass of wine in hand, Dorothy pulled out the address book. The wine had given her a warm buzz and she thought she might call her daughter. She looked up the phone number and began dialing it. But halfway through the number she hung up. It was Wednesday night, and her daughter would be at her class.

She finished off the wine in her glass and poured more. She couldn't call her son because his wife had requested that Dorothy only call before dinner time, so that the family schedule wouldn't be interrupted. Dorothy hated to think of herself as an interruption that had to be scheduled in at the least inconvenient time, so she had stopped calling her son. It would be so good to talk with him but she would only cause trouble with his wife.

She poured more wine into her glass. She needed to talk to someone. It was pathetic, really, but that was what it came down to. There was her sister, but her sister would know she was drinking, like the last time she had called. And then all Dorothy would get was a lecture and she didn't want another lecture.

Dorothy filled her glass again. She opened a drawer to put away the address book and she saw the tree man's card. She picked it up and read it again, then remembered their conversation. You can do anything I need? she wanted to ask him. You can keep my tree from dying? You can make my grass grow? You can fix the gutters and sharpen the blade on the mower the way that Charlie used to? You can tell his jokes? You can bring him back to curl beside me in bed at night?

Without thinking, she picked up the phone and dialed the number on the card. She wanted to hear a voice. Any voice. She wouldn't say anything.

The phone rang and rang. Just as Dorothy came to her senses and was about to hang up, the ringing stopped.

"Hello."

Dorothy recognized the tree man's voice, but she said nothing. She gripped the receiver tightly in her hands.

"Hello? Hello? Anyone there?"

Dorothy held her breath. Then the man hung up. Dorothy put the receiver down and poured the last of the wine in her glass. She felt her heart beating so wildly in her chest that it hurt. Maybe she'd die of a heart attack like Charlie, she thought. One moment she would be alive and the next she would have crossed over. She had watched him die, but she never knew exactly when it happened. When she kissed his face, it had already lost its warmth.

The phone rang. Dorothy jumped, spilling a little of her wine. Then, without thinking, she picked up the receiver and held it to her ear.

"Who is this?" she heard. It was the tree man's voice.

Dorothy almost dropped the phone.

"I know you called us," the man said, sounding angry. "My wife got this call-back thing for us. So you may as well speak."

"Yes," Dorothy said, her mind racing frantically. Could he really find out who she was? "I talked to you about a tree today," she said.

"Oh," his voice softened, "you're the lady with the willow."

This surprised Dorothy. Could it be the same man who had talked about lightning?, she wondered.

"You knew it was a willow?" she asked him.

"Yes, ma'am. Did you decide anything?"

His voice was matter-of-fact but friendly, as though there was nothing odd about a would-be customer calling him at eleven at night to discuss a job.

"But before you tell me," he said, "I gotta be honest. Sooner or later that tree's a goner."

"You said you could make it beautiful again," Dorothy said. Her words were slurred, and she was ashamed of herself—drinking and calling strangers. She should have called her sister and gotten the lecture she deserved.

"For a year, it would look just fine," the man said. "But that's about all you could hope for. They're pretty trees, but they don't last, ma'am."

"It's hard to lose them," Dorothy said, and to her horror she found herself beginning to cry.

"Yes, ma'am," he said.

Could he tell that she was crying? Dorothy put her hand over the receiver and cleared her throat. She hated showing weakness. Charlie had been the same way. It was the wine doing this to her.

"You know what you need, ma'am?"

"What?" she asked.

He didn't answer right away, and Dorothy found herself waiting expectantly. She wanted to know what he would come up with. Even if he said she needed all of her trees cut down, she just might give him the job. He had looked like someone who needed work. Why hadn't she let him take the tree down for her?

"What you need is to sell that place. That's a house for a young family, if you don't mind me saying so, ma'am."

"No," Dorothy said. She felt more like herself again; the tears were gone. "I don't mind. You're right."

"Have you and your husband ever been to Florida?" the man asked her.

"Yes, we were once. In winter."

Dorothy remembered the wonderful break from winter they'd taken the year before Charlie had died. She remembered the clear ocean water at low tide, the palm trees everywhere. And Charlie's delight in seeing his first coconut outside a grocery store. Charlie had meant for them to go back.

"That's where I'm going," the man said. "I might not even wait till I'm older."

"To go to Florida?" Dorothy asked.

"If I can convince my wife to leave here. You know, her mother's here. Do you have a daughter?"

"Yes. But I don't see her much."

"Well, ma'am. Maybe if you didn't have so much house to work at, you could get around to a visit. But I'm sorry, if I'm talking too much. My wife's gone for a few days and it gets too quiet around here, you know?"

"Yes," Dorothy said. "I know."

"Well, did you need me to do some work for you?"

"Yes," Dorothy said. "When can you come?"

He could come the next day. He would be there around ten o'clock.

"But what do you need?" he asked Dorothy. "I never gave you any prices."

They could talk tomorrow, Dorothy told the man. He could tell her what he thought she needed done and they would talk about the price then.

"Yes, ma'am," the man said. He thanked her. "You won't be disappointed in my work," he added just before they hung up.

Dorothy put her wineglass down beside the phone. She unlocked the front door and walked outside. Charlie had been a stickler for keeping the door locked, even when they were just outside in the yard. But now she could leave the door wide open and step outside barefoot, something else Charlie had bothered her about.

She stepped off the front porch and onto the slate walk. In the moonlight, the yard looked dark and lush. At the edge of the lawn, the yellow of the marigolds glowed against their leaves and the fireflies flashed on and off as they drifted through the trees.

"What I need," Dorothy said aloud.

She remembered standing out at night, watching her children chase fireflies. When had they stopped needing her? When had the whole thing turned around on her? When had she become the person who needed more than she was needed?

The night was full of cricket noises and the distant sound of cars on the highway outside her neighborhood. She bent down to swat a mosquito from her ankle and saw the silvery trail of a slug on the flagstone beside her. In the morning she would put out pellets to lure away the slugs that were eating away the marigold leaves.

Dorothy saw something on a slate a few feet away from her and she took a few steps before she recognized the handiwork of the little boy up the street; a trail of yellow flowers lay on the ground. She ought, by all rights, to be angry. Charlie had chased children out of her gardens so many times over the years to keep them from destroying her work. She picked up one of the marigold heads and its soft, wet pedals filled her palm. She wasn't angry at all. The gardener in her knew that snapping off flower heads kept a plant strong and productive. And the mother in her knew that the little boy couldn't resist the pom pom heads of the marigolds.

She tossed the flower into the ivy and, as she moved, something tickled her leg. Bending down, she saw that it was a weed. A plant not on the desired list, living where it hadn't been invited. As much as she hated the sloppy look that weeds gave a garden, she secretly admired them. She had tried to explain this once to Charlie, but he thought she was joking and he roared with laughter.

She would weed in the morning until the tree man came. He needed work and she needed help. She had never hired anyone to help before, because Charlie had never approved of it. He would roll his eyes when a truck pulled up across the street with the painter or the plumber. Dorothy could hardly see the house now; in the darkness it was only a fuzzy patch of light on the other side of the trees. The same couple lived there, the same people who Charlie had been fond of at the same time he'd gently mocked their inability to fix anything. But Dorothy understood now that it was more than that.

Charlie believed in self-sufficiency; he'd shown it every time he refused to let someone else paint the house or help him carry bags of topsoil to the car. But he was wrong, Dorothy realized. Needing help wasn't such a bad thing. It was the other half of being needed, and the only people who weren't involved in the exchange were the dead.

Gerri Brightwell

MR. SWEET PIE

By the time Travis's old pickup lurches into the driveway, Paulie's tired of waiting. Up since six because they were supposed to leave a half-hour ago and instead he's been standing at the kitchen window eating cold beans from a can because there's no cereal, no bread, no milk in the fridge, though there sure as hell is a twelve-pack of beer for when his mom and Dwayne get up and want to kill their hangovers.

Paulie's a skinny kid, tall for fifteen so he has to duck to watch Travis's truck strain up the driveway. It's an old blue thing scabbed with rust, and behind it unfurls a long flag of exhaust that hangs between the trees. On the small apron of dirt by the garage the truck pulls around then stops at a lazy angle, hood aimed at an old birch, like Travis means to take it out when they leave. A couple of heartbeats later he hits the horn—blatt-blatt-blaaatt. Like he's saying Hurry up. Like Paulie's the one who's late.

Paulie licks his spoon and lets it clatter into the dishes in the sink, tosses the half-full can of beans into the trash bag slumped against the wall. It lands with a wet thud, like maybe beans have splattered out on the floor. He doesn't glance back.

This day feels ruined already. The slick skins of beans caught against his teeth, Travis arriving late like it's no big deal, like Nenana isn't fifty miles away. He snatches up his gear bag from the foot of the stairs and slings it over his shoulder. His hand's already reaching for the doorknob when he stops himself and steps back, tweaks the radio on with the volume up high. A wash of Aerosmith follows him out the front door and he slams that door good and hard, never mind that it's a cheap piece of shit and the frame's rotting so the slam's more of a shudder. Still, if Travis's horn wasn't enough to wake his mom and Dwayne, maybe that shudder's done the job and now they're turning over in bed wondering what all that goddamn noise is, and why the hell there's Aerosmith playing downstairs at seven in the fucking a.m., and in a moment they'll yell for him to shut it the fuck off. Except, here he is heading down the front steps and into the driveway—if they want the music shut off, one of them'll have to get up and serve them right, promising him a ride then yesterday deciding no, it was Beth's birthday and everyone was heading to the Klondike Bar and sure as hell they didn't want to be up crazy early for some fucking taekwondo tournament, and besides, hasn't he got a stack of trophies already?

Fuck them. That's what Paulie thinks as he kicks his way to the truck, dirt blooming into the air behind him like the driveway's smoking hot. Fuck them for bringing friends over at one in the morning, and slamming doors, slamming the fridge, shouting to each other across the house like he wasn't upstairs trying to sleep.

Another blast of horn. No way could Travis have missed Paulie coming toward him—there's his face peering out, pale and blurred behind the dusty windshield—and now he gooses the gas as well, sending a filthy puff of smoke across the driveway, and Paulie thinks, yeah and fuck you too.

The engine has an odd lurch to it that makes the truck tremble, like it's a half-tamed thing and Paulie shouldn't risk getting in. But they're late. He goes to open the door, has to yank it hard. With a groan it swings open and there's Travis, fat as a beaver, thin graying hair scraped back across his scalp and curling at his collar, his pouchy face flushed and shining. Seven a.m. and he's smiling, but then, he's always smiling. "Ready to rock and roll, bud?" he calls out, one thick hand on the gearshift. "Then toss your bag in the back, and hurry it up. This old truck's not what she used to be." Paulie's barely had time to climb in when Travis shifts into first and the truck lunges forward, just missing the old birch, then roaring out onto the dirt road.

The cab smells every bit as bad as Paulie'd imagined. Stale tobacco, the sharp reek of old sweat, plus something sour and muddy. Travis is the guy who shows up for class in a dobok turned piss-stain yellow, whose thick toenails curl toward the mats like claws, whose filthy hair flaps around his ears as he puts his considerable weight into each move of his patterns. He reminds Paulie of Pig-Pen from Peanuts, as though this is the aging guy Pig-Pen would have grown into with that cloud of soiled air still flickering around him. And yet, you can't dislike Travis. Never a bad word. Never one to slug you in sparring because he's mad you got him with a turning kick to the head, like that's a fair move when his knees are so stiff he can barely get his own feet a few inches off the mat. A third-degree black belt who'll go over each move of a new pattern with you, over and over until you get it, like you aren't stupid, like this is how he likes spending his class time. The kind of guy who'll say, "Hey bud, if your folks can't give you a ride tomorrow, no worries, I'll take you," and Paulie had waited for someone else—anyone else, for fuck's sake—to offer instead, but the other black belts were mostly kids like him, busy fake punching each other in the shoulder by the water fountain, so he'd nodded and muttered, "Great, man, thanks."

Now Travis tosses him a Coke from the fridgepack between them on the seat. "Have yourself a little caffeine to kickstart your morning," he says, and Paulie can't help resenting it, that sweating can that lands in his lap, like now he's supposed to be grateful for this too. Still, it's a Coke, and it'll wash away the floury taste of the beans, and maybe with his mouth full of Coke he won't be able to smell the fug of the cab, so he pops it open and pours in a good mouthful, holds it fizzing in the hollow of his tongue.

This early, the skies have a worn-out look from all the brightness that won't let up, and no wonder when the Arctic Circle's just an eight-hour drive north. At this time of year the sun doesn't do more than tilt away behind the hills at night so there's no such thing as darkness anymore, like time's stuck on pause, like whatever you do, nothing's going to change. Paulie takes another swig of Coke, lets his eyes drift to the trees flashing past, as though he's too tired for much else.

Soon they're on the paved road running along the edge of town. Just past the gas station Travis takes a left onto the highway, a two-lane road that leads all the way down to Anchorage. Here it cuts through the end of the valley—a few fields, then forested slopes, and above them the university's huge dishes cupped to listen in on the skies.

Paulie has wound down the window a few inches, but now as they barrel along the highway, Travis says, "Here, close up that window and I'll crank the ventilation." A few moments later a moldy smell fills the cab.

Travis drives with one hand on the gearshift and the other gently holding the wheel close to the bottom so his arm can rest on his belly. Every now and then he says something like, "Hope there'll be a good turnout this year. Last time only a couple of schools from Fairbanks showed up, and those folks down in Nenana must have been pretty disappointed," or "You wouldn't think a place small as Nenana would have such a good school but boy, they've whupped our butts a few times, I can tell you," and Paulie says, "Yeah," and "Yeah?" then goes back to staring out the window.

Soon they're climbing the hill out of town, the engine working hard and the truck slowing ominously, and just when it feels like they're not going to make it, like the truck's about to churn to a stop, they hit the crest and start the long slide down the other side, gathering speed, blasting along at fifty, then sixty, the truck shaking like a rocket taking off into space.

***

Hundreds of thousands of kilometers overhead a knobby asteroid the size of a small couch slowly executes a rotation, end over end, as it has been doing for the last few million years since a collision knocked it out of the asteroid belt between Jupiter and Mars. Now its orbit brings it wheeling through the solar system in the general direction of Earth at twenty-one kilometers per second, a preposterous speed, if you think about it, and Travis has, frequently.

Travis is a man who thinks about speed and trajectories. He is a man who has felt himself become untethered these last four years, his wife dead and buried after some coward in a blue pickup hit her outside the clinic where she worked, hit her so hard the cops wondered why she hadn't crossed on the crossing, except she had, only the impact sent her flying through the air to land yards away by a bus stop. So said a witness. No license plate. No description of the driver. The driver had simply kept going—down the street, on with his or her life as though nothing had happened, whereas Jeannie's life ended a few weeks later, and his had been knocked out of its orbit: medical bills for the weeks it looked like she might make it, bills from the funeral home for burying her. Their house sold, his life reduced to what would fit into a rented cabin, a place with an outhouse and no running water.

Across the great divide between Before and After, the only elements in common are his days in front of computer screens as he tracks great silent rocks plunging through space, and his evenings at the do-jang putting himself through the moves of his patterns, spinning and kicking and blocking. If he lets himself think too hard, he wonders: Isn't it too late? Those forearm blocks, those hook punches and elbow strikes, aren't they empty gestures because no assailant's coming at him, no danger's dogging him out there on the mats? The worst has already happened and he wasn't there to stop it.

He was Jeannie's Mr. Sweet Pie. He was her Sugar Babe. Now he's just Travis at the do-jang, or Mr. Lawson when the master's asking him to do something in front of the color belts. At work he's Dr. Lawson. At a conference down in the Lower Forty-Eight last year someone called him Asteroid Guy, and it's true he wasn't wearing his badge, he'd lost the damn thing just like he'd lost his boarding pass at the gate, and the slip of paper with the hotel address on it somewhere on the plane. That's his life these days: everything spinning away from him as though, despite his two hundred and thirty pounds, he exerts no gravitational pull whatsoever.

This kid—Paulie—sitting beside him as he pushes his foot hard against the gas, this sulky kid who doesn't say thanks for the Coke, or thanks for picking him up, what does he understand about a life that's been broken apart? About how you're doing your best but somehow you forget to set your alarm, and you can't find your keys, damn it, so you show up late and feel bad when really, how is it your fault?

***

Taylor's a good kid. Seventeen, waitressing at the Marriott downtown for the summer to pay her parents back for her car, a twelve-year-old Subaru when what she really wants is a Honda SUV like this one her friend Melody is driving, its hood glinting a cartoon apple red through the windshield, the music from Melody's phone—Drake, he of the soft voice as though he's a gentle soul through and through—channeled into an all-around warm throb through the speakers. All she has in her Subaru is the radio and a CD player, when who on earth buys CDs anymore? But then, Melody's dad's a surgeon, and her family takes vacations in Europe every year like it's no big deal. It's a whole different ball of wax, Taylor's dad says, from being a state employee for Fish and Game.

Beyond the glass, nothing but trees and the faded gray of the road, rucked up from frost heave that sends the car gently bouncing. Everywhere the same scrawny spruces she's grown up with, the same hills that stretch forever, a let-down after two days in Anchorage because that's a real city, and maybe it's because of not having slept (Why sleep when they'd pleaded a few extra hours in Anchorage, never mind it meant leaving after midnight?) but everything feels dreary and washed out now, like she's not just going home, she's going back to being a kid when she's seventeen for crying out loud.

When she blinks her eyes are dry and gritty. With her fingertips she rubs them, lets them close for a few moments and feels the tug of sleep. Her mind tilts away into the start of a dream. A crowded street, a wall of store windows, the comfortable bumping of a bag against her hip.

"Hey." On her bare arm, Melody's hand. "I need to pee, then you're driving, OK?"

Taylor takes a breath, opens her eyes into an unbearable brightness. "Sure," she says, "I can do that."

***

When two objects collide, their kinetic energy—dependent on their mass and velocity—can be transformed into other forms of energy. For example, though a significant proportion of an asteroid's energy when it hits the Earth is simply transferred as kinetic energy to the rock and other material it displaces, some is converted into strain energy as rock is deformed, and some is turned into heat and sound. Many asteroids, however, are simply unable to withstand the huge forces exerted by air resistance as they travel through Earth's atmosphere at fifteen to twenty kilometers per second. These asteroids explode before impact with a bright flash and a shock wave that can, though rarely, be powerful enough to damage structures and cause injuries.

Of course, most asteroids in our solar system do not come into contact with our planet but orbit harmlessly in the huge void of space.

***

Settling into the driver's seat comes as a surprise to Taylor: how it feels like she's about to captain a spacecraft, something sleek like the *Enterprise*. The dials with their elegant arrows for speed and fuel. The buttons that give with a satisfying click at the push of her finger. The screen that shows inside and outside temperature, and wind speed, and wind direction, and that, when she swipes her fingertips across it, lists radio stations, and gas stations, and directions to her destination: Follow Alaska Highway #3 north for seventy-four miles. As though there is any other way to get home, out here where it's just trees and a single road cutting through the hills.

Taylor adjusts the seat, just a little, forward, up, the back a little more reclined, until it cradles her just so. Beside her Melody's yawning into her fist. "Christ," she says, voice thick with sleep, "it's just a car. Stop playing with it and get going. My mom'll have a fit if I'm not back in time for orchestra practice."

But it's not just a car. It's a car whose steering wheel she can tilt so that, even though she's only five foot three, it faces comfortably toward her chest. It's a car that builds a landscape of music around her, so minutely detailed that, even though she's been listening to this album for the last month, she notices how Drake's singing into her left ear now, like he's just a few inches away, and how there's a touch of echo here, and here, and here. It's a car that, when her sandal touches the gas pedal, surges forward, the whole mass of its glass and metal and electronics bursting from the pull-out onto the road in a shiver of gravel, and even as she lets out a quick "Sorry!" to Melody she's laughing at the sheer craziness of it, her face stretched with joy at the way the car's dragging the road toward them, gulping it down as though all the spruce and dust and hills beyond the windshield are just a backdrop.

***

Exactly 10.8 miles away on Alaska #3, Travis's old pickup is doing nearly fifty, leaning a little on the bends, Travis nodding along to a Bon Jovi number pulsing out of the radio, the sound of it half washed away by the hiss of air coming in through the window because the kid has cracked it open again. The kid's got his head leaning against the door, eyes closed as though he's sleeping, but he's not: his face has got a hard held-in look, not the softness that creeps through flesh when someone's mind has loosened its grip on their body.

So much for company, Travis thinks. So much for doing someone a favor. It just isn't right. He clears his throat, says over the rush of air, "Hey, Paulie, you thinking of testing for second degree in the fall?"

The kid's eyes open. Dark eyes that turn toward him for a moment, then away to the landscape beyond the glass. "Dunno," he says and shrugs.

"You don't think you're ready?"

Another shrug. "No one's said anything to me about it."

More than anything, Travis wants to dig his cigarettes out from his jacket pocket and suck hot sweet smoke into his lungs. Wouldn't it ease the annoyance tightening his throat? Wouldn't it at least give him something else to think about? But this is a kid next to him, so instead he coughs into his hand then drums his fingers against the wheel.

If Jeannie knew he was smoking again she'd kill him—and isn't that the biggest joke of all? Because there's no point not smoking now. No Jeannie. No log house that was their home, small and a little dark but full of the smells of bread and home-cooked chili on days Jeannie didn't have to work. It wasn't a place to foul with his tobacco so he'd quit, just like that, and when he'd had the urge to light up, he'd made himself sit on the sofa by the woodstove, and close his eyes, and breathe in the pure good smells of the place instead, and tell himself how lucky he was—him, Travis Lawson, married at last, forty-five years old, for Christ's sake. So what if they were too old for kids? What did that matter when he wasn't alone and unloved anymore? And now, twelve years later, here he is back where he was before Jeannie, back in that emptiness of an unshared life.

Beside him the kid's turned away. Travis says, "What's up? You go to bed late last night?" and he adds a smile because he's Mr. Nice Guy, isn't he? Mr. Nice Guy at the do-jang. Friendly Dr. Lawson at work, the research professor who'll look over your assignment with you and put his finger on the exact spot where your calculations are wrong. And on his own? He's nobody, that's what he thinks now.

He waits for another shrug, but Paulie stares at him. "Yeah," he says at last, "something like that."

Travis opens his mouth to say more, but whatever it was he'd had in mind is gone, pushed away by the sight of the kid. Something about the droop of his mouth, the way he tilts his head when he looks back out the window. Some sort of sadness there, Travis thinks. "Hey," he says to Paulie, "no worries, bud, you let yourself go, catch a few zees while you can." And the kid does.

Before long there's the river up ahead, milky gray and furious with snow-melt. Travis pops open another Coke, feels its coolness track down his throat to his stomach. For a moment he lets one hand rest over the angle where his chest meets his belly, his thumb nestled into a crease in his T-shirt while the other hand steers the truck gently into a curve. His thoughts are pulled toward Jeannie, but what good would that do? Instead he makes himself list the asteroids he's been tracking, picturing their trajectories. Sometimes on the weekend he goes into work. Not because he has to but because there's comfort in the office with its dimmed lights, and the screens with their asteroids and meteoroids and comets glowing in the darkness, and the photo of Jeannie on the beach in Seward taped above them on the wall. There's his old chair squeaking when he sits down. There's his mug, warm in his hand, *Sugar Daddy* in swirly red on its front. A Christmas gift from Jeannie just after they were married.

He's only got as far as asteroid Tiva, the couch-shaped asteroid that, in a few hours, will come tumbling past just four hundred thousand kilometers from Earth when, steering into the sharpest part of the bend, he notices: an SUV well over the center line, sunlight glinting off its apple-red paint. It falters as the driver tries to correct, and like that, before it seems possible, Travis is yanking the steering wheel hard, pulling his truck out of the path of that SUV, only there's nowhere to go except off the road toward the river. His can of Coke sprays down his shirt then hits him in the face, damn it, and he's trying to steer when there's nothing but air beneath the truck. He brakes for all the good it does, brakes so hard his whole body's stiff. He's thinking, this is it, this is really it, an end to a life he has no more use for, a way out when he didn't have the guts all these years to end it himself.

But it doesn't work like that. There's an impact that jolts him forward, then the windshield's filled with a tumult of water and broken glass as the river rushes in. As freezing water sweeps up to his chin he lifts his head and strains his face toward the roof, and his hands, numb from cold, try to fumble his seatbelt loose. Soon he's clawing at the belt, his body churning as he tries to break free, water slopping over his face so he's gasping.

A shadow. The kid, looming over him. The kid bending close, his hands searching for the buckle, and as his breath burns in his lungs Travis reaches out and hauls the kid's head to his chest, this kid, his savior.

A hard jab in his belly and the breath he was holding spurts out in silvery bubbles as the kid escapes. Now there's nothing but the savagery of the water.

***

Sitting by the river, clothes dripping, shivering hard as the breeze chuffs around him, Paulie knows he'll never escape Travis now. On his head lingers the ghostly pressure of Travis's hand holding him fast, against his arm the softness of Travis's gut from when he elbowed him. Wherever he looks swim the bubbles of Travis's last breath as he buckled and let go.

A sick feeling forces its way through Paulie's belly until he vomits, over and over, spilling the cold beans he ate, the Coke Travis gave him, into a filthy puddle between his feet. He stares at it. He already senses the sort of nightmares that will make him thrash in his sleep like a drowning man for years to come. He senses the way people will look at him when he says he tried to save the guy, he really fucking tried.

Spitting the skins of beans out from between his teeth, Paulie feels cursed because he doesn't know better. He doesn't know that he's no longer a person who'll take the batteries out of a smoke detector to replace the ones in the TV remote, and that he won't die in the fire that starts in the kitchen of his mom's house six months from now. He doesn't know that in just over eight years he'll stagger out of a bar and, suddenly swamped by air cold as river water he'll shove his car keys back in his pocket and go home with a woman he'll never see again, a woman he's kissing (long and deep like he means it when in truth he just wanted a place to sleep off too many beers) at the exact moment that the moose that would have stepped into the road in front of him lopes across the blacktop and vanishes into the trees on the other side.

He doesn't know yet that he'll die an old man, far older than Travis, a man who at his own end, when his grown daughter's hurrying off down the hospital corridor to find the bathroom and suddenly he's gasping for breath through the fluid in his lungs, fingers grabbing at the sheets, at the nurse's hand, crushing it, he'll hear that nurse whisper, "Time to let go." And how glorious that release will be, no need to breathe anymore, no need for anything as he falls back into the darkness from which he came. Soon the nurse'll pull her hand free and bend over him, watching, something come loose in her now that he's gone. She'll lean closer and look into those eyes that see nothing. Like staring into a void, she'll think, then she'll smooth them shut before his daughter gets back from the bathroom so it'll look like he just fell asleep. When she steps away from the bed she'll flap her hand a few times, ridding herself of the feel of the old man because it's late afternoon and her shift was over a half hour ago, and she has groceries to buy, and her son's Christmas concert to go to, all those little kids singing like angels, it's enough to break your heart.

Kathryn Chiariello

DOCTOR DELACRUZ MEETS HER MATCH

D r. Inez Delacruz needed a new bra. She needed a vacation. She needed to retire.

Professor Andrew Keller needed meds.

"I'm a genius. Now kindly go away." The new admit placed his hands in his lap like they had nothing to do with him and looked down at his toes.

For the last three days, Dr. Delacruz struggled, unable to make any progress with him. A suicidal theoretical physicist from Johns Hopkins who refused to participate in the therapeutic process. Acute mania or possible psychosis. Today they met in his room instead of her office. It was a single, with a long bed barely wide enough for his frame. He sat on the bottom edge of it and with all his considerable weight resting there, she couldn't shake the feeling the whole thing was going to flip forward towards her, that the whole room would. She sat on an upright chair one of the nurses dragged in for her from the day lounge. It put her at disadvantage to meet in his room, but she hoped to make him more comfortable. And more compliant.

"Not quite yet, Andrew. Let's start a little further back."

"Family of origin far back, or a bit further, perhaps? Roman Empire or further? Phanerozoic or further? Precambrian? Further? Reionization Epoch? Hadron Epoch? Quark? Inflationary? Electroweak? How far, Doctor Delacruz? All the way back to the big shebang, shamalama ding dong bop sho wa ba wah? Blues Brother brother, may you rest in peace."

"I was thinking of last week. When you took the overdose."

"Touché! You *do* have a sense of humor. You've been a little loathe to show it in our previous encounters. I was beginning to doubt." His hand explored the bottom ridge of his skull behind and beneath his ear.

Professor Andrew Keller was older than she was, but only by a couple of years. They were both on the backside of their careers, both graying, and both, she suspected, annoyed with each other. She hadn't been invested enough to be this annoyed by a patient in a long time.

Why wouldn't he just take the meds? He'd been on and off them most of his adult life.

The wife was no help in convincing him. She had medical power of attorney, but objected to any and all medication too, as long as the patient refused what he called a chemical straightjacket. She agreed he needed to be in Sheppard Pratt for his safety, but said he deserved final say on what happened in and to his brain—for his survival. They made quite the pair, the petite wife dressed like a modern Isadora Duncan, all diaphanous layers and scarves and bangles, and the bearded, burly professor with no apparent interest in a comb.

Today he had on the same pair of jeans faded to baby blue that he'd worn each day Inez Delacruz had known him, and the same dark gray sweatshirt with stained, frayed cuffs. She shouldn't judge. She wore her standard outfit too. Black slacks, a V-neck silk sweater, red pumps. Well, they'd been red when she started at the hospital almost forty years ago. The ones she wore now were more cordovan, even if she still *thought* of them as red.

"Why are you here, Andrew? What happened last Tuesday?"

"Tuesday, the 23rd? Let me think. I believe Dan and I had lunch in his office. He had a turkey on rye. No mayo. Or maybe you meant more globally? The earth continued in its orbit around the sun at thirty kilometers a second, per usual. My heart—and yours—beat approximately one hundred and fifteen thousand times. And, yes, Dr. Delacruz, I see we are both carrying some extra weight around the middle, and so I used a rather less than optimal eighty beats a minute, if you don't mind my saying, about the weight I mean of course, since as a scientist, to the extent that psychiatry, or even medicine, is a science, you no doubt recognize the improbability of a sixty-beat average for either of us. Whatever our degrees."

"How did you feel when you woke up in the ICU?"

"Do I look good in green?"

"Why did you take the pills, Andrew?"

"Because a gun is too violent. Hemingway always *was* a bastard to the women in his life."

Inez Delacruz resisted the urge to write down a note. It could be perceived by patients as a power move. It often was. She'd attended a mindfulness class twice a week for the last six months—part of an effort to feel alive again, to lose the weight she kept finding, to remember that being alone didn't have to mean being lonely—and had begun to catch her thoughts more often. Her impatience, her need to control. Her tendency to think she understood and merely needed to receive confirmation from the client, as if she was a cop, and these sessions were confessions. It hadn't always been that way. Had it? Back when her shoes really were red? Back when she went home and cared for her daughter and read good books and didn't have peppermint–chocolate chip ice cream every night before her second glass of wine?

"Delicate, as always, if not in all ways, Dr. Delacruz. Your silence speaks volumes without volume. So no to the mint of that hospital gown. But what about hunter? Perhaps it would bring out my eyes? Stefania always says it does. Consequently, I have quite a few shirts in that shade. She does my clothes shopping for me, you see. I'd be content in a burlap sack. Though why must sacks always be burlap? Strike that from the record. My skin is quite sensitive. A cotton or cashmere sack. Depending on the season. Even the waistband of these jeans can feel too hard on my waist. See aforementioned comment on girth."

"Would you like to talk about Stefania? How did you two meet?"

It wasn't much, but it might get him to share something more personal. Not that Inez knew what that was like—sharing something personal—not now that Marisa was all grown up and out in California, busy with her job, her husband, her kids, and rarely came back East, and Inez's colleagues were younger and younger and treated her more and more like a myth or an object of study than a woman.

"We met in grad school. Or a former life. As a physicist I have become quite humble about the nature of nature. All the universe is a physical phenomenon, but quite a lot of it is unsolvable."

Inez noticed her heart speed up. That word—unsolvable—it felt like a wedge she could use to split him open. Wait. That was the wrong image. He was *already* broken. She was trying to help him put himself back together. Still, it was an opportunity. She reached to her side ribs and tugged the bra band flat where it had curled and dug into her flesh.

"Tell me more about 'unsolvable.'"

"Surely you know about the wave/particle duality of light? At this point, that grand mystery is considered tame and plebeian. Paradox, Dr. Delacruz, it is all around us. Quack-quark. Likely even more in your mind-field than in mine, and mine is a minefield. For instance—and to throw you a proverbial bone, since you so clearly want to know what I am thinking—is the carpet crawling beneath my toes? Yes *and* no. Did my mother beat my deceased older sister's back black and blue with belt buckle in front of my tender young eyes—oh do write it down, you so want to, *n'est-ce pas*—again yes *and* no. Does information carry entanglement? Is entanglement information? Physically speaking? Metaphorically? *Peut-être*."

She could not allow this to become a game, even though she felt the urge to win—an urge she needed to resist. She looked down at Andrew's feet. The bare, long toes and their long toenails folded and unfolded themselves on the gray carpet tile.

"Was she a physics student as well?"

"Stefania, you mean? Well played, Dr. Delacruz! I thought for certain you would go for the chum."

"Was she?"

"Yes."

His first direct answer. She didn't push it by asking another question. The sky above the parking lot outside the window was clear, and the turning leaves showed soft motion. For a breath, she could believe it was an autumnal paradise out there, that this hospital was, after all, a space for contemplation, recovery, redemption—that fall would be followed by winter, but after that, somewhere beneath the detritus of the past, spring waited and would bring them new life. If they could make it that long alive.

"So we beat on, boats against the current, borne back ceaselessly into the past." His voice was a song, almost a whisper as he recited the line. Then he continued, as before, the clever chatter absent himself. "*The Great Gatsby*, of course. By another brother blue. For the likes of you."

"You know, Andrew, I used to be quite a reader too." It was a risk, but risks were what had made her the famous Dr. Delacruz, Patron Saint of Unmanageable Cases. "When I first starting working here, I thought it so interesting that Zelda Fitzgerald was a patient here once. Scott's wife. His muse."

"Why, Dr. Delacruz! Are you threatening me?" He brought one of his paws to his chest in mock horror. "She died in a hospital fire, did she not?"

"She did. But not here. Don't worry." She pointed to the two sprinklers on the ceiling with her pen.

"Oh, but I do, Dr. Delacruz, I do." His hand slid down his chest and lay limp and heavy in his lap again. "Don't take it the wrong way when I say you cannot *begin* to imagine."

She watched a sad half-smile come to his lips. He blinked slowly, as if to block out some outer sight, or revisit some inner one. Slowly, she let her breath fall into sync with his.

The universe is arbitrary and cold and infinite and none of us amount to anything although we experience our lives as if they are everything. She wished someone could admit that to her and show her the face of love anyway. She wished someone could see her as she was when she was a little girl and her *abuela* let her fill the chipped china cup with sugar and drip, drip, drip the coffee into it—but not so much that the sugar melted all the way—and sat with her while she ate it with a spoon and listened to her talk about how boring school was and how mean Yuniel Diaz was to her during recess, just because she was smarter than he was. She wished she had been a better mother to Marisa, had been the kind of mother she never had herself, instead of being so much like the one she had. She wished Marisa had never been born, had had a hundred sisters, had stayed in Maryland, had called last night. She wished she had made a difference in the world, for more than her patients, for even her patients. She wished there was no such thing as evil, that no one ever suffered, and that she had worn a different bra.

"Why don't you try me, Professor?" She granted him the respect of his title, and of her wholeness. "I might surprise you."

He looked at her, relieved. He looked at her.

"But Inez, I think we both know you just did."

Chris Cleary
PERSPECTIVE

His tiny voice ran looplike through her head.

Mommy, I have my beach ball and so we have to go down to the beach.

Felix, six years old here, always to be innocent, tens and tens and tens of copies of the same photo, trimmed, cropped, laid one atop the other, scanned, rescanned, pencil-sketched, water-colored, tempera-painted, each addition echoing out of the central original like ripples upon a lake surface emanating from the point of disappearance and loss. Who knew how long it would take her? As long as it took. A puzzle she forced herself to solve.

Here he was six and already full of fond remembrances of Stone Harbor, the soft burning grains of sand upon the soles of his feet, then the cooler sturdy wave-soaked band nibbled by the tide, his toes leaving dime-sized indentations that quickly evened away into the surface's stubborn flat sameness. The inflated ball would bound and bounce, sometimes blown back by the draft, sometimes seized by the invading surge so that Daddy would hold up his hand and run to retrieve it while he waited, inspecting the pebbles and shell bits and paperish crab claws and popply seaweed below. With squinty eyes he would follow the airplane as it inched along the hot sky with its little red letters in tow. He was begging to return there as the ball called to him through his memory, for the backyard patio was only the backyard patio, but the beach was the beach, and they had to tell him he had to be patient.

She shuddered. Suddenly it was there for her. Or at least as close as it was going to get this time. She would have further opportunities to walk around it and around it and maybe even complete the recapture. But for now it was close, close enough to be outweighed by the urgent desire to roll up the whole battleground on which she had fought and slide it into a mailing tube and hurl it like a javelin into the beautiful house on Cascadia Street.

Mommy, how did you and Daddy meet and were you in love right away?

Oh, yes, immediately! So handsome in his suit and tie behind his desk! If that drunk driver had not totaled her car as it sat a helpless target on the street outside her apartment, she didn't know what she would have done. She had been teaching at Middletown Middle for almost five years, and my God she was so lonely! The children kept her busy, even allowed her on good days to slip back in age herself, but after the dismissal bell rang, nobody took her hands and kissed her deeply, nobody the least bit aware of the mousy enigma in Granny glasses and high-buttoned calico blouse. She faded for the evening until expected at the chalkboard once again the next morning, and passed the time drawing portraits of the icicles hanging from the branches outside her window in the winter. She was vaguely aware of the being she indifferently called Ellie Childs—she barely sensed it waiting in some form there beneath a blanket of routine and abnegation—but it was enough that the children required her, and more often than not she felt that what she gave them was all she had within. She read in a novel one night what a shame it was that to fire others you constantly had to be wasting the matches within yourself, but that was Captain Ahab who said it, and he was a selfish meanie.

Bob Cadmus looked over her claim when she visited his office on the corner of Cherry and Butcher. He took command of the paperwork and knew exactly how to resolve it. Aplomb—that was what he had that first attracted her. And an easy smile, a kindness in his manner. And so meticulous in his dress. True, he inclined a little toward the pudgy, and a boyhood scar on an otherwise smooth jaw line arrested attention, but nevertheless quite attractive. As he guided her through the process, his attention lingered upon her face more than she was used to. She knew he knew she was single. What would he do in the end? Awkwardly formal, they shook hands. She surprised herself by stepping to the window. Was that Llynmawr Lake he could see from his office? He joined her. Yes, it was. What a lovely view. On their first date, he revealed the fact of his divorce three years before, and she knew that he also had been lonely.

Felix in his Easter suit. Felix sledding down a hill. Felix on the deck of a Tall Ship on the Delaware. Felix in his baby pool. Felix reeling in a big fish. Felix astride a huge pumpkin. Felix marching in the Fourth of July parade. Felix rolling down the Avalon dunes. Felix opening presents Christmas morning.

She wondered what she was to discover as she held each captured joy in the cheerless present. With all that she possessed of him, could she eventually reconstruct the totality within herself? She would need to see him differently, that much she acknowledged, that much had she lost irrevocably. So what did she mean by found art, little Allie had asked her in her final year of teaching. Little Allie had been staring at the piece of driftwood hanging by a string above her filing cabinets.

"It's not art," she complained peevishly. "You didn't paint it. You didn't carve it. You just took it and hung it up there."

Mrs. Cadmus nodded her head patiently. "And where was it before I hung it up there?"

"Dunno. Guess on the seashore."

"If you had seen it there before I got to it, would you have asked what it was doing there?"

"Well, no."

"Why not?"

"'Cause it belongs there."

"There you are. It's found art not because I found it. It's because *you* found it. Just now."

"Huh?"

"You're asking questions about it that you would have never asked. So your new word for the day is *context*. An object changes when it changes its context. It basically means what's around it, what we see around it, and its *relationship* to what's around it."

"Con...test...."

"Context. Here, try this. Look at Cory over there. What's he doing?"

"Playing with Austin and Jason."

"How do you feel about him being over there?"

"Good. 'Cause he's not bugging me. He's a poop-head."

"Allie, we've talked about that kind of language. Now let's call that landscape. Cory! Yes, dear, you. Would you walk to the middle of the room for me? Now, Allie, we'll call that still life. How would you describe him now?"

"Well, he's closer to me."

"Good. Cory, come over here to us."

Mrs. Cadmus placed him face to face with Allie, less than a foot away. Cory squirmed and giggled.

"This is portrait. Allie, don't back away. How does he make you feel now?"

"Yuck! Make him go away!"

"Why?"

"He's not supposed to be this close!"

"Do you see anything else besides him?"

"No, just his ugly face!"

"OK, don't be mean. Thank you, Cory."

Cory backed away a few steps, gave her a thumbs-up, bowed deeply from the waist, and resumed his play.

"That's what I'm talking about. He's different for you—your feelings are different—when he's up close than when he's far away. That's one of the results of changing context."

"Well, if that's context, I don't think much about it."

Mommy, why do you draw so many circles before you paint a picture?

She guessed Bob had taken her there to show her he was cultured too, at least when he wanted to be, although he clearly didn't know what he was getting himself into. She had asked the school for a week off in November to go with him to visit his parents outside New York, and as a treat he secured a couple of tickets to some kind of performance at the Met. He knew nothing much about it. Something about Einstein. He guessed that she would appreciate it because in her own quiet way she was sort of artsy. Maybe something more. Had he divined something deeper? Had he secretly peeked beneath her blanket?

They settled into their seats, the lights dimmed, and as the performers began counting, vocalizing the beats to establish the rhythm, she felt she was about to partake of something utterly unfamiliar and inexplicably dangerous, a tortuous pathway into a sinister forest that seduces and transforms you, never to let you depart whole again until it was done with you meandering in circularities of sound and movement that prolonged resolution, perhaps even denied its very existence, hypnotizing her into self-absence, the solfège of *re-mi-fa-mi* resonating into *right-before-me* and *rain-befalls-me* and *rape-me-love-me*, the sheer vanity of the assault upon her senses, devoid of any denotation, forcing her to search for significance by seeking out someone she barely believed she really was, and her heart raced (she gripped his arm, and she thought she heard him whisper, "Hey, are you OK?") and kept on racing as if it were about to explode as entire sheets of the ordinary sheered away and avalanched from her, and four hours later, by the time that the spaceship had climbed the skies to an arpeggiating violin, her mind had been dyed.

She sat in silence during the cab ride out of the city. "You're not upset, are you, Ell? Holy cow, that was weird. I didn't get it at all. Did you?" She said nothing. She was imagining an infinity of rotations from the hum of the tires upon the road, a road she imagined as stretching forever if you simply ignored the exits. The turns of the taxi (south, southwest, west, south, southeast, east, south) slowly disappeared the patterns of stars beyond the borders of her window and replaced them with new ones. There would always be stars regardless of what direction you faced. Yes, things would be different from now on. That night in the hotel room, she made love to him again and again. She lost count of the number.

Mommy, why do you have to watch me so close when I run on the grass?

He wasn't exactly whining, but his face contorted with curiosity the second before she took the photo. It was a fair question, and he deserved to know why, so she told him about his allergy. She didn't want him to hate bees. Bees are our friends. They make honey, and she knew he liked honey on his oatmeal in the morning. She also didn't want him afraid to explore, to close himself off in a cocoon out of fear. She knew there was a danger of doing that herself, becoming overprotective and smothering like so many mothers of a child who after a difficult delivery they found out was to be their first and last, and so she let him run on the backyard grass. Bob had resodded to eradicate the clover, but just to be safe, she kept him under the aegis of watchful care. They had found out the bad news the best possible way, no rush to the ER with him gasping breathlessly. She had asked Dr. Sutton to have Riddick Memorial run the tests. You see, she told him, her little sister had it, and she didn't know what in the world to do, being all of fourteen years old when she noticed Nattie staggering across the hay-laden barn floor, wheezing and turning blue. She left her there where she fell by the bales and tore down the dirt road to the house to call the ambulance, chilled with guilt and doubt over leaving her, but by the time the ambulance found the farm, Nattie was gone and in her stead a lifeless little body, swollen to horror. Her parents told her there was nothing she could have done, but still she blamed herself, and taught herself what she could have done, what she should have done, except now it was too late. She swore nothing as awful as that would happen to him, so the allergist began immunotherapy as soon as the boy was able to withstand the venom, injections month after month, building up the allergens so the desensitization would let him love life with impunity.

Mom, put the camera away, I'm not in the mood.

He was so petulant on his eighteenth birthday. There didn't seem to be any photos of him smiling that January evening after dinner when he grudgingly blew out his candles. She asked if he had wanted them to throw him a party, but he said no. She asked if he felt he was too old for cake and ice cream with his mom and dad, but he said no. She asked if there was something going on at school, souring his senior year, but he said no. She asked if he... But he peevishly interrupted, "What's with the third degree? Leave me alone," and skulked off to his room. Bob also tried to ferret out the root of his moodiness, but he got nowhere. He stopped seeing friends. His grades dipped from their A's. Nobody seemed to know why. She would crack his bedroom door and stare at him trying to drown out his demon with the violent music pouring through monstrous earphones muffling his head. His funk lasted the rest of the winter, and they were already lining up child psychiatrists when suddenly he was himself again. In fact, more than himself, irrepressibly jubilant, excelling once again at Rosebaron, driving to friends' houses and going out to movies, engaging and communicative, save for the reason behind his abrupt emotional restoration. Some sort of chemical imbalance, she worried, but Bob hushed her. "He's happy again. Let's not rock the boat. Teenagers are like that."

His exuberance lasted through graduation and propelled him through the summer headlong into his freshman year at Princeton. She worried about a difficult acclimation spiraling him back into sullenness, but on the whole, everything went well. He was close enough to Middletown to return on the weekends periodically, but that was simply his being homesick. Nothing odd about that. Breaks at Thanksgiving, Christmas, Easter. "All systems go," Bob whispered in her ear, hugging her from behind as she watched him drive off to complete the year, and she had to agree.

They were dead wrong. She couldn't bear to confront it all over again, wrestle out some explanation, and she would never have any definitive answer anyway. Instinctively she reached for her box of photos.

Felix crabbing on the Chesapeake. Felix pretending to ring the Liberty Bell. Felix dressed as a scarecrow for Halloween. Felix on Santa's knee. Felix setting up the camping tent. Felix riding his first horse. Felix with her parents. Felix with Bob's parents. Felix at Cape Kennedy. Felix tubing on the Brandywine. Felix taking his first communion. Felix playing Ring around the Rosie.

She circled around and around, like some kind of wildcat stalking her prey. If only she could accumulate all the infinite perspectives, then perhaps she would finally understand. The mere data she knew by heart. His blood alcohol content was .28. There were several people in the park that late afternoon, although none in the immediate vicinity. By the time the family closest to him had figured out what had happened, he was already lying face down. He had been stung repeatedly, although it was not anaphylactic shock that caused his death. It was something as simple as drowning. It had been ruled an accident. But why was the hive on the ground beneath the tree, lying crushed beside his bookbag and a large rock?

Round and round she went, and still it made no sense, except for what she kept seeing, a speck of sawdust in her eye she could not blink away. He did not want to live without her, but she was married, with a family and career to consider, and her being almost twice his age, and other rational objections she must have cited. When he argued love was more important than all those things, no doubt she became cold and clinical and cruel, as if she had had enough of him and his childishness, and needed to rip him out of her life at once. He still had some of the liquor from the last dorm party of the year hidden in his trunk, so he headed to Llynmawr, dragged himself down to the lake to luxuriate in his self-pity, wanting desperately to reach out to them but for the shame of his year-long affair. Yes, to Llynmawr, where maybe his father would catch sight of him from his office window and call home so she could run right over and sweep him up in her arms before he did anything stupid. But as he drank and drank, hiding himself from the occasional picnickers passing in the distance, he dwelt more and more on the way she dismissed him as some callow idiot, stupid enough to have been born too late for her, and blinded by hopelessness, the clouds spinning hectically above, he noticed the hive hidden in the branches of the nearby tree, and—here was the critical part, the conclusion she did not want to reach—knowing he could not survive long with all that venom in him, he impetuously strode forward and lobbed a rock, then stretched his arms wide, an invitation to his proxy, but as soon as they were upon him, instinct kicked in, and he flailed about in futility until he realized that diving beneath the water was his only salvation, and so he flung his body into the lake, burrowing down and down and down, then blacking out, never to see the surface again. My God... My God... That can't be it. Not her sweet boy. There had to be another explanation. Ashes. Ashes. Not her child. Not her boy. Look at the wealth of his life. Where did she go wrong?

Felix posing before the Statue of Liberty. Felix watching an air show. Felix on a merry-go-round. Felix skipping rocks on the Wissahickon. Felix with his arms like an airplane at Kitty Hawk. Felix at a performance of *The Nutcracker*. Felix celebrating a hole-in-one at Putt-Putt. Felix at the Smithsonian. Felix hiking in the Poconos. Felix searching for Easter eggs. Felix arms aloft on a flume ride. Felix standing beneath the LOVE statue in JFK Plaza. Felix in his crib.

She had needed a twelve-letter word for *casuistry*, but what was a casuistry?, so she consulted the dictionary on the desk in his bedroom, and that was when she found the note, stuffed into the pages, written in the assured hand of an adult. "It just wouldn't work out. I can't leave him. We need to talk. Bellbridge Mall food court. Next Wed. 2 p.m." There was no sudden jolt. Instead, it spread like burning sickness as she worked backwards through his recent life, especially his excitement upon his return from Princeton, eager to get back to something undisclosed, and then his abrupt shift back into sullen hostility last Saturday. She phoned Bob, who agreed with her that they would never be able to wring the story from him. Trusting that the Wednesday in the note meant the day after tomorrow, and confirming it when he suddenly left the house in his car that day at 1:15, she had Bob leave the office and pick her up.

They pretended to browse the three-ring binders in the stationery store across from the food court, watching for the woman to join their son at his table, and there she was, right at 2:00. She appeared to be in her mid-thirties, baseball cap over her blonde curls, and large, black sunglasses that veiled her identity. "Who the hell is she?" she muttered, and Bob was ready to confront them both, but she held him back, respectful of the humiliation that would fall upon her boy. No, they would see how it played out. The entire scene took less than five minutes of his reaching across the table, trying to seize hold of her hands, before she shot out of her chair and out of the food court.

"We're following her."

"What about...?"

"We'll talk to him later. He'll be fine for now. We need to know who she is. Now, Bob!"

She lived on Cascadia Street in the fashionable neighborhood west of the northern station. The mailbox read Sowyers. She was out of the car before Bob could stop her. The venom within her burst uncontrollably. She spewed in such frenzy that Bob was forced to hold her back. The Sowyers woman, frustrated by her hands shaking so at the lock and unable to flee into her house, spitefully confessed. Only later, when Bob told her in their kitchen, moments before the police called with news of their son's death, did she vaguely remember the kinds of words she had never used before.

She would never see the Sowyers woman again, but she would find a way to stay in touch.

She sealed and addressed the mailing tube to the house on Cascadia Street as she had every month since then. There was nothing she could say to anyone, no evidence to back up what she had discovered, for her boy must have stopped at the house to retrieve the note from the dictionary before going to Llynmawr Lake. There was nothing she could do but ensure that the woman never forgot. The woman would receive every month her gift of found art, various portraits over which she had labored, portraits of her boy, now redefined by a context of pain and retribution.

His tiny voice ran looplike through her head.

Mommy, I have my beach ball and so we have to go down to the beach.

Katie Cortese
BEFORE THERE WAS LIGHT

"In the beginning God created the heaven and the earth. And the earth
was without form, and void; and darkness was upon the face of the deep.
And the Spirit of God moved upon the face of the waters. And God said,
Let there be light: and there was light."—Genesis 1:1-3, King James Bible

We got along fine. Before the light we still had heaven and earth, even if we couldn't see them very well, which wasn't so bad since everything was formless and empty. Relatively speaking. Volcanoes sputtered. Glaciers drifted. And we roamed, the people who lived here, in The Before. We didn't have the sun to freckle us, or the moon to pour its silver over the deep, but we stayed clear of the waters anyway. The Spirit of God patrolled them in the shape of a twister, lightning-lit from within when He was pissed, which was often even then.

Plus, we had fire. I mean, we weren't helpless. My wife made the best torches in the village. She carved the faces of the old gods into the handles, the ones who'd split when they realized how jealous the Spirit could get. He wanted us all to Himself. He's single-minded like that. Even though technology's advanced some, I still use her torches for sentimental purposes, because she's gone now, no thanks to the light, which did neither of us any favors.

In the hundreds of years I've been around, I never met anyone who could wield fire like her. Take her cooking. My favorite dish was her mushroom and mouse kabobs, rotisserie style. We had a favorite patch of velvety dirt outside the hut where we'd eat and ogle stars. The heavens were distant and lovely and all ours before the Spirit commandeered them.

My wife's story isn't much different from the rest, but it smarts more when the loss is your own. The day the light came, Diklah saw it first. He was tending his herd of mole-rats—which I always thought tasteless next to my wife's fresh-roasted field mice—when there was a disturbance above. The sky opened, parting the pearl-gray clouds that kept us cool during the day and sometimes spat down drinking water. Between two cottony mounds appeared a diamond-shaped patch of what we later called "blue." It was the same shade as my wife's eyes, which I'd admired by firelight since we were nomads, before she took up whittling, before she learned to reach beneath my loin cloth after a hunt with a how-do-you-do that almost always led us back to the hut so we could know each other—as the kids say—biblically.

Well, Diklah was terrified, of course, so he called for Vophsi, who came out of their hut with Mnason in a bat-wing sling. It's lucky their older kids were down by the waters, the first to discover that the Spirit of God had taken off for higher ground. I like to imagine them happy down there before the screams, splashing in the shallows, grinning wide as the clams they'd harvested for lunch with their toes.

When the patch of blue appeared, naturally Diklah pointed and they both stared, along with little Mnason, who was strapped to his mother in such a way that his eyes couldn't help but seek the heavens. That's when a burning orb blotted out the gap and baked their retinas to smoking black discs. The sun was hotter in its infancy. Ignorant of its strength. A ball of fire burning with no regard for the flammable world beneath. Their screams brought others, including my darling in her best river-reed sheath.

Diklah and his wife were found kneeling over Mnason, clawing at their own faces. "Don't look," they cried, but human nature being what it is, you can guess how that worked out.

My wife called for me with eyes fused shut, though from the right one seeped three neat drops of blood (eventually we'd name it "red"). This was before we learned to fashion headdresses of leaves to shade our faces, before children were warned against staring into the sun. So hot did the orb burn that its heat kept burrowing into the mysteries within the unfortunates' heads long after they'd averted their gazes. For three days my wife glowed with fever. All her life she'd ruled the fire, but now it mounted its revenge. I tended her as best I could, fingers blistering where I sponged her; my lizard broth evaporating on her tongue.

Of course, it was bitter stuff anyway. I have nothing of her gifts.

In the end, she held out longer than anyone, especially Mnason, who was mercifully gone at first glance. Sixteen of us fell that day, and lots of folks have forgotten. They've learned to love sun-dried furs and lush fields, flowers blooming in so many colors we haven't named them all yet. And maybe it's not their fault. When your average Joe lives eight hundred years easy, he sees a lot of folks born, a lot die. Too much suffering in between. But I never remarried, and that makes it harder to forget.

My wife, she thought we had plenty of time for children. *Maybe next century*, she'd say, and I'd agree because I wasn't ready to share her yet. I wanted more of her cooking. More of her laugh. More of her hair long enough to wrap around the both of us like a cloak. Joke's on me, I guess, because now she's all I have. Those old memories swirling through my brain like the damn column of fire the Spirit still appears as when he's pissed at us, which, if you ask me, is more often than we deserve.

But how can I make it real for you—the world before the Garden and the Fall? Before the beasts of the field or their names. Before Eve tried to make vegans of us. Before Adam was the Spirit's pet, the anointed, the blessed. Even we didn't appreciate the way we roamed the earth with abandon, eating what we gathered, camping where we tired, loving who we wanted—for centuries, if we were lucky.

Lucky. Fortunate. Chosen. Just a handful of words we didn't need before the light, when the wide, wild world was ours.

Daniel Coshnear
PROXIMITY

The first time I lost Lucy was at the women's march in D.C., 2017. She was three then, forty pounds, and I carried her on my shoulders until she began to squirm and the ache in my neck became a pounding in my head. The moment I set her on the ground a push from behind sent me into the back of a coworker from my hometown in northern California. "Kate, what a surprise!" said my new boss, Marta, and beaming with tears in her eyes, she threw her arms around me. "Meet my husband, Jim," she said, and he threw his arms around me, too. I didn't dislike them, not at all, but I barely knew her, and him I'd never seen before. Such sudden shows of affection make my blood shy. So, in fact, do marches and rallies. I have a low tolerance for public expressions of emotion, be they love or rage, both of which had been maximally on display for hours. What was I doing there, so far from home?

As Marta reached into her bag to give me a pin and a pink hat, I turned to look for Lucy. Her pigtails, tied in pink ribbons, were lost in a sea of crotches. So began the most terrifying fifteen minutes of my life. She couldn't have been more than twenty feet away, but in which direction did she go? I couldn't move. I couldn't stand still. I made my search in ever-widening concentric circles, pushing at times against the forward thrust of the crowd. Lucky for me Lucy chose to sit cross-legged on the pavement. Lucky for both of us she wasn't trampled.

Fast forward three years to the May Day march in Santa Rosa, a Wednesday midafternoon. Lucy is six. Marta is still my boss, a lawyer at the Immigrants' Legal Defense Center, and I am still a paralegal. I am still separated from my own Jim, still a single mother. What's different in this case is that Marta and several other lawyers from the ILDC have planned an act of civil disobedience and I've agreed, somewhat reluctantly, to be the contact person, to collect cell phones and purses and information lest any of my fellow workers be carted off to jail.

Also, worth noting, at age six Lucy still has Downs syndrome. The thumb of one hand is almost always in her mouth and with the other she tends to tug at the waist of her T-shirt. Like many children her age, she is easily disoriented in crowds, but strangers, well intended or not, tend to look at her and then look away. She refuses to wear a harness, and well, I don't blame her. She permitted me to tie the string of a powder blue helium balloon around her wrist.

I'd had trouble finding a babysitter (always!), so in the weeks before the march and action, I did not attend the CD training nor any of the planning meetings. I was fuzzy on the details. We'd meet on Sebastopol Road, walk roughly a mile with the full procession to downtown Santa Rosa. Most would gather on the plaza in front of the mall, but our small contingent would cross the street and protest in front of Wells Fargo, effectively blocking the entrance/exit from the B Street side of the bank. Wells Fargo is heavily invested in two private, for-profit prison contractors which house illegal immigrants and asylum seekers detained by ICE or agents of the Border Patrol.

It is true, what you've heard. They separate families. They hold children in cages. I've seen pictures. I've heard the wailing of toddlers on YouTube. I've met some of the cousins, uncles, grandmothers all these miles from the border, bereft and weeping. I can't imagine the pain the children feel, or the psychological harm that will persist for years to come. I think I can imagine what their mothers are going through, but I will not allow myself to dwell on it. I can't.

For now, Lucy has half of one hand in her mouth and the other is in a fist gripping the back pocket of my jeans. Marta, Celeste, and Rodrigo (also lawyers) are several paces ahead in this crowd of roughly five hundred. Rodrigo is leading the marchers in a chant, "Wells Fargo, you're the worst, put our immigrant families first," and "Hey-hey, ho-ho, detention camps have got to go." I see a sign that reads Justice for Palestinians, and a large banner: Fight for Fifteen. I see a man with a faded T-shirt, a familiar-looking logo: *It's Mueller Time.* One big war; fighting on so many fronts. And when I turn to make sure that Lucy isn't drooping, the powder blue balloon brushes my face. It could be Jim, the proximity (no one other than Lucy was ever so close); it is the color of his eyes. It is a reminder of my internal preoccupations, not that I need one. We were engaged. He was twenty-five, I was thirty-one. We never fought, or not so that anyone witnessing would have perceived it. He wasn't ready to have a child, but willing to think about it. He'd wanted me to abort when we learned Lucy would be born with a disability. "Why now?" he said. "Why bring more suffering into the world?" he said. "We'll bring more love into the world," I said. I believe wholeheartedly in a woman's right to choose, but I simply could not make the choice he wanted.

King Solomon said: *Go on, then, and pull your relationship apart.*

Fifty feet ahead a five-piece marching horn section punches up the energy. A dozen men and women in Mayan headdress perform a ritualistic dance, though two are working with Hula Hoops, two others on rollerblades. Lucy tugs. She says, "ABC Mommy." She's referring to our favorite YouTube video, the Jackson Five, the only song she knows by name. She waddles when she walks and often rocks when she sits; when I play "ABC," she rocks full tilt. I turn and squat, kiss her on the cheeks. She smiles. She's a trooper for now, and I'm so proud of her it nearly chokes me. "You and me against the world," I sing. She gives me a wet high five.

Because it is a permitted march, we have the SRPD on motorcycles as escorts. The tail end of the procession hits the beginning of rush hour. Some motorists signal support with a beep of the horn or a pumped fist, others look on annoyed, and some few flip us the bird. As we get closer to our destination, Marta and Celeste offer a fuller description of our planned action. Two (names I instantly forget) will go inside the bank with a banner and leaflets describing the reasons WF should divest. They have a letter they hope to deliver to the bank manager. They will sing a few classic protest songs. If police ask them to leave, they will leave. It is important not to startle or frighten customers. As for the other part of the action, a handyman constructed for us a facsimile of a cage, a four-by-four square of chain-link fence, roughly four feet high. Marta, Celeste, Rodrigo, and another, a name I didn't catch, will carry the cage across the street from the plaza and set it in front of the bank doors. They will stand inside the cage. I'll stand beside them, outside the cage. Marta had not anticipated that I'd bring Lucy, and I think she's unhappy about it, but it's too late to make any new arrangements.

Is it possible I'll be swept up by the police, arrested along with the others? I simply can't let that happen. It is terribly unfortunate Jim is out of town—he would have been here if I'd called. In spite of our differences, and his choice to live apart, Jim's always had my back when I need him. He'd said in the months before Lucy was born, he wasn't sure that he could love her, but once she came into the world, there was never any question that he did. And she worships him. And here I am thinking about Jim, the sad turn in our lives, the desperate hope he'll change his mind, the subtle signs he might, when I should be helping carry the cage across B Street.

Lucy lets go of my pocket in the middle of the crosswalk. She stops to point at a larger-than-life puppet with an enormous orange papier-mâché head. Beside the puppet, a man is selling frozen desserts from a cart. Of course, that's where the fun is, but we need to press on. I take Lucy's hand and pull as she tries to sit in the middle of the road, all seventy-five pounds of her. I am strong enough, barely, to drag her to the sidewalk in front of the bank. Bikes, cars, and buses whizz by. I cajole and bribe: you're such a big girl; Happy Meal; rainbow-colored snow-cone. I lie; soon, very soon. She slumps beside the wall of the bank only a few steps from where I must stand.

The cage is in place; lawyers in the cage. It's loose, it feels good, lawyers trading lawyer jokes. Soon the protesters from inside the bank join us on the outside pulling their ten-foot banner, chanting, "*Sin justicia, no hay paz.*" And soon, a tall, bald man in a suit pushes the bank doors open a crack and speaks to Marta, Celeste, and Rodrigo. "You need to move," he says. "You're blocking the door."

"We know," says Marta. "We're not going to move."

"I will call the police," he says.

He retreats. A moment later he is back. "You are creating a fire hazard," he says. "You're putting the customers in danger."

"They can exit on the other side of the bank," Marta says.

"You're making a terrible inconvenience," he says.

"That's the point," says Celeste.

The police arrive as promised. I count two SUVs, ten motorcycles, roughly a dozen cops on foot. After a lengthy conference at curbside, one emerges as spokesman, approaches the cage. Though I am close, I cannot hear the exchange because a young man with a megaphone standing only a foot away roars "*Si se pueda, si se pueda.*" I feel a rush of adrenaline; it's in the air. Rodrigo calls me closer, tells me the group has decided not to go limp if arrested. His pupils are double sized, and his voice breathless. Lucy is still sitting, sucking on her wrist. She seems to be trying to pry off the string, the tether to her blue buoy. My blue buoy, my Jim. I'm being totally stupid.

Marta calls me over to the edge of the cage. She's an old hand at this. She wants me to know how things are likely to unfold. "Now the police have dispersed, it is quarter after five, and they might simply wait it out. The bank closes at six."

"Oh," I say. "Are you disappointed?"

She shrugs. "We'll be in the paper tomorrow," she smiles. "It's just the beginning."

Celeste comes to Marta's side, gives her a squeeze. To me she says, "Thank you. I know it wasn't easy bringing your little girl along for this. By the way, where is she?"

I point to the space where she is not. If you're a parent, you must know this moment of terror. I turn, see the powder blue balloon blowing across B Street, feel the weight of wet sandbags in my legs, see the broad side of a bus, hear the screech of horns, the squeal of tires. It takes a lifetime to cross ten feet to the curb. I see a man, a stranger, lifting Lucy off the street. I wave frantically as he carries her toward me. She is unharmed, oblivious.

And now I see that the boy who held the megaphone leapt into the onrushing traffic. Later I will learn his name is Pedro, he is a student at the Santa Rosa Junior College, an activist and an advocate for day laborers, an amateur accordion player, an undocumented immigrant from Guatemala, a rabid Warriors fan, a pot-smoker, an embarrassment to his friends on karaoke night. Both his legs were broken, and he incurred a severe concussion, unconscious for twelve hours. He nearly died. He stopped the traffic. He didn't hesitate.

Suffering and love. Come back, Jim. Do you see, we've only touched the surface?

Zane deBlosat
CUPID, VALENTINES, AND LSD

The DUVALIERS moved onto Sparta Avenue sometime over the summer of 1971 but nobody who lived on the street quite knew when. One day the Schmaltzes were gone from the house and the next day the Duvaliers slunk in, the brood-mother apparently wearing enough colored scarves for one neighbor woman to peg them "U-Haul gypsies." The house was a red brick three story with five bedrooms. The mother, then a widow, had her own room of course. The eldest son who was then twenty-one occupied his own room and being an artist filled the room with oils he had done, mostly of Aphrodite, Medusa, other goddesses and heroines of mythology. There was one other male, a ten-year-old, who likewise had his own room and constantly went through costume drama phases, dressing up like characters whom he admired. Finally, the last room was shared by two teen girls, eighteen-year-old Cassandra, a senior at Carrick High School, who was dark haired, always deep in thought, and full of herself. Her seventeen-year-old sister Helena, a junior at the same school, was something of a sex kitten. Within a month the boys on the street pegged her as a young Ursula Andress type. When they whistled at her, she'd first giggle approval, then twitch her nose at them, , and then let loose a "humph." Her nickname was "Craze" because she could go off like a firecracker, especially if on a first date a guy would attempt to put his hand down a blouse or up a skirt.

It just so happened within a month of arrival at their new lodging one sunny Sunday midmorning there was a knock on their door. It was a teen Helena had met the night before, clad in blue jeans and shoulder-length brown hair. They had met near the local pizza shop, the usual Saturday night street corner loafing, and he was eager to see her again to get the ball rolling so to speak. Helena had seen this one in the school hallways during the year and thought him sharp.

Behind the door he heard a string of several cuss words from a voice he recognized to be Helena's and muttered to himself "Nice girl." The door opened and there stood the younger brother wearing white underwear, gossamer wings, and holding a bow and arrow—the arrow having a plastic sucker tip.

"Your sister home, Cupid?"

"Which one? There a couple."

"One with the mouth."

"Oh, you want Craze."

"Outta the way, nimrod!" came a girl's voice from behind the kid and suddenly Cupid was to the side, revealing Helena, "Craze," with tousled hair, half dressed, with one shirttail tucked in her blue jean skirt. Her right hand reached behind to scratch her ass, and then she yawned. "Oh, you're the one from last night," she said flirtatiously. "Come on in." When she saw him staring momentarily at her feet, she raised a defiant black-soled foot near his face, her blue jean skirt falling up her thigh to her waist. "Wanna smell my piggies?" He saw no underwear; she was obviously aware of the free shot she was giving him. She turned around, just missing an arrow.

"Shoot me in the ass one more time and I'm bustin' all them arrows, hear me?"

She turned back to the stranger and shook her hair in a lame untangling attempt. "You just caught me in a midmorning younger brother battle and about to have some Lucky Charms. Want some?"

"You stir the sugar with your piggies?"

"For you I should," she said and turned back away from him again with a little flip up in the air of her backside.

Once inside the door he could see the arrow shooter, in his tighty whities, a ten-year-old with valentines strewn all over the living room floor. "Sorry for the mess," the girl apologized. "My little brother's weird. He keeps his schoolmates' valentines and brings them out and messes up the living room floor with them."

"He also doesn't put on pants, does he?" the guest said.

"Goodness me," she said in this sarcastic voice, putting both hands in a feigned aghast expression to the chin. "I'm not *wearing* any? It's only for the expected uninvited."

"Where'd you learn to talk like that?" he laughed.

"What's your name again?"

At that very second Cupid hit Helena in the rear end with a sucker dart which didn't stick but fell to the floor.

"Parrish."

"I think I'm in love," she said smiling, moving up close to his face and batting her eyelids rapidly in a mockery of what happens when the cherub's arrow hits one and smittenhood begins. "Your name sounds classic, noble, like a prince's name."

"I was named after the family dog who died before I was born. That's noble."

The guest was led to the dining room and told to sit down at a large table. "Like I said before, we were about to indulge in some Lucky Charms. Want some?" Before he could answer, she commanded her younger brother, "Get us all some Lucky Charms, retard."

The little Cupid brother went to the kitchen, spied Helena's purse, mumbled, "I'll show her how retarded I am," finding a little square of paper laden with a tab of LSD. "This'll do him better than any sugar." Within a few moments, he returned to the dining room table. "These are *real* Lucky Charms, loverboy," he said and set a bowl down in front of the newcomer, his sister, and himself.

"What are you grinning about, retard? Look like a Cheshire cat."

From upstairs boomed a voice. "Better save some for me or I see impending doom in your future!"

"That's our sister, Cassandra," said Helena. "Don't mind her. She's always pissy."

Parrish took a spoonful of the cereal and nodded to the living room floor, strewn with the Valentine's Day cards. "So what's the deal with all those?"

There was the sound of footsteps from upstairs, then swanning into the dining room like a pseudo-Olympian goddess came the older sister, Cassandra, in a purple summer dress. Having overheard Parrish's question, on her way she scarfed up two cards off the floor. She tossed her long wavy black hair over her shoulder and fanned her face with the cards. "He matchmakes them like some half-assed Tarot, though they're all one card." She put one valentine close up to Parrish's face with her left hand and repeated this motion with her right. "The Lovers."

Parrish shook his head. "Ridiculous. Well, how does he know if whoever signed these cards gets together?"

Cassandra looked at her sister and then at him, slowly lowering and raising her eyelids, giving him the once over lightly. "That's for him to know," she said smiling slyly, "and you to find out."

"Oh, well," said Parrish, "if we're going to play that game," and went back to his cereal.

At one point while he was eating, he suddenly felt a big toe creeping up the bottom of his jeans. He stopped his spoon from reaching his mouth in midbite and kept it there.

"Suspended animation?" Helena laughed. "Whatsamatter? You look like a zombie. After kissing me behind the pizza parlor last night, should this surprise you? I'm a fast filly when I want something." She withdrew the toe, wiped her mouth with the back of her hand, and kept eating.

"Charming," her little brother said, imitating the sarcastic tone of the newcomer.

"Watch it, fuckface," Helena warned him. "I like this one and want him to come back."

"I think," said the younger brother, "since there are no purple Lucky Charms, that we should *add* one. Well, at least we'll do it with music." He went into the living room, put on the stereo, and within a moment Jimi Hendrix's "Purple Haze" was playing.

When they were finished, Cassandra's ride came, her boyfriend Troy, and they all went out the front door to marvel at the "pony," a sparkling 1965 black Mustang convertible.

"Oooh," sighed Helena.

"I got this practically for nothing from some Greek in south side. This lights your fire?" asked Troy.

"Sure does, cuz," she said in a singsong. "Come on! We're going cruising in a pony," she shouted, grabbed him by the arm, and soon the four of them were in the hot Ford convertible. "When you get in one of these, you never know what kind of person you're gonna be when you come out of one."

"Yeah," said Cassandra darkly, "and sometimes the ones who get in and out are unexpected visitors."

"I met him last night and I want him along," said Helena. "Now, don't be your typical cooze self and rag on the afternoon with one of your typical 'prophecies of doom.' We're out to have a nice Sunday ride in the country. And we're going skinny dipping at Mingo Lake. Right, Troy?"

A half hour of riding and reflecting on school, they played a game of Getting to Know You and the question arose what could you not do without? Parrish answered, the purple shirt he was wearing. "It's my cloak of power, of mystery, of prophecy."

"Wait a minute," said Troy. "*You're* not the one who started the purple shirt fad this year, are you?" He told how this rumor spread that wearing a purple shirt in a darkened room playing a whole side of one's favorite album would bring some revelation. "If you're the one, I'm your biggest fan. That scam was really clever."

"Ooooh," gurgled Cassandra, shaking her hands in the air above her head as though casting a spell, "that's what made the Carrick cliques squeal with delight! I'm the one who started this nonsense from a dream I had."

"That's not true," said Parrish.

"Yes, it is true," said Helena. "Before this fad started, Cassandra had this dream that a purple velvet cloak with gold trim covered the whole school one day and through everyone's favorite albums would be a mystical experience of some kind. You're just the—"

"Midwife," Cassandra said, "by which it was possible."

"Will I ever be a midwife again?"

"Oh, yes," Cassandra said and nodded vigorously. "You will be one by the time you get out of the car today."

"What's that supposed to mean?"

"Never mind."

It was at this moment everything changed: purple was no longer a color but a state of mind, a plane of existence, an entity that existed beyond time and space and yet commanded utmost respect and allegiance.

"This fortune teller once informed me that if a purple shirt was worn at night while listening to a song which is most important to the listener that some sort of truth will come."

"Then you *are* the one who started all this," said Helena.

"I'm seeing things, purple hobgoblins," said Parrish and looked outside one window then the other in a nervous agitation. "What was in the cereal I ate? It just dawned on me that I *am* purple and purple is me."

"Oh, our cute little brother," said Cassandra. "He slipped a tab of purple haze into your Lucky Charms."

Parrish spread out his fingers in front of his eyes like a Japanese fan, examining them as if never having seen them before. "Snakes. I have snakes. One night in my purple shirt I turned out the lights and was listening to *The White Album.* I heard some song about a séance, and out of freaking nowhere I thought I heard McCartney wanting to come back from the dead—I threw off the headphones and turned on the lights before I had the screaming meemies."

"I just got chills," said Helena. "Hug me," she said and put her head on his chest and her arms around his neck.

"You've got snakes coming out of the top of your head. Your snakes won't bite, will they? You're not Medusa, are you?"

"I'm Helena," she said, "a pretty goddess you have the hots for," and French kissed him hard.

"Your snake is in my mouth," gasped Parrish wide eyed with confusion.

"That's my tongue, dope-o."

"Your brother, the retard Cupid, shot me with an arrow of LSD."

The radio was playing America's "A Horse with No Name" and they stayed silent, listening. Parrish hugged Helena and it seemed his flesh was melting into hers. She pushed her hair away from her face and smiled. "My goddess has a beautiful smile with huge white teeth." She thought this amusing and rained more kisses on him, her tongue now so familiar inside his mouth like it had found a home.

At one point Troy kept one hand on the wheel, but reached inside his back pocket and pulled out a piece of paper folded into a small square.

"Anyone read this?" he asked.

"Give it to me," said Cassandra beside him and when she unfolded it grimaced.

"It's in some kind of mystical language," Troy said, "which I cannot decode."

"It's in shorthand," said Cassandra.

"Give it to me," said Parrish. "I just finished my first year of the class. I can read shorthand."

"Shorthand? For a guy? Are you gay?"

"I wanted to be a cryptographer."

"A crypt*what*apher?" asked Cassandra.

"It's a codebreaker, asswipe," said Helena.

Cassandra closed her eyes, putting her head back trancelike. "I predict cancer of the potty mouth for you, Helena."

Helena kissed Parrish on the cheek. "Parrish doesn't mind, do you, Parrish?"

"I've never forbade anyone to speak freely when around me," he said and waved his fingers in front of his eyes. "But back to what Troy said—implying I'm gay. True: I was the only male taking shorthand. He hangs out with the jocks. Me? I'd rather be in a room full of pretty girls than a field full of ugly sweaty guys."

Helena and Cassandra laughed, Helena saying, "Touché! That was a strike at the old Achille's heel."

"Well, whatever," said trumped Troy. "Read the letter to me."

"No!" said Cassandra. Cassandra had wild eyes, wild in that they darted sometimes like an animal caught in a trap, desperately looking in all directions for an escape.

"Why not?" he asked. "What are you afraid of?"

"It may say something horrible." She relented and gave him the paper.

"Always the prophetess of doom," sighed Helena.

Parrish looked over the page full of lines with loops tilted left and right, odd-looking little circles with half moons attached. He was able to decode it and began to read aloud: "'Whoever can read this will tell my beloved...' They're just noodles," he said. "Now the noodles are swirling in time to the song on the radio." The Stones' "Wild Horses" came over the radio. "Do you know," he said, "that these are what killed Dracula?"

"Noodles killed Dracula," said Helena and they all laughed.

"He was a vampire," said Troy. "The version of Hungarian goulash he ate must've had garlic in it. Garlic in the sauce of his noodles killed him."

"No, seriously," said Troy, "these noodles—I mean shorthand—killed Dracula. He tried to read the letters of his prisoner Jonathan Harker, to make sure Harker wasn't signaling his fiancée Mina of his being a prisoner, but he couldn't read the letters because they were written in shorthand. He cursed the noodles and then ripped the letters up."

"Cursed the noodles," Helena laughed. "I knew my retarded Cupid brother did the right thing in slipping you the purple love dart of LSD."

"Dracula couldn't adjust to the new world around him," said Parrish, "which had changed and ultimately destroyed him."

"And if the Beatles had gotten Dracula through the séance," said Troy, "he would've warned them not to eat noodles. Now, seriously, tell me what the note says."

"It's a valentine," said Parrish.

Little purple hearts popped above Helena's head. "I've just been awarded purple hearts!" he laughed. "Isn't that for valor? The purple heart for valor. What did I do that had any valor? Did you ever notice," he said seeing the curious expression she had, "that valentine hearts look like little rear ends?"

"What?" everyone chimed.

"Their shapes look like little asses, little red asses. But in my case, purple," said Parrish and suddenly couldn't stop laughing.

"So," Cassandra said, "they symbolize how asinine everyone becomes over this ridiculous 'pay-or-put-out' holiday women have to succumb to as a means of emotional blackmail to keep her man. And what are valentines, anyway?" she asked, darting her eyes in different directions and raising her arms in a perplexing manner. "Little cards, notes, that must *remind* one they're loved. And if one doesn't get one, what then? Has one forgotten the history of love bestowed up to that point? Does one cease to believe they're loved if the card has not been given, not sent, lost in the mail—or halted by the Fate Sisters? Does one cease to be? That there's no more purpose or pleasure?"

"My sister the existentialist," sighed Helena.

"Huh?" asked Parrish.

"My sister the soothsayer has been reading Jean Paul Sartre."

Cassandra said, "Or valentines mean something else. By what you said about their shape, Parrish, something else. Something much simpler."

"What else?" Troy asked. He was over the moon about Cassandra, hung on her every word, tended her every whim, but always afraid she would leave him.

"Obsession with anal sex," she blurted out in a huff.

"I don't mind *that*," Helena moaned with a low seductive growl and nudged her elbow gently into Parrish's side. One of the hearts above Helena's head popped in a fireworks display of fairy dust; springing from the center was her little brother, still in his Cupid accoutrements and winking.

"*See*? I knew she was for you! Just remember: if a girl really loves you, she'd *let* you."

Cassandra suddenly had a zombie face and said, "Someone here is anally obsessed," in an unearthly tone.

"Oh, wow," said Parrish, "you really are a prophet."

"Yes," Helena said, raising her eyebrows, "she *is*."

Out of a lull came an unforeseen rumor war of the senses, "I heard that—," "I saw that—," "I felt that," marching out of their mouths like soldiers of misfortune, each statement a thrust at someone or some incident; such is the high school way for petty amusement.

"I heard that this Purple Shirt Prophecy fad was really working," said Helena and she went on about how some kid wore the shirt in the dark and was listening to Emerson, Lake & Palmer's "From the Beginning" and thought it had to do with Calvin and predestination.

"I saw that kid one day—Nosepicker Ned he's called—and he said he made it up," said Cassandra.

"I felt," said Troy, "this purple shirt bit was probably someone's clever idea from the beginning—just to give us all a sense of solidarity or something." He momentarily looked over at Cassandra, and Parrish saw red love bubbles popping over his head.

"I should've guessed this was something from only someone as gifted as you, darling." Cassandra leaned over and kissed him on the cheek.

"But how," Troy asked, "does wearing a purple shirt give anybody the power of prophecy?"

"Ooooh, but it does," said Parrish. "Purple is the color of power, the Pope's color. Purple is a mystical color, the color of a weird sunset that promises an even weirder night. Purple has major powers."

They traveled through a few suburban towns and eventually were in rural areas and pulled up to a waterhole known as Mingo Lake. "Watcha See Is Watcha Get" was the last song on the radio before they got out to start stripping near the edge of the water.

Once in the lake, when Helena was close enough to Parrish and he could see her breasts, perfect as cantaloupes with huge pink eyes, he said, "Are these the tits that loosed a thousand lips?"

"Maybe," Helena laughed. "Watcha see is watcha get," she cooed. Then she turned her ass toward his front side in the water and rubbed it against him. "You can put *your* arrow here any time," she wiggled.

"Cheeky little monkey, aren't you? You'd do that?" Parrish said and felt a tingle down there where she was rubbing.

"If a girl really loves you, she'd *let* you."

"Your little brother Cupid just said that to me in the car."

"How'd he get here? Oh, never mind. The acid talking."

Again in the water, Troy brought up the shorthand letter.

"It's just a gushy valentine," said Parrish, "most of which was a lot of lovey-dovey jazz. I wasn't able to decipher to whom or by."

"Well, that's disappointing."

The four of them splashed around in the water for a while. Cassandra overheard Helena tell Parrish she'd "be whatever" he wanted her to be, meaning what exactly who knew. But at one point Cassandra caught Parrish alone and whispered, "A prophetic warning, loverboy: Don't get in over your head. My sister's exiled herself for others before you. A cruise in the cooze is not a home in the heart."

Parrish frowned and after a moment said, "Funny how some girls forever sing that one line from the Carly Simon song."

"And what line's that, loverboy?" Cassandra huffed.

"The one that says she's always someone else's something else, never herself."

Instead of rolling her eyes, she patted him on the back. "Bullseye! Now you're getting it. So, don't let any arrow break your heart."

Not long after, they headed back to Sparta Avenue. Troy left the three of them off. Cassandra turned to Parrish and told him that she left it up to the Fates: she had a girlfriend of hers write the letter in shorthand, sneak it into his locker, and if Troy would find out what it said, she'd leave him; if not, then not. "I could tell you knew what it said, so why didn't you tell him that I was considering breaking up with him?"

"Not really knowing what I was to do, I decided to play it safe. I didn't want to jeopardize my being able to come around your house." He put his arms around Helena's waist and she winked at him, a promise of further adventures. "And something else."

"What else?" asked Cassandra.

"I didn't want to see the destruction of Troy," he said.

Gabriel Don
EXTRAORDINARY RENDITION

It's not a normal bus. Looks nothing like the buses back home. The bus traveling to Karachi airport is funny, covered in mosaics and patterns, adorned with colorful and kitsch decorations, big bright red flowers drawn over the yellow undercoat and gold chains dangle down in front of the windshield embellished with Urdu script. The roof has a low railing to pile up people, too many passengers to contain inside. It is around one o'clock in the morning as we go down the mountainous path in the dark. The landscape of Pakistan is a scary place. It is my first time being away from Sara since we got married. I miss my wife and children. I miss Australia. Two young boys from Germany are sitting next to me. We are nearly at the airport when the bus is pulled over. Four men board the bus demanding that the German boys go with them. I stand up. The boys are only eighteen and twenty and don't speak English or Urdu. They don't understand what is going on. I am aware of Pakistani corruption and I'm not just going to let them be taken away.

"Who are you?"

"We're police."

"What do you want from them?"

"We want to talk with these guys. If you want to be with them, come with us."

"I'll come with you."

I don't believe they are going to take us away. I can defend myself. What are they going to do? The bus is full of people. Maybe they are going to ask us questions and let us go. As soon as the German boys and I get off the bus, the four men surround us and force me to get my luggage. I have no choice. I take my luggage and the boys' bags too. The bus leaves and the men blindfold us straight away. In handcuffs and shackles, we are pushed inside their four-wheel drive.

***

After two and a half years of marriage, I fell pregnant, Kareem and I lived in a valley, the northern bank of Sydney's Parramatta River—Parramatta an aboriginal word for "the place where the eels lie down" or "head of waters"— and I had my first child at twenty-one. In labor for over sixteen hours, Kareem was with me the whole time. He was so good. We had a bet that I was not going to cry and I didn't but tears were coming out because I was in so much pain. The doctor said, "We can't wait. The water has burst and it's very dangerous for you and your baby." They had to do a cesarean and I was scared. The hospital staff put something in front of me so I couldn't see the procedure but I was awake during the operation, Kareem beside me. They let him stay with me. Kareem sat right next to me holding my hand.

I remember how my newly born Yusif was crying in the nurse's arms. I think Kareem was crying too. I stayed in the hospital for ten days. We had our third wedding anniversary there and Kareem brought cake for me and the nurses. He bathed his child and changed his diapers. I was terrified to touch Yusif but Kareem, who was more confident with the little baby, encouraged me. We went home to our house in Parramatta, greeted by friends and family and lots of presents. Our home was near a park, fertile soil, a riverside walk, scarred trees, red gums marked by cut-out bark, removed with a stone axe by ancient locals for canoes and ceremonies, a reminder of the past, a reminder not to take more than you need, the scent of eucalyptus, muddy-looking water sea creatures loved for its nutritious mix of salt and fresh water, a ferry station, a greeting sign that said *Gi walawa and nalawala at Baramada*, please stop here and rest at Parramatta, boats sailing to where river meets the harbor. I remember breastfeeding our first child, my husband helping me. I remember kind kisses and cuddles, my husband so happy.

We have always kept to ourselves, stayed together as a family—Kareem, our four children and me. I had all four of our children by cesarean and Kareem never cut a cord. Australia is a family place and I had beautiful children. I always tell my kids, "If someone ever asks for help and you can help, always do it. One day if you need help, someone will help you. Never hesitate if you can help somebody." Kareem helped me build up my confidence and made me realize that education, knowledge, and honesty are so important. He has made me a positive person with lots of pride and strength. He encouraged me to do a receptionist center course and further my career. After completing this course, I worked several temporary jobs with government departments. I worked as a clerical officer and a data operator at the police terminal, in the immigration department and the department of public prosecution as a clerical assistant. Then I became permanent in the police department. When I was working in the police department I would work day shifts and Kareem would work afternoon shifts with his cleaning and security business. No one else looked after our kids. We used to look after them. When I was breastfeeding Kareem would bring Yusif at my lunchtime break. After I breastfed him, Kareem would take the baby and go. When I'd finished work Kareem would pick me up and then he'd go to work. We've always shared things together.

Life is for enjoyment and freedom is essential. We worked so hard. Made money. Went overseas. We loved to travel. Once we had saved up money, we would go and spend it traveling then come back home. We never cared about money. We are not greedy. Some people just work hard to make money, more money, too much money. What's the use of having money if you don't enjoy yourself? No, we worked hard and then we went and enjoyed ourselves. The six of us would squeeze into a car and drive around New South Wales, camping in lots of different places. We would be on the road for hours and hours and never fight. Our car would pull into Yamba, a fishing town at the mouth of the Clarence River—on the edge of the Pacific Ocean—and we'd watch the foaming sea and set up the tent ourselves. Even the littlest one pitched in. Kareem always made sure our two girls knew how strong and capable they were. He would take them to taekwondo to learn self-defense. Kareem and the kids were very close. He's a family man. My favorite thing to do was to go fishing with my family or have a cappuccino with Kareem. Spoon-feed each other the white froth sprinkled with chocolate and cinnamon. You know, a beautiful life.

*** *** ***

We don't know who they are. The people claiming to be Pakistani police take us to a secret jail. The secret jail looks like a regular house where a nice family lives; inside this house there are two cells. I am put in a cell alone. The two German boys are locked up in the other. I can hear and see them. We keep asking, "What is going on? Why?" They tell us the reason is, "We're trying to save you from the Americans. They kidnap a lot of tourists and we don't want to have a problem in Pakistan." That's what they keep saying. I don't believe them. Neither do the boys. They tell us, "We're going to contact your commissioner. If your commissioner doesn't take you then we'll take you ourselves. Make sure you fly safely." I argue, "Don't worry about me. Just let me go. I will be safe." Three days I wait. Finally a guard informs me, "We're going to take you to your official Australian commissioner."

Blindfolded, handcuffed, and tied up tight, the men take us in a Jeep and we drive for eight hours. We are transferred to a military place. There is a huge area with twelve similar small cells in the middle. The cells are so scary. Inside every cell I can see metal circles on the walls to hang people off by their arms and legs. I can see a man hanging like Jesus on the cross. I can see a man with his arms chained above his head, his arms higher than da Vinci's Vitruvian man, his arms higher than an overeager child in class who knows the answer to a question and wishes his teacher would call on him.

As soon as I go into my cell I'm frightened because aside from the wire on the front where the guards can look in, it's made of cold hard concrete and less than five feet, smaller than the average man. It is freezing. Not cold but freezing. Freezing to death. My skin becomes all cut up, incisions from the freezing cold. Through the wire, which makes me feel like a chicken in a coop, I can see military people walking around. Behind our cells is another area that goes underground. People are taken down there for torture.

We can hear the torture. We can hear people being beaten and getting electric shocks. Every day people go in and out. For the twelve days, before the boys and I are transferred again, we see a lot of new people being brought in. We can see that they were kidnapped and brought here too. People constantly being taken to the place under us and tortured. We can hear people scream.

The new place we are moved to like dead bodies in a bag is an underground secret jail in Islamabad. I can't see into the other cells. Sometimes I am alone, sometime the Germans and I are in the same cell. They keep moving us. The Pakistani captors tell us, "We're finished. We are sending you home. We're sorry for what has happened to you. You're going to see your commissioner. We'll talk with him and he'll take you home."

***

I used to fast on Mondays and Thursdays because the prophet Mohammed (peace be upon him) used to do that. It was Thursday the 20th of September 2001 and Kareem was away. The plan was for Kareem to visit Pakistan to investigate schools and see if it was worth moving the family there for a while. I had just picked up Fatimah from school with my barely one-year-old baby girl Hala on board—my boys were already at home—and when I started turning into our driveway, I saw people surrounding it. Three or four cars were parked next to my house. A man approached my car and said, "Mrs. Aswad, we've got a warrant to search your house and your car. Can you please just park here?" I ignored him and just parked right up at the top like I usually do. They all followed me. I wasn't sure why. I was confused and shocked. They showed me a piece of paper.

A warrant. I read through it. The man said that they needed to search. Because of the shock and because I was fasting, I said, "All right. You have to wait while I photocopy this and I want to talk to the kids and explain things to them."

The man said, "No, we don't have time for you to explain anything to your kids. You can photocopy it."

I took the warrant and I photocopied it. I gave them back the original and I left the copy in my photocopier. Sixteen people—Federal Police and ASIO, the Australian Security Intelligence Organization—all dressed in suits went into my house, a house without a husband home.

I held Hala, not even a toddler yet, in my arms while they raided my home. Fatimah was nine years old—her older brothers were fourteen and sixteen—and these people were following us everywhere in our own home. They were there from four o'clock in the afternoon until ten o'clock at night. I was fasting and I couldn't pray. When I tried to pray, they stood there staring at me like I was a monkey in a cage. When the sun set I couldn't break my fast, how could I eat? There were strangers in suits searching my house. I was so confused. I couldn't work out why this was happening.

When I realized the copy that I had made of their warrant was not on the photocopier, I asked the man in charge, "Where's the warrant? You took my copy?"

"Yeah I'm not allowed to give it to you."

"After I asked and you said I can photocopy it? Get out of my house."

I was really cross.

"Let me make some phone calls," and he went outside.

When he came back he told me, "OK, here you can have it." I took it and put it in my handbag. They continued to search. Inside my room, searching my stuff, opening everything, my private things. They were not respectful; they were a bunch of criminals attacking a woman with four children for no reason.

After a while my eldest son Yusif came to me and said, "Mum, I'll tell you something but please don't be angry."

"What's wrong?"

He said, "I saw him opening your bag and he took the copy."

"No way." I went to my bag and I swear to God I couldn't find it. I was so upset. There was one more room left for them to search, my daughter's room. I went up to their leader.

"You took the copy again? You pinched the copy out of my bag."

"I'm sorry, I can't give it to you."

"You lied to me again."

I was now really angry so I went outside and I couldn't believe the view of our backyard. My family's possessions dumped around the place. Our house upturned.

Strangers in my backyard and me standing at the door looking at the mess they created under the trees behind our house. Everybody was so quiet and I said, "I put God witness to what you are doing to me and to my kids and to my husband. One day you are going to be sorry for what you have done. One day we are going to be in heaven and you will be in hell and you'll be suffering the way we are suffering now. Get out of my house all of you. Just get out." Yusif said, "Mum, please just let them finish Fatimah's room, then they'll leave." I didn't say yes or no. They continued and finished my daughter's room.

They took our belongings and put them in bags they had labeled Item Number such and such. Each bag had so many of our documents, our tax returns, our diaries, our photographs, and our letters. They took our laptop. They took all our mobile phones. They had our SIM cards. They took our phone book. They had all our addresses and numbers. I couldn't contact anyone. You wouldn't believe how much they took. I have a list of things I've written down but I will never be certain of everything they took. I don't know what was inside every bag they filled. Seven hundred dollars Kareem had left in the filing cabinet for us to keep in case we needed it for something while he was away went missing during their visit. They took all our possessions and they wanted me to sign a piece of paper at the end. I refused, saying, "No, I am not signing anything." So the man in charge just signed it himself. They took everything and put it in a van. I asked, "When are you going to return our stuff?" The man mumbled, "Ahh, it's going to be... shortly, shortly."

***

We are in the secret jail for fifteen days before the Australian and German commissioners come.

I ask my commissioner, "Why you want me to do this? I haven't done anything. I didn't do any crime. Why these people keep me here?"

My Australian High Commissioner informs me, "You're never going to see your family again. Australia canceled your citizenship. You are not an Australian citizen anymore." I don't believe him, but I have a feeling that something is going on because it has been at least twenty-five days since I have been taken away and if Australia sends me home now it's going to look very bad.

He tells me, "If you want us to inform your family, just sign this paper for me."

I say, "No problem," and I sign it. I want my family to know where I am. The paper says sign here if you want to confirm you are under arrest in Pakistan.

My commissioner says, "There are new laws now. You don't know what's going on after September 11th. The world has changed. America has declared war on Afghanistan."

The Australian government official tells me, "I believe your citizenship is being canceled. You're going to Egypt."

***

Kareem had left a message on the answering machine saying, "This is Baba. I'm on the way back home." We were relieved because of everything that had happened recently like September 11th and the police and ASIO raiding our home. Then in October, I was lying down in the afternoon, the sun was sinking to the horizon and at around four o'clock I received a phone call from a lady.

"Mrs. Aswad?"

"Yes."

"I'm from the Department of Foreign Affairs. Are you aware that your husband has been detained in Pakistan? He hasn't been charged yet."

"For what?"

"I don't know. That's all that we've received, some information that he's been detained and that he's taking his medication and he's fine but he hasn't been charged with any offense yet."

"Can I talk to him? Can you send a message for me so I can speak to him?"

"I will try and do what I can."

***

The next day they take me to an American camp to interrogate me. I refuse to talk with the Americans and I am being rude to them. Before this time, I didn't believe that they were going to keep me for long. The Germans had gone home.

When the German counsel came he said, "Twenty-four hours I want my citizens released," and they released the two boys. Before the German boys left I gave them my phone number. I told them the name of the commissioner who had seen me. I told them to tell my wife what had happened to me. I said they should wait seven days then call because maybe I would be released by then and I didn't want to worry my wife and kids. "If you find me at home—end of story. Don't worry about it. If not, tell my wife."

***

Fatimah has started having severe nightmares. It is her first time without her father. She tells me she saw him in her dream but he looked like a skinny stranger. Just completely different, nothing like what he was, a walking skeleton.

***

I don't go home. The Pakistani Intelligence brutally interrogates me. Everyone steps on me and hits me. A Pakistani hits me in the head with a gun. They all have their faces covered with masks. They all wear the same black T-shirt and gray pants. Suspended on a wall, string tied around my hands holding my arms above my head, a guard beats me. Slaps me across my face. A guard points a gun towards me as another guard shoves my head in a bucket of water. I am interviewed by the FBI and the CIA with ASIO present. An Australian agent comes to Islamabad three times to interrogate me in late October. An Australian federal police officer is present at two of these. The Americans are in charge. When they beat me, the Australian says, "Oh don't talk to me. Just talk to these people. Try to cooperate, Mr. Aswad. Try to cooperate."

***

A German man called me and said, "We were kidnapped off a bus. Your husband was with me. He told me to let you know that he's all right but if you don't hear from him in one week get him a lawyer and speak to the media." How can I get a lawyer in Pakistan? I was so confused. Suddenly everybody knew as the news spread: "Sydney man has been detained." One report said he was from Afghanistan and that he was picked up on the border.

***

I am detained for about a month in Pakistan when I am taken to the airport and handed over to Americans. The American Central Intelligence Agency transfers me on a Gulf Stream jet to Egypt. They aggressively cut off my clothes with scissors. The men have a very bad manner. It is scary. I feel them force an object up me. Someone puts a nappy on me. They give me a gray tracksuit. I think I'm wearing the same shoes. They surround me with chains until I am a spring roll. They put on handcuffs and shackles. My whole body is chained up. They put stuff in my mouth, duct tape wrapped over. I am blindfolded. They put a black bag over my head. They put goggles over the top of my hooded head covering my eyes. And they just roll me onto the flight.

***

The woman from the Department of Foreign Affairs rings me again.

"We believe your husband is no longer in Pakistan, we have a strong belief that he's in Egypt."

"How can he go to Egypt? His ticket doesn't mention anything about Egypt? His ticket says from Sydney to Dubai, Dubai to Pakistan, Pakistan to Dubai, Dubai to Singapore, Singapore to Sydney."

"Nothing to do with his ticket. We just have a strong belief that he's been taken to Egypt."

***

I lose everything in Egypt. At the beginning—because of the drugs and what I'm going through there—I lose everything. Everything. I don't know my name. I lose my memory. I am wearing a nappy like a baby boy. Baby boy. You see a baby boy: that is everything that I am. In the very early morning, sometime in November 2001, I am shackled, blindfolded, and transferred through the city of Cairo in a van to an underground state security detention center where I am tortured and interrogated. The prison cell in Egypt is unbelievable. I can't stand up. The ceiling is so low. I can't stand all the way up. It is not as tall as me. It is all concrete and cement. I cannot straighten my body. The windowless room is smaller than my body in every way. The door is two steps away with a metal bed next to it. I can't relax in the bed. I can't lie straight. I am halfway open, my body bent. They put me on drugs. I'm not concerned about food. I'm on a hunger strike because they put drugs in my food. I'm on brainwashing drugs all the time. They want me to confess or admit I'm a terrorist. There is only one small blanket that barely warms. A naked light bulb hardly lights my small compartment.

After I arrive in Egypt the guards show me what happens to prisoners if they don't cooperate.

"We'll show you how we treat people."

They start kicking a tall bulky man bent with his hands shackled under his knees down on the floor. He can't breathe. One of the guards picks him up and says, "He's dead." The very first day they prod me with an electric gun. I sit shackled in a chair. A guard gives me 320-volt electric shocks all over my body. I thrash and convulse in pain. I don't fear death because to die is better than the torture. They force me to turn over, handcuffing me in a straining position and beat the soles of my feet until they are big and swollen. When my feet get really bad they treat them with cream until they heal. Then the beatings start again. The guards put me in a box with only a very small hole that a tiny stream of light shines through. It is smaller than a coffin. I could relax in a coffin. This box is too small to relax in. I don't know how long I am in the box.

I wonder when they are going to get rid of me, to kill me. The only reason I continue to survive is because of all the drugs they are giving me. They give me a lot of drugs. The drugs make the torture easy. I don't feel anything. In between the torture they interrogate me. They try everything to make me confess. An Australian official attends some of my interrogations. When I don't cooperate they get sick of me and put me back in my dim cell. I believe in God and God makes it easier for me. The guards handcuff me and put me in a dark black windowless room. The room gets smaller towards one side. Lower, lower, lower, and lower. They try to scare me. Water starts to flow into the room. I can hear the sound of the water rushing in. I can feel it on my legs. They put electricity into the water. I can feel it but I can't see it. I can't see anything. I can't see the water. I move to the other side but the concrete ceiling gets lower and the floor higher. I feel the water rise past my shins, my knees, past my thighs. The water rises up past my stomach, to my chest. I don't know when it is going to stop. I scream but I know no one can hear me. It comes to my neck. It comes to my chin. On my tippy toes, I try to stand as high as I can. The water stops. I'm tired and standing on my toes. I am left suspended in water for hours with my head touching the ceiling.

***

It is hard to be a mum and a dad at the same time while Kareem is away. It has been four years without him. The children are growing and without their father. Being a father and a mother at the same time is impossible. The government has put me on a pension. I don't like being on a pension. I thought pensions are for people who are disabled, sick, or elderly. Welfare has put me on a single-parent pension. I think my connection with God is what really keeps me going. Looking at the kids, that is what charges me up. I have to work hard for the kids. I'm still a human being. No one's perfect. I get moments when I am weak. I get moments when I am strong. When I am weak I can't talk to anybody. I just go and have a shower. Face God. Pray. Speak to God. Cry to God. I have to remember, I know myself, that I haven't done anything wrong. I know who he is.

They say, "Maybe he's done things that you don't know."

I say, "No."

I know that he didn't do anything wrong and if he had he would have told me. All my secrets are with him and all his secrets with me. We've always shared everything. Sharing, that's very important between a husband and wife. I heard a lot of people say thing about us. I'm not going to listen. Kareem and I have been together for so long. Twenty years and then they snatch him away from our family.

❋❋❋

The interrogators question me using information that must have come from my wife's mobile phone.

"How did you get that?" I insist. They tell me they got this information from my home. The Egyptians say the Australians gave it to them, the numbers of my family, mechanics, and plumbers.

They go through the numbers asking me, "Who's he? How do you know him? Where does he live? Who is his family? Why are you connected to him?"

Every single person. Everyone: The people who used to work with me in my café, my next-door neighbor, my sister-in-law. After they finished the questioning I am returned to my cell awaiting the men who would make me suffer. I haven't eaten or slept in a very long time. I am very weak and can barely hold my head up. One time they tortured me by removing my fingernails. They pulled them out until I had no nails. Almost all my fingers were broken. Two are especially bad. I urinate blood. I can't stand up straight for very long because I'll fall down. I can't walk on my left leg. My body is in awful shape covered in burns. The captors have hung me from metal hooks like a monkey. They shock me with high-voltage wires and beat me. The guard lifts me up and handcuffs me so I have to hang there. He hits me with a stick. They do this repeatedly. Unprovoked beatings are routine. One time when they came back to where I was suspended, they took my clothes off. I was naked upside down with my face on the floor. My hands, legs, and feet were shackled. They had dogs with them and they told me that the dogs were going to rape me. I tried to believe that they were just trying to play with my mind. Make me worried. They tell people that the dogs will sexually assault them. Intimidate me so I'll confess. After six months, I tell the Egyptian interrogators everything they want to hear. The electric shocks in my ear, my groin, the injections they give me.

I tell them, "I was originally going to be one of the nine September 11th hijackers."

I admit to whatever they want me to admit. If I confess I'll go to trial.

"I'll tell you whatever you want."

I pray they will stop tormenting me. I agree with them that I had advanced knowledge that September 11th was going to take place.

I confess, "I trained the 9/11 hijackers in martial arts."

***

I witness my children's suffering and depression concerning their father. Fatimah and Hala are too young to be able to help the family so most of the burden falls on both Yusif and Abdul's shoulders, an early responsibility. Abdul has dropped out of school in year eleven because he felt he had to. Hala, the baby of our family, is missing out on having a father. I've always tried to make her understand who Daddy is. She has not seen him in years. She was only a year when he left. She sees him on the television and has a little key ring with his picture in it. Every night she kisses it, kisses him good night. Every morning she kisses him good morning. She has a little jewelry box where she keeps her key ring with Kareem's picture. Hala misses out on a lot because Kareem isn't here. We all pray for the day we can be back to normal like the family we used to be. For now we don't know when we'll see him again. I leave my trust in God. As long as you have good intentions to speak the truth and not to harm anybody, he tests you as much as you can take. Never be afraid of the truth. I believe in God and that God will never give me more than I can take.

***

The American military police transfer me from Egypt to Kabul then to Kandahar then to Cuba. I keep saying, "I can't walk." The officers attach all of the prisoners to each other, twenty people chained up in a line. I am very sick, my head flopping to the side like a rag doll. I was going to Guantanamo Bay. The eight-hour flight from Pakistan is the worst. Flying in a sack like a rubbish bag is torture enough. You can't breathe. The Americans chain my shackled legs to my cuffed hands, cover my face, blindfold me, and put goggles on top. I wouldn't be able to walk properly even if I could keep my head up. They carry me onto their secret CIA plane, drag me along on the floor with everyone else being forced on the flight. There are no seats. There are kids amongst us—fourteen-, fifteen-, sixteen-year-olds. Young kids being taken to Guantanamo Bay. I was fainting throughout the flight, my head leaning to the side, my body unbalanced. What the Americans, the military, has done in front of my eyes. They take the pants off a young boy, push him under and rape him, in front of my eyes, in front of everybody—and that's the military. These people are meant to be looking out for human rights and searching for justice and this is what they do. The Americans want to scare us. They are criminals. The men aggressively yell and curse at us. They intend to harm us. If they did this in a war I would have said, "All right," but they kidnapped people. All these people on this plane were kidnapped from their own homes, from their flight, from the airport. Most of these people are not fighters. Our captors spray us with stuff that makes us sick. Abusing isn't even the word for it. Abusing means nothing in comparison. An American flag flying in the plane, they are proud of themselves, they take photos, they are happy, they send the photos everywhere saying, "Look we did this to people!"

***

In August 2004, I still didn't know where my husband was. I had not heard his voice in years. I had been hearing stuff about Abu Ghraib and was very concerned. I take the kids to the movies one day and every single movie in the previews contained violence. Our society is sick. Why do people want to watch bombs, wars, torture, fight scenes, the murder of children? There is not one film without violence and some of them are meant to be funny. Violence is not funny. We heard some news that a British guy who was in Guantanamo Bay for a year and a half had just been released. He wanted to speak to me before he talked to the media. A TV station arranged for me to go meet him in London so I left the kids and I went all the way to England with my lawyer. We met him and he told me about Kareem. He let me know that

Kareem had been suffering and that he's been through a lot. He saw Kareem when Kareem first came from Egypt and was put in Guantanamo Bay, saw him all the time through the cage, locked up opposite him. He revealed that Kareem couldn't balance his head and used to fall on the floor, that he used to bleed from his nose, from his eyes and from his ears, that the guards used to leave him like that for about half an hour before they'd turn up and when they did instead of looking after him, they used to bash him. He informed me that Kareem thought his family had been killed, that Kareem doesn't believe that his family exists. When he said that, I cried. I don't like to cry in front of anybody. I've always tried to keep myself strong in front of everybody.

✻✻✻

On arriving to Guantanamo Bay I was taken from the big gray plane to Camp Delta. Camp X-ray, the temporary camp, was now gone. I can't hold myself up. The heat is unbearable. We are in the middle of the Cuban wilderness. The other prisoners think I'm in appalling shape. They say I wake them up in the middle of the night screaming. I can't sleep properly—too many disturbing memories. In the beginning the military police with crew-cut hair, dressed in full combat gear, gave me a white T-shirt to wear which soon changed to orange. Delta is divided into many different places. Block A, Block B and so on. I can see through the eyes in the sides of the mesh cells. There is wind blowing through. Rain comes inside. Mice, rats, snakes, and scorpions wander into my cell. I can see the shadows of the person in the next cell through the green tarpaulin. There are gates and wire fences around each individual cell block with military police guarding each cell. The guard that stands outside my cell is dressed in a military uniform with a flak jacket, a gas mask, and a M16. In the cells there are metal beds and squat toilets. They want you to be isolated. Noise moves through the cells. We can talk to each other but we don't know who we are talking to. They have a fan in the block that makes a big noise. If the military don't want you to talk they keep the fan running. The guards take you outside to have a shower. There is no hot water at all. Even in the wintertime they shower you outside under pipes. There is an area of around four meters square for recreation where the guards will take from your cage to exercise you for fifteen or twenty minutes once a week depending on the interrogator. The military are just the guards. The interrogator wants you to talk. Everyone in Cuba is interrogated. If the interrogator doesn't allow you to go outside for recreation or a shower, you don't. There is nowhere to go. Beyond the twelve-foot-high steel fence that is always locked there are plants and rocks for as far as you can see.

The prisoners are assigned to four different levels. If you cooperate your interrogator will give you a level one. A level two if you are cooperating but not much. Level one is the highest—and those detainees get extra-special treatment. They are allowed two blankets and two sheets. Their uniform is shorts, shoes, and a T-shirt. They can change their uniform twice a week. Other levels are only allowed to change once a week. Level two only has one blanket and two sheets. I was always a level three or four. Everyone in Cuba is treated differently. The only thing that is the same is your cell. The interrogator treats you however he wants depending on what he wants you to do. This is mentally disturbing because you are in the same block as people of different levels. The interrogators try to make people jealous of each other. The guy next to you has two blankets, a cover and everything while you have nothing in your cell. Another detainee is taken every three or four hours to go watch television. The guards bring one person McDonald's to his cell. You get disturbed. The prisoners turn against each other, thinking that the detainee getting special treatment is a spy. People start to talk about it. That's what the interrogators want to play with. There is a main interrogator but you don't know who that is. You never know. You never know who's dealing with your case.

During this time the interrogators were not interested in me. What do the military do with people like me? They put them in isolation for twenty-four hours a day. I was in isolation with nothing in my cell apart from my uniform, which was sometimes shorts, sometimes a full uniform. I was level four with CI Lost. Confidential Item Lost. You have nothing. Most of my time in Cuba I am in isolation or in level four with CI Lost. I can't see anybody in the one-and-a-half-meter square closed cell. They have a toilet inside and one metal bed. It's all metal. No mattress. There is nothing in there and that's all I've got. The isolation rooms are similar to the other cells but in the isolation cells the walls are metal so you can't see outside. My treatment was very bad. I was in isolation for the first year, year and a half, or two years in Guantanamo Bay. Sometimes the guards would take me from isolation to Camp Delta to see other people. Not for long though, maybe one or two days and then they put me back in isolation.

There is another block called Block Romeo. The detainees in Block Romeo are fully naked. The guards will sometimes give them shorts. The cage is similar to the others except it has a heavy plastic over the mesh caging. You can see through it but your hand can't get out. The people in Romeo are there for serious punishment. There is no blanket. You have nothing all the time. I've been through this. I've been in every bad block. They hate my guts. They hate me. Romeo is punishment. The interrogators take you there to make you suffer. You're not allowed to have anything. To taunt you, the guards will give you a blanket at eleven o'clock at night then they'll take it away at four or five o'clock in the morning. The time you need the blanket the most, they take it from you. A lot of people don't ever accept the blanket off the guards, because what is the use? If I take the blanket at eleven, when I am warm and asleep the guard will wake me up and take it from me. The guard will come at one o'clock—see me sleeping—and he'll knock on my cell shouting, "Hey, hey." Once he makes sure he's woken me up, he'll take my blanket. "Why'd you give it to me for?"

An hour later when I'm asleep again, he'll knock, "Hey, hey." Then the guard will give me my blanket back. It's hard. To play with people's minds is terrible.

The guards take me to Camp Echo, which is built like a house divided into two parts for two detainees. You can hear this person when he goes to the toilet. You can hear him when he talks but you don't know who he is. In this block, everything is inside the cell. The cell is around one and half meters square with a bed, toilet, and shower within. You don't have to go outside for a shower, which means you have twenty-four hours inside the cell. There is a camera in the cell and there is a door to a large area for the guard just outside. He sits at his table and chair watching you through the mesh. Camp Echo is for people who are going to see their lawyers or are going to be sent home. So no one will know. They take people to Echo if they don't want anybody to know what's happened to you. It is far from everywhere. You don't know what is happening outside. Sometimes you can get information depending on your relationship with the guards. I used to hear children. A guard confirmed the American military detained a ten-year-old and a six-year-old, Afghani children, at Camp Echo. They put them far away so no one will know about it. I found out because some of the guards don't like the Americans, especially the Hispanics. The non-American guards release too much information to us. When you speak English and other languages you can take information from people. Especially me, I speak Italian and the Spanish-speaking guards understand Italian.

There is another new big two-level building called Camp Five built, I was informed, to contain ninety-nine people. It was built like a cross. You could hear people at opposite ends but not the people near to you because it's curvy. Hearing was made hard. The room was about two meters square and inside everything is concrete, even the bed. The lights are very bright and there are cameras everywhere. There is a door in your cell that leads to where the guards are. The guards have a cover they can put over the door, which they can open and close whenever they choose to look at you.

Four years of my life in interrogation. The interrogator tries to keep you angry. In Guantanamo Bay the guards will approach me whilst I'm lying down in my cell and say, "You spit on me?"

"Huh?"

"You spat at me. You swore at me."

And then bang, he hits you.

"I swear at you, what's wrong with that?"

"All right, punishment."

The guard goes inside my cell, takes my blanket, takes my cover, and takes everything from me until I'm naked. They try to scare me. They know what makes me upset and they use it against me. If I say, "Get lost," I'll get punished for it. I know what they do. I know the system. I know how they are playing the game.

I have nothing to cooperate with. They know that. And I'll tell them. For me there's nothing to cooperate with. You know what to cooperate is? You lie about other people. That's cooperation. It depends on you. But it doesn't even matter if you confess. The interrogator will ask, "Did you see this person?"

"Yeah I see this person at this time he was there. Yeah I saw him, he was doing this and that."

"Thank you very much."

The next day they want more. That's why they have levels because the more people "cooperate," then they can move up levels gradually. It depends on how many people the detainee will give a false confirmation about. They lie and say they have witnessed things. Cooperation does not mean cooperation.

The interrogators drive people insane with their games until they "cooperate." They put them in solitary confinement, deprive them of their senses, tied up in excruciating, painful positions until they crack. Some prisoners are put in stress positions, straining postures, limbs in places they shouldn't be, for so long, the body begins to torture itself but the guards are technically not torturing you, you're doing it to yourself. They did this in Vietnam, Viet Cong prisoners captured and placed in submission position, tying boards between their arms. Some prisoners are masked and water is dripped onto their faces for hours on end until they feel like they are drowning and suffocating. Nightmares invade my head. I see Sara when I am awake even though I know she is dead. The Americans told me my whole family was dead. The interrogators put pictures of my wife and children over the carcasses of dead animals.

Until this, Australia was the best country in the world, the safest. How could Australia allow this to happen to my family and me? Detainees tell me stories of what has happened to them. Imagine.

"I am in my home. I have my kids. I have my wife. I have all my family, my father and my mother, in the house—and somebody breaks into my house. They injure and rape my children, my wife, my father, and my mother, in front of my eyes and I can't do anything about it. What do you expect me to do? If I blow myself up and I blew up these people, is this too much? If you lost everything in front of your eyes and they rape you. They rape your family and kill them, in front of your eyes. What do you expect? If you saw your own daughter, five years old—and you as a father witness her rape. What you feel? So much spite and you can't do much."

It's a true story. This has happened.

✳✳✳

I heard from the Department of Foreign Affairs. They were going to arrange a phone call with Kareem for us. The children and I went to the city. We had to be there at nine o'clock in the morning. We all sat in a conference room with a loudspeaker and Kareem picked up the phone.

"Hello, who's that?"

It took us about ten minutes to convince him it was us. He wouldn't believe it was his family.

"OK prove it to me. How would I know it's you, Sara?"

"Do you remember the day we had our marriage registered? Where did we go? "

"Yeah, where?"

"The cinema."

Then he started to ask me questions and said, "Remember the movie *Lock Up*? Watch this movie and you know how I live."

I knew this movie. Kareem and I watched it together. It's about how the government tried to set up Sylvester Stallone and they tortured him in an isolation room.

The general took the phone from Kareem and told me, "Get the person in charge."

They made rules: we couldn't speak in Arabic and Kareem couldn't speak about his situation. The phone call was only for half an hour and they stopped us in the middle for chucking a few Arabic words in. We weren't doing it on purpose. It comes out naturally when we speak. The kids all spoke to him for a little bit. All this in half an hour and we were not allowed to have more.

***

The guards tell me, "You're going to have a call with your wife." Four guards blindfold, handcuff, and shackle me and escort me into the general's office.

I go inside and the guard behind me makes it clear.

"Listen. She'll call and you'll talk to her. Tell her you're good and you're happy. You are being treated well."

Even if you're under torture, you have to say the truth. Lying will harm one thousand five hundred people there because if I'm treated well that means they are treated well too. It is not fair for me or for them to let anyone think that we are treated well here in Guantanamo Bay.

The general stops us in the middle of our phone call, "Hey, hey don't start trying to pull tricks."

I said, "Well, that's my life. I'm talking about my life."

"No, no, enough, enough."

The general stands up and takes the phone from me and starts talking on the phone with I don't know who.

I start telling the guards, "I speak the way I like whether you like it or not. Just kick me out."

One of the guards starts to beat me but I don't care. They are not allowing me to talk. Someone bashes me in the head, then they start to talk nicely, "Are you all right?"

"Do you think I'm all right?"

"Tell them you're all right."

"Why I'm all right?! Do you think I'm all right?" and I swear at the guards.

I don't even care that they're beating me. I don't care. I said, "Do you believe I am all right? You are cowards. Why are you scared?"

"We are American, we are not scared."

"OK, OK… let me tell them that you are Americans and you're an idiot. Let me tell them that."

"Be nice."

"Why be nice? What for? You are just cowards. Why you worry if I say what I want to say? It's the truth. I cannot tell them the truth? I'm not going to lie. I'll tell them what it's like here."

"No if you talk anymore about that you're not going to have your phone call."

Then they start to talk nicely again, "Your daughter wants to talk to you."

I wasn't happy with the rest of the conversation. They'd already taken out fifteen minutes of our half-hour call. I tried to say more but they don't allow me. I couldn't focus even when my children were speaking to me. The guards were not happy. The general got up and started moving closer to me.

***

I found out that lawyers in America had been acting on Kareem's behalf, without me knowing for two years. *Hamdullah*. The group of lawyers in America invited my lawyer and I to go to Chicago so we could discuss the situation. They wanted me to sign some documents and write a letter to Kareem but I didn't want to write a letter to him. Kareem had told me on the phone, "Do not send me any pictures or any letters."

They were being used against him. The guards in Guantanamo Bay were putting them on top of animal carcasses and doing lots of disgusting stuff. So I wrote a letter to the lawyers saying, "Thank you very much for inviting me and acting on behalf of Kareem."

He will read it and know that I've been to Chicago with the lawyers and those people are acting for him. When I talked to the head lawyer Tom privately I told him something that only Kareem and I know. This way Kareem will hopefully trust Tom. It is very important Kareem sign the document Tom gives him so we can actually go to court. If he refuses the lawyer the first time he sees him, he misses out.

***

Tom had no lunch. The guards treated him badly, keeping him outside in a line for two hours after they searched him. Took everything away from him. The only thing they left with him was some chips and lollies.

I told Tom when he first sat down, "I'm not going to trust you."

He's an American. I grabbed a bunch of his Pringles and ate them all at once.

"Kareem..."

This is the first time I hear my name in a long time.

"Kareem can you eat one by one? I had no breakfast like you."

"I haven't eaten for a year." I'd been on hunger strike.

"I accept that but I'm hungry. Leave me some," Tom jokes. "Doesn't matter I can get one when I go back."

Tom was interested in the torture and I didn't know why he wanted to talk about it. I want my case out there but there's no need to talk about torture because torture is disturbing and pointless.

Tom argues, "The only way to get you out of here is if we explain how you have been tortured."

"In my case they have nothing. I haven't done anything. Why am I here?"

"I don't know. But they are going to accept your case in the court at this time only. Today. They will accept your case because we have important media reports outside about Abu Ghraib. If we file your case now, we're going to push the government immediately to look at your case."

"Abu Ghraib?" I had never heard of it.

Tom informs me he will come back tomorrow. "You have to sign this for me. I'll let you think about."

He hands me a bunch of papers. "Read through this. This is your case. We are going to take it to court. I'm not coming to play a game with you. I'm not CIA. I'm not FBI. I am a private lawyer. And we want you out."

Tom came back the very next day like he said he would with salad sandwiches.

"All right. I'll sign."

Tom was happy.

"Maybe one year. Maybe six months. Maybe eight months. I'll see you after. I can't promise you."

"Why you here? Why you coming? You think when you come back after six months or eight months you're going to see the same person? I'm finished. I'm dead."

"No you stay strong and write to me."

"Write? I never see pen and paper. How am I going to write to you?"

"I'm going to ask and I'll get permission from the commissioner in the United States. I'm going to send them this permission here to give you paper and pen to write to me."

Then Tom left.

***

My daughters and I were sitting down in the afternoon watching television, snacking on sticky baklava, my sons Yusif and Abdul were out, when we received a phone call from the Department of Foreign Affairs.

It was a man and he said, "Mrs. Aswad?"

"Yes."

"We have some news from the United States. They've decided they are not going to charge your husband and he's going to be released soon."

"Excuse me, can you repeat what you just said again?"

He repeated it.

"Are you telling me that he's coming home soon?"

"Yeah, once the Australian government puts in an application to have him repatriated."

"So he's coming soon?"

"As soon as they do the application. Yeah, he will come."

"Can I speak to people? Can I let people know?"

"Uhh... Yeah, the Attorney General, Phillip Ruddock, is going to be announcing it soon in the media and it's going to be public."

Oh my God. I hung up the phone. I couldn't believe it! All of us dropped to the ground and bowed. We prayed and did *sajda*. Then I rang Yusif.

"Where are you?"

"I'm driving."

"Pull over!"

"Why?"

"Did you hear the news?"

"I heard the news. Is it true?"

Yusif stopped the car and he did the same as my daughters and I. In the middle of the street, he thanked God that this is going to happen.

Aaron Emmel
THE LISTENERS

Ryan knew what the blood bank receptionist's answer would be before she looked up at him. "Sorry," Debbie said. "We can't accept more than two donations a week."

"I've got to get back to New Mexico."

Two days earlier, Debbie had asked him to teach her a card trick. Now she avoided his eyes. "It's a regulation."

"I need the money. I've got to see my son."

Debbie looked down at her computer screen.

Ryan watched her for a half a second before he headed back out to his battered Civic. It didn't matter that the job that had brought him here to the East Coast had paid a decent salary before he got laid off. It didn't matter that his magic career always seemed like it was about to take off, even though it never did. It certainly didn't matter that he'd promised Sheila he was never going to gamble again. All that mattered was that he was going to get back to Caleb.

That afternoon he pawned his sound system and his vinyl collection and cleared out his bank account. He walked into the Maryland Live! Casino with eight hundred dollars in his pocket. Enough to pay his next month's rent, or to get to Caleb, but not both. And when he finally saw his son, he knew he couldn't show up empty handed. So here he was.

Two hours later, he sat across a poker table from a gray-suited older man who looked frustratingly familiar, his hand hesitating over the last of his chips.

"Are you in?" James asked.

Ryan sighed and shoved out the small mound of colored counters. Both men turned over their cards. Ryan had a straight. James had a full house. He pulled in the pot. That was the moment when Ryan realized where he'd seen him before.

Ryan scraped out his chair and stood up. He had nothing left. The server came up to him and smiled. "Another Black Russian?" He shook his head and walked out.

He wasn't thinking about the money. He wasn't even thinking about Caleb. He was thinking about his dad the night he was taken away. He pushed aside the slow-moving automatic door and escaped into daylight.

A group of teens and an associated pair of parents were heading past the parking lot toward Arundel Mills Mall. Ryan caught up with them. He didn't have a plan. He just knew he had to do something to escape the memory of his father, and there was only one thing that never failed him. He dug a deck of cards out of his jacket pocket. "Want to see a trick?"

One of the boys glanced his way. He was clearly the couple's son. "I'll find whatever card you pick," Ryan promised him. The boy looked like he was about to brush him off, so Ryan peeled the top half off the deck and handed it to the girl he'd been talking to. "In fact, I'll make it even harder. I'll identify both your cards. At the same time."

The girl stopped walking, and the boy halted beside her. Ryan handed him the remaining cards. The adults approached to hurry their son on, but when they saw what was happening, they paused, and soon several other passersby had also crowded around to watch.

"Shuffle your cards," Ryan directed the teenagers. While they were doing so, he continued, "Each of you, when you're ready, pick a card, any card, and memorize it. Don't let me see it." After they had both looked at their respective cards, he said, "Now trade cards—remember, don't let me see them!—and put the other person's card in your stack. Now shuffle again, as much as you want." He waited a dozen or so seconds. Another family and an elderly couple joined the small crowd. "OK, are they thoroughly shuffled? Completely randomized? When you're satisfied, hand the cards back to me." They did so.

Ryan took both stacks and fanned them out in his hands. He quickly selected a card from the first half of the deck. "Is this yours?" he asked the girl. "Two of clubs?"

"Wow," she said. "Yeah."

He showed another card to the boy. "I think this is yours?"

"The nine of hearts," the boy agreed. "How did you do that?"

"Magic," Ryan said, shuffling the entire deck so that no one would be able to tell that before the trick started it had been divided in half between black and red. "The art of illusion. Would you like to see something else?"

If Caleb had been there, Ryan would have told his son that people started to lose things the moment they were born. They left behind their childhoods, their schools, their parents' homes, eventually their careers. As they got older, they lost their friends and family members. Everything ended. So the greatest of all illusions was to convince people that things could be retrieved from the chaos. That no matter how thoroughly you scrambled the deck, it was possible with the right gift to reach into the disorder and pull out the single card you'd been waiting for all along.

Just over ten minutes later Ryan thanked everyone for watching and put his cards away. A few people pressed bills into his hand as they moved on. Back in his run-down sedan, with its history of misfortune publicly recorded in its decade's worth of dents and scratches, he took out the bills and counted them. Four dollars.

After he had turned on the engine, but before he had let his foot off the brake, he put his hand over his phone and imagined calling Sheila. Then he thought of all the questions she would imply but not ask about hospital bills, and he sighed and eased the car out of the space.

He was almost out of the parking lot when James walked past. Ryan braked and swerved into a bus drop-off zone. "James," he called as he stepped out.

The gray-suited man stopped and turned. If he was surprised, he hid it well.

"You knew my dad." Ryan walked up to him. "When I was a kid. My name is Ryan Tillman."

James raised his eyebrows and gave a slight smile. "Ryan. Right. Your dad was Steve. You had the big house by the lake."

"There was a trick he used to do. I watched him practice. The Shift, I called it, but I don't know if that was its real name." Ryan stopped, waiting for James to show a look of confirmation or confusion, but the man still wore the same almost-smile. "He wouldn't—he didn't get a chance to teach it to me. I figured out most of it, I think. But I never knew the break cards."

Just for a moment Ryan saw a flicker of satisfaction pass behind James's eyes. It was as ambiguous and fleeting as his look of recognition in the casino earlier. "He was good with cards." He seemed to study Ryan more closely. "You should give me your number. We can catch up sometime."

By this time Ryan had come to the conclusion that he didn't like James, but Ryan had been the one to stop him, and James had known his dad. So he and James exchanged contact information.

James was a few steps away, when he glanced back and said, "The trick you mentioned. Try the four of clubs, queen of diamonds, ten of hearts, and jack of spades."

That night Ryan stood in front of his bureau in his boxers and picked up his deck again. He started shuffling, as he often did when he was thinking.

For the first time since his dad had been taken, he let himself remember all the times he'd seen him practice the Shift. The long afternoons he'd studied his father's careful moves. The longer nights when he'd tried to reenact them himself.

Ryan was holding an old deck branded with the Las Vegas Riviera logo, a souvenir of the night that had won him the cash he'd used to buy Sheila's ring. He could still summon the thrill of seeing the jack of hearts slapped down on the table in front of him and knowing he had just landed four of a kind.

His unconscious default when cards were in his hands was to practice his overhand shuffle while he used the little finger of his left hand to maintain a break over one particular card, occasionally palming the card into his right hand, then returning it to the deck and resuming the break, so that no matter how much he shuffled he always knew where the particular card he had chosen would end up.

The Shift applied the same premise, but the deck had to be ordered precisely beforehand, and the controlled card passed between other specific cards in order. Like the teeth of a key fitted against the correct pins. When he was younger, and the Shift had taken up a significant portion of his thoughts, he had speculated that there must be different types of keys and different types of locks. Cards were only one way of opening the unnamed door. But this was the one he had watched his father practice, over and over, that summer before the Listeners had come for him.

He remembered the concentration on his dad's face as he'd committed the motions to muscle memory, first in their airy house and then, once they'd lost that, in their small second-floor apartment. He remembered the day his dad had declared his refusal to continue to be bound by the Masters' rules. Remembered his dad screaming the morning the humanlike things clawed their way out of the portal and dragged him away.

Ryan grimaced until the memory was gone. He arranged the cards with the new information James had given him and performed the operations that observation and practice had burned into his mind. He was going to see his son.

And then it was done.

He looked around. The bedroom was unchanged, but he felt a slight weight on his head and shoulders, as if something insistent but invisible were pressing down on him. His heart was pumping furiously in his chest. For a moment he saw his dad's face, the way it had been at the end. He scrunched his eyes shut until the memory passed and went to brush his teeth. When he returned he shuffled the deck randomly, flipped the cards over, and fanned them out. They were divided by suit. Even though he had been expecting something to happen, the astounding improbability of what he was looking at was vertiginous. The Shift had worked.

He shuffled again, not maintaining a break or controlling a card, and turned the cards over once more. They were still divided by suit, and now the cards of each suit were ordered Ace through King. Again he turned the cards over and reshuffled. Again when he flipped them face-side up they were organized in a series of four straight flushes.

He set the cards on the dresser and opened his wallet. The bills he had received in the parking lot were no longer there. Instead he saw a neat stack of twenties. Forty, to be precise. Eight hundred dollars.

An hour later, as he lay on his uneven mattress, he heard muffled voices from the corners of his room. He sat up quickly and turned on the light. The voices stopped.

The Listeners.

He breathed heavily, staring up at the ceiling with the light on, until finally exhaustion tugged him back down to his faded blankets. He was almost asleep when the voices returned, faintly, as if coming from a long distance. He opened his eyes, suddenly alert, and this time the voices continued. He strained to listen, continually certain he was just about to make out what they were saying.

Ryan finally fell asleep close to dawn. When he awoke a few restless hours later, the first thing he did was open his wallet, just for reassurance. The twenties were gone.

"That's as long as it lasts?" he asked out loud. He rolled up into a sitting position, his feet on the floor, and shuffled his deck. After seven shuffles he flipped through the cards. Their order was random. He performed the Shift. The pressure on his head and shoulders returned, and this time it felt stronger. He checked his wallet again. The eight hundred dollars was back.

Ryan took his duffel bag out of the closet and packed. The bag went into his trunk along with his tackle box and both fishing rods. His own pole, and the still-unused rod he had bought three years ago for Caleb. His first stop was Walmart, where he bought a red Mongoose freestyle bike. He had planned on going to the gas station next, but when he started up the car in the parking lot he saw the tank was already full. He counted the cash in his wallet and found the same eight hundred dollars he had started the morning with. He put the car into drive and headed for the interstate.

I never wanted to move away from you, he would tell Caleb. But how was I supposed to make enough money to support you in the middle of nowhere?

I understand why your mom wanted to stay. We had a life there. We had a house. But when you get a good job offer...

And what would he say next? Would he talk about being laid off from his sales job? About continuing to send money he no longer had to Sheila for Caleb's hospital visits because another job always seemed like it might be just around the corner?

I made a mistake. I should have been there with you. I should have been holding your hand when you got the neuroblastoma diagnosis.

No matter how long he drove, the needle swung to Full every time he started the car. He had the same number of bills before and after he stopped for a burger for lunch. The same number after his barbecue dinner.

That night the voices around his Econo Lodge bed were louder. He kept his eyes shut because he was certain if he opened them he would see what was speaking.

When he woke up in the morning his money was gone, but his head and shoulders still throbbed from the invisible weight. After he performed the Shift, the pressure increased.

He knew he was running up a bill he had no way to repay. But he drove anyway, chewing Tums after horrible rest stop food, popping Bayer tablets for back pain exacerbated by hours of sitting, and downing pints of cold coffee to keep himself from falling asleep at the wheel, because Caleb was worth any tab he could build.

The next morning, he felt like bricks had been piled onto his skull and upper back. Ryan performed the Shift anyway.

He called Sheila just outside of Indianapolis. "I'm coming to see Caleb," he said.

There was only the slightest pause. "He'll be glad to see you."

"How's he doing?"

"They think they'll be able to get it all with surgery. Overall, he's young and healthy. He has a good chance."

James contacted him after his car had started its climb into the mountains of northern New Mexico. "How does it feel?" he asked as Ryan put him on speaker. "To finally be able to take as much as you need?"

Ryan nearly drove off the road. "What is this about?"

"I want to help you."

Ryan realized he was speeding up and pressed down the brake. "You don't know anything about me."

Ryan could visualize James's tailored suit and not-quite smile. "I know a lot about you, Ryan. I know that one day when your family returned from vacation all the locks on your beautiful house had been changed. I know that your dad never owned the house; he had been a caretaker, and he—you—were kicked out when he took you on a fishing trip without giving the owners notice." The speaker buzzed as it amplified James's voice. "That's when you moved into the apartment and he finally used the Shift he'd spent all that time practicing."

Ryan's fingers dug into the wheel and the speedometer surged back to the right.

"Do you know how I know?"

Ryan just shook his head, even though James couldn't see him.

"Because your dad was my initiate. I chose him. And now I choose you. I need a new initiate, and I feel an obligation to you. I know how much you need this. I understand what you've lost."

"You don't know me," Ryan repeated, slowly and firmly.

"You think you're opening doors. You're not. You're seeing through the illusion that makes us think walls and doors exist."

Ryan shook his head again.

"The Listeners are all around us, but they can't see us anymore than we can see them. We can take from their world. We can take as much as we need. We can tear down the veils between us at will." James's voice changed. It became insistent, precise. He was emphasizing the significance of his message. Ryan no longer saw the speedometer, barely saw the cliffs on either side of him or the road being consumed beneath his wheels. He only barely saw James's face in his mind's eye. He saw his dad being dragged away. "But you've felt the weight, too, haven't you? The burden it places on you? That's one of the ways the Listeners can find you."

"Who are you? Why are you calling me?"

"I will be your mentor, Ryan. You will accept part of my burden. That means for a time you will only be able to take small gifts from the Listeners for yourself. But eventually you will find initiates of your own, and you will pass your burden on to them. When that happens, you will be on the path to becoming as powerful as I am. Those are the rules."

Ryan stabbed the End Call icon.

Sheila's house was a brown trailer on a half-acre parcel, the front yard filled with flower beds that were losing a one-sided war with weeds, a half cord of wood stacked near the fence, apple and apricot trees growing in the back. He smelled pine and juniper. Ryan had enjoyed a handful of good years here, but that life had done what all lives did and ended.

Sheila met him halfway between the driveway and the porch. He recalled his satisfaction at building that porch, and how they had both agreed it made the trailer feel like a home; now it looked weather-beaten and old. "There's a motel down the road. I made a reservation for you."

"It's good to see you, Sheila."

She pushed the brown hair out of her face. Split ends and a hard mouth, but behind them she was still pretty. "I've put up posole with red chili. You're welcome to stay for dinner."

"Where's Caleb?" he started to ask, but then the door clanged open and his son was on the porch. At eight, he was no longer the little boy he had remembered. He was tall and wiry. His hair was no longer wavy. But his big brown eyes were still luminous. Ryan strode past Sheila up the steps and took Caleb in his arms. His body felt like a bundle of restrained energy. It was hard to believe that deep in his abdomen there was a knot of flesh devouring him from within.

Caleb half-hugged him back. "Hi, Dad," he said uncertainly.

"How are you doing?"

"Fine."

"I've really missed you." Caleb stared at him. "Here," Ryan said, "I have something for you." He almost dashed back to the car, but he forced himself to slow to a brisk walk, unlocked the bike from the rack, carried it to the steps, and set it down proudly. This didn't seem to inspire the enthusiasm he had anticipated, so he prompted, "I got you the bike you wanted."

"Say 'Thank you,'" Sheila prompted Caleb.

"Thank you."

"It's for after your surgery. After you recover. Something to look forward to. Do you like it?"

"Yeah."

"It's like the one you wanted."

"Yeah. Thank you."

"He has a bike," Sheila explained to Ryan. It's been three years, her expression implied, and his life didn't stop when you weren't here.

After dinner, with the dishes drying on the rack, Ryan showed Caleb a card trick. "Pick any card," he told his son. "Once you've memorized it, put it back on top of the deck, face down." Caleb did as instructed. Ryan took the deck in his left hand, placed his right hand over it, and shuffled.

"The card's in your right hand," Caleb said.

Ryan paused. He started to deny it, then decided against it. He had palmed the card when he started to shuffle. "You saw me take it?"

"No," Caleb said, "it's just what I would have done."

"You're a smart kid."

That night in his motel room when he heard the voices, he opened his eyes. He saw the carelessly cleaned walls of the small room rising up around him, the drawn shades, the red glow of the digital clock on the nightstand. He heard the mini fridge's low hum. But now he could also see around the walls, with a cubist's converging perspectives, to larger rooms beyond this one, to a long, tiled hall between his bed and the bathroom door, which he felt he should be able to enter if he could just figure out how to approach it from the right angle. Past the new rooms he saw other windows and other doors, and beyond them a forest with trees that swayed slowly like kelp disturbed by underwater currents, beneath the dim stars of an unfamiliar sky. In the new rooms around him, beside him, creatures moved. Even though several were no more than a few feet from him, their voices sounded as if they were coming from far away. They looked almost like men, or women, but taller, and occasionally instead of walking upright they dropped onto all fours and scuttled across the floor or up the walls.

Ryan lay frozen on his back on the bed, breathing shallowly, staring at the closest of the creatures. After a moment it stopped and looked back at him. Ryan grabbed the mattress. The creature stretched out its hand. It had thick, broken nails. Ryan clambered back across the bed, but although the hand kept coming closer it never reached him.

"We are coming," the creature said. It sounded like a long sigh.

Ryan sat up. "I can understand you."

"We have been listening," the creature said in its faraway voice. "Every time you have been stealing from us we have been listening. We know you."

Ryan blinked, and he could no longer see the creature, or its rooms or the rest of its world. There was just the motel room, the shapes of its furniture indistinct in the darkness. But he could still hear the creature, breathing, sounding as if it were at the end of a long tunnel, from its concealed place just beside his head.

The next morning Ryan took Caleb fishing at the creek up the road, which the state still stocked with trout. There was a deep, slow part of the brook, curving into the bank, where a large rock jutted out over the water, and when he had lived here Ryan had found the biggest fish in the rock's protective shadow. Ryan showed Caleb how to bring up his rod, let it load, and cast it down. For a moment he forgot everything except the presence of his son, the movement and sound of the water, and the scent of sun on stone overlaid with the fragrance of mesquite and acacia.

"My dad didn't talk to me much," Ryan said as they stood side by side beneath the cottonwood trees. Even when his dad had spoken, he had eventually learned, he couldn't always trust the words. "But whenever I go fishing I feel like I'm close to him."

Above them the bright green leaves stirred with a sound like rain.

"What do you think?" Ryan asked Caleb, nodding at his rod.

"It's kind of boring."

Ryan avoided performing the Shift for most of that day. He knew from the heaviness of his head and limbs that the Listeners would be able to reach him the next time, or perhaps the time after that. Twice he heard the Listeners' voices from some invisible place in the air around him, and he instinctively froze both times. It made him disoriented and cold to realize that they could reach him even outside, even in daylight.

Sheila let Ryan stay over that night. "On the couch. Caleb's excited you're here."

Ryan called James after the others had gone to bed. He was afraid to go to sleep but afraid to stay awake alone. He didn't want to speak to James, but he wanted answers.

James answered immediately, as if there were nothing surprising about receiving a call at such a late hour. "So, you're ready."

"No. I just—I want to understand."

"I feel responsible for what happened to your dad, and I don't want it to happen to you," James told him. "If you become my initiate, I can help you."

Ryan didn't answer.

"This is a gift, Ryan. This is a power that presidents and billionaires don't have."

Ryan hung up.

He didn't want power. He wanted his son to grow up. He wanted to be a big enough part of his life to watch it happen. He had already given most of the money he'd brought to Sheila to contribute to Caleb's hospital bills.

That night while the others slept, Ryan performed the Shift again. When he looked up he saw a large cathedral-like room surrounding the small trailer bedroom. Now the angles between that world and this one seemed less acute, and he could visualize how the Listeners would be able to step across their invisible border and take him away. A small crowd of Listeners had gathered in the cathedral room, and they were all watching him. Some of them carried faceted round objects in their hands. He recognized one of them as the Listener who had reached out to him the night before.

Ryan walked to the kitchen, ignoring the Listeners' voices and avoiding glancing back in their direction. He put a stack of bills on the table. He had left himself just enough to get back home, if there were no emergencies. He didn't know yet what he was going to do about his rent. But enough time had passed that at least he'd be able to give plasma again.

He knocked softly on Caleb's door. When there was no answer, he entered the room. Caleb stirred and sat up on his elbows. Moonlight leaked around the edges of his curtain and gleamed in his eyes.

"Caleb," Ryan said, "I have to leave."

"Why?"

Everything ends, he could have told his son. But it wasn't the answer he wanted to give, and he didn't know what else to say. "How are you feeling?"

There was a long silence. "Sometimes it hurts."

Ryan took his hand. "It's all right to be scared. But you're going to be OK. You will be."

"Are you coming back?"

"You know that I didn't want to move all the way to Maryland. I got a job offer and I thought I needed to take it." It sounded like an excuse, so he stopped talking.

Caleb didn't answer.

"Every minute I'm away from you, coming back is all I think about." Ryan swallowed. In the distance he heard the Listeners whispering. "Tell your mom I'll call her."

"She doesn't know?"

"I don't want to wake her up."

Caleb looked at him the darkness. "I love you, Dad," he said timidly.

There were a dozen other things Caleb could have said. He could have been angry, or self-pitying, or dismissive. Any of those emotions would have been justified. "I love you too, Caleb," Ryan answered, and hugged him. When he left, he shut the door gently behind him.

Just over the Oklahoma border Ryan pulled to the side of the road. He stared for a long time at his reflection in the visor mirror before he stepped out of the car. He was going to give everything he could, every last dollar, to his son.

Everything ends, he would have told Caleb if he were there. But not your story. At least not this way, not now. You're going to have a long life. Even if I won't get to see it.

He performed the Shift with his back to the interstate and a dry plain stretched vastly before him. On the other side, in the Listeners' world, a walled terrace jutted over a wide ravine. On the uneven paving stones in front of him, halfway between him and the wall, was the familiar Listener, its eyes locked on his.

"I'm not going to wait for you to take me," Ryan said. "I won't be dragged away screaming. I'm going to face you. If you're going to take me, take me now." He reached out with his hand and watched it twist around a corner that had more than 360 degrees. The Listener stretched out its own long limb and their hands locked, a bridge between the worlds. Or between two ways of seeing this world. Ryan felt the Listener's muscles strain and prepared to be pulled through. But instead the Listener hauled itself into the bright Oklahoman sun.

"A human creature who can open doors for us, who knows we can come to get it at any time, is a useful creature. An ally, perhaps. Yes?" The Listener's voice was familiar, but now it was startlingly loud and present. The creature shook itself, and Ryan realized it wasn't expecting an answer. It was a rhetorical question.

"What...what do you want?" he asked.

"To hunt," the Listener said. It stretched out its arm and its hand vanished to the wrist. When it reappeared another hand grasped it, and the first Listener tugged another creature just like it out onto the roadside. The second pulled out a third. And then a fourth and a fifth.

The Listeners dropped to all fours. The first one twisted its neck to stare back at Ryan. Then it loped away from the car, and by twisting through angles between both worlds it was suddenly several hundred yards away. The others followed, snarling in low voices. They ran east, toward James, perhaps, or one of the other Masters who had eluded them and their kind for so long.

Ryan blinked and slid the deck of cards back into his pocket. There was pressure on his head and back, a dull chronic pain, but it was something he could eventually learn to live with. He knew, without checking, that there was eight hundred dollars in his wallet. He climbed into the car and made a U-turn, accelerating as he headed back in the direction of the only place he wanted to be. "The rules are changing," he said to himself. And soon he would be able to tell that to Caleb.

Greyson Ferguson

THE WOMAN BY THE SEA

The woman awoke to the sea's breath. It twisted about her hut, leaving her filled with its salty-sweet musk. She rubbed sleep from her eyes, complete darkness giving way to silver outlines of her hut's opening. She filled her lungs with the morning's crisp air before dipping hands into a clay pot of water. She drank and splashed her face, snapping what senses had remained asleep to attention. The sun waits for only the dead.

She slipped a bag over her shoulder, the once scratchy, irritating fabric worn smooth. It now tickled her exposed skin when she moved about the sand dunes. The mark on her wrist rubbed against the smooth fabric. Once a raised scar from where she had been branded, it too had worn smooth. The woman removed a comb carved from a turtle shell and ran it through her hair, pulling out tangles and knots formed during slumber. Sometimes she wondered if spirits came while she slept and tied strands together. The village had already punished her, banishing her to the other side of the island. Perhaps the spirits wanted their say as well.

Violet water carried in the morning's first light, leaving bubbling foam on the gray sand before returning to the sea. The woman walked along the line between land and water, following its curve into a small cove. The sand gave way to a black volcanic stone, yet her feet walked over the coarse rock without flinching. After years of isolation, her feet had developed calluses as thick as any sandal.

The warmer water of the cove trapped fish of all kinds. Food had rarely been a problem. Once, early on, the storms brought with it cold water, and the cold water pushed most marine life away. She nearly starved that season. Instead, she learned how to prepare for the future. It hardened her. It callused her.

The woman removed a patched, aged net from her bag and cast it out into her cove. Early in the morning, the fish were mostly subdued, so it usually only took a single cast to catch what she needed for the day. She kept one or two for herself, discarded any with a noticeable illness, and released the rest.

Tails struggled and mouths flapped as the woman pulled the net onto shore. She selected her pick of the day, slapping its head against a nearby stone until its body stilled. The rest of the fish looked healthy, so she opened the net and let them return to their families with stories of being caught and the miraculous escape that followed.

The purple sky gave way to pink and finally gold by the time the woman finished preparing her fish. She kept a few of the bones for sewing needles and discarded the rest back into the water.

Satisfied with her work, the woman sat, her toes in the water of her cove, her prepared fish next to her. She closed her eyes and absorbed the warming morning light. Every morning she considered leaning back, letting her body fall back into slumber, yet every morning she opened her eyes and returned to her hut to continue preparing food for the rest of the day.

Today proved no different. She opened her eyes, but what she saw did not align with previous mornings. At the edge of the cove, caught amongst the volcanic rock, something bobbed and reflected the morning light into her eyes. The woman stood and made her way to whatever reflected. Trapped in the stone, she found a glass bottle.

Before her banishment, or as the men who came to her village said, her excommunication, the strange new people had come with glass bottles full of many liquids. The glass corked, she had hopes of the bottle containing such a liquid, yet upon picking it up she knew it to be too light, but it felt like it contained something.

She clawed at the cork, but it would not budge under her slender fingers. Not wanting to break the glass, as the bottle could be useful, she decided to return home.

***

Embers from the dying fire glowed in the center of the woman's hut; smoke curling up through a small constructed hole and several others that appeared over time. A pot of grains and the fish she collected simmered. It would take several hours to cook through.

Sitting in the entrance of her hut, the woman shook free curled paper from within the bottle. The paper felt of coarse sand and did not spring open upon exiting its glass tomb. It cracked and split as the woman unrolled it. The paper would not be good for much, had she not seen ink scribbled within the forced scroll.

As the stew simmered and the flavors mingled, the woman slowly worked the paper open. The ink faded to nothing in some places, and in others liquids of many kinds stained over whatever there was to be read.

The men who had come to her village taught those who could understand how to read their language. As a young girl, they spent time teaching her and others like her. The children were eager to learn. But they had very little to read, except for the same book each had been given.

A man named John wrote the letter from the bottle. It read as if he wrote it to himself, and yet hoped another would discover it. The man named John longed for a woman from a home he did not know if he would see again, for he had been on a boat more days than he could count, and even longer since he had seen her.

Some of the words the woman did not understand. But the man spoke of love and the woman could feel his love. A man who writes such letters to nobody and hides them away does not do so for show. He does so because he is so overwhelmed with feeling he must get it out, or suffer from keeping it in.

The woman felt sorry for the man and yet spoke his name to the wind, thanking him for allowing her into his world of love. She too had once found love. And now she clung to the other side of the island, cast out from society.

***

The second bottle showed up much like the first: clinging to volcanic rock, as if afraid it might wash back out to sea and lose all hope of being found. The woman spotted it as she watched her net cast out into the cove. Perhaps while she slept the rock cast its own net to bring in messages from beyond.

She did not wait to open this bottle, a clear glass version of the muted blue she had found weeks earlier. Cleaning her catch could wait. Her curiosity could not. The paper proved not as stubborn as the last. It felt smoother to the touch. It did not break as she unrolled it. And the ink was easily visible. The woman did not need to read the signed name to know the handwriting came from the same man named John as the letter before.

The man named John detailed his days at sea. The washing of decks, and the long hours of doing nothing but thinking of the woman back home. He wrote he hoped the bottle would somehow find its way to her.

The woman accepted the love the man named John signed his letter with. She prayed the rightful owner would forgive her for it. But she knew how isolation felt. She had pushed the idea of love out of her mind long ago. She pushed it out with the hate she felt for those who reported her own secret love. The hate would do her no good on her own. Nor would love.

Yet now she felt the love return. She wondered if hate would as well.

***

The woman no longer went to the cove in search of only food for her body, but food for her soul. Some days a new bottle would cling to rock, waiting for her to make claim, while most other days she left with only food.

With each bottle and the letter it contained, she felt a closeness build between herself and the man named John. Much like the love he feared never seeing again, the woman knew she would likely never meet the author, and yet it did not stop her from loving him.

The love gave each day purpose. It separated the days she received new correspondence from those she didn't. But the arrival of each new letter did not bring only the one emotion. With it, she felt the weight of isolation. Of the need to feel wanted in return. She believed the man named John shared similar feelings.

His letters had become dreary. Sad. As if he could see an approaching finality nobody else knew of.

The men who came to her village taught her to pray, yet she did not believe. She never saw anything come of such words spoken by others. But maybe she did not see anything come of such spoken words by others because she did not believe. So she said something to the wind about keeping the man named John safe. If someone were to hear, then so be it.

***

The woman went without finding a new bottle for many weeks. She lost track of the number. She wondered if he no longer wrote, or if the water took the bottles elsewhere. She spoke to the wind for his safety and even to let him find his love, although part of the woman hoped he didn't so he could continue to write.

So when the stubby green bottle washed into the cove, she felt relief. She removed the letter without casting out her net that morning. The fish and her stomach could wait. The scrolled paper felt new against her callused skin. It sprang open, unlike the first letter she received. The man named John must have only recently written the letter. She wondered how close he might be.

But then she read what he had to write and her heart sank. He would write no more, as he no longer had hope of seeing his love again. He didn't believe he could live without her and wished to die before he could no longer see her in his dreams. He apologized if she ever should come across the bottle, and he hoped she would take a new love.

The woman felt the man named John's pain deep within her own chest, as she too knew the feeling of lost love and abandoned hope. When the men that came to her tribe discovered her with a man promised to another woman, they proclaimed all involved must be punished. They were branded for their crime. Members of her tribe managed to convince the men to simply banish her. She did not know what happened to the man she had loved.

And now she felt a similar love for this man named John. A man she would never meet and yet knew deeper than anyone else would. She had his letters and understood the torment of his soul.

The woman did not return to her home that day. She remained on the beach, by the cove of volcanic rock, as if he might appear before her. She fell asleep in the sand, the sea nipping at her toes.

***

The crack of thunder did not wake the woman. But the groan of wood and the scream of men did. The blue sky had given way to a swirl of gray and black clouds, hungry for what they could devour below. Explosions of lightning highlighted the mist of roaring water and outlined the sinking hull of a great ship in the distance. The swirling wind tore at the ship's sail. Her hair whipped and twisted in the air as she looked to the raging sea.

A small captain's gig cut around the ship's stern, fighting against waves clawing at the edges of the wooden vessel. Lightning painted the sky in a flash of silver violet as water gripped the lifeboat like the tentacles of a great sea beast and snapped it in pieces.

As the woman watched, she saw men from the great ship jump overboard. Some sank and never returned to the surface. Others grabbed hold of what they could. Deep within her chest, she knew the man named John must be one of them. So she did what any lover would do, and dove into the sea.

The current pulled and threw the woman, warning her not to enter, yet she continued on. Fists of water hammered her head, pushing her under. Wreckage floated past, and yet she could not see any man in its midst. A splintered plank caught her arm and she bled, and the salt of the sea punished her for not heeding its warning.

Clinging to broken barrel she saw a man. He did not move. His face pushed against the wood. The woman could not tell if he was alive as she moved him to his back. Waves spat and hissed. She slid him into the crescent barrel and swam for the dark shadow of the island.

With her back to the sea, she could not prepare for the final capsize of the great ship, nor the wave it unleashed. In a last effort to claim the woman, the wave crushed overhead and pulled her underneath the surface, before something struck her head and the world around her went black.

***

Sun cut through the crack between the woman's eyelids as a headache threatening to press her head to a pulp shot her awake. The sea had given up its anger and lapped at the gray sand. The golden hue of morning offered an apology for what had just consumed a ship and its men.

The woman sat for a long while before seeing the man and the half-barrel tucked into the sand next to her. His long hair twisted about like discarded seaweed, the man's clothes were ragged and torn, yet did not fit him. He looked as if he had worn the same tattered pants, the same ripped shirt, for years.

She leaned over the man, his face tanned and cracked from a never-ending time at sea. Ravines creased around his eyes, blisters peeled away and regrown pocked his hands, and yet the woman did not believe him to be as old as the signs of work and sun suggested. The woman touched the man's hand but the skin felt cold. She shook him but he did not make a sound. She held her ear to his mouth but did not feel breath or heat. She pressed her hands to his chest to force free lodged water but felt a leather pouch under his shirt. Removing the leather from around his neck, she found a vial of black ink and a tattered goose feather quill.

Her hands returned to his chest and she pushed, now more than ever determined to save this man. Possibly the man named John. She threw her weight into the press, watching his mouth for the spurt of water. Once as a girl she saw the men who came to the village save another they thought drowned by forcing water from his lungs. No water came. She looked over his body frantically, hoping for something of use, when her hand grazed over his wrist. She stopped. Twisting his wrist over she found the mark. The branding. The same branding as on hers. And her eyes began to erase the wrinkles of time around his eyes, and the deepened pigment of his skin, to reveal the boy she had once loved long ago. The boy who was now the man named John.

She pushed into his chest. Harder and harder. Faster and faster. Liquid spilled from his lips and yet he did not breathe. For the first time in many years, panic consumed her. She shook him violently but he would not awake. She stood and paced, trying to think. Trying to hope. She spoke her wishes to the wind. She spoke a prayer to the god of the men who came to the village. Yet he did not move. Falling to her knees, she slammed into him. A fountain of water sprayed from his mouth, like a cork exploding from a bottle. She hoped his words would follow as well. The woman pressed her ear to his lips and listened.

Shelby Settles Harper

FEATHER

My father died alone, on a survey, in the middle of someone's twenty acres of Oklahoma pasture. The owners of the land were still in shock when I, his only child, arrived, tasked with driving his truck fifty-seven miles northeast, back to his house.

They hadn't found keys on his body, which had collapsed not far from where I stood, shifting from one foot to the other, dreading what I had to do next.

You reckon he's got a set of keys in the truck?

When I was a little girl, Woody had kept his keys under the driver's seat. I felt around until the bundle was in my hands and held them up.

The look on their faces was clear: they didn't think I was in any shape to drive the truck back.

Woody's truck was a manual transmission, which I hadn't driven in over a decade, since I was a teenager. I put a tentative foot on the brake and a foot on the clutch and slowly eased the car in reverse, backing away from the place where Woody had died.

The empty county road turned in to an empty highway. I pushed the radio power button and the Traveling Wilburys filled the truck. There was the time Woody had called, excited about the band, a union of so many of his favorites from the '60s and '70s. I had only half listened. It had been my turn to be distracted.

The truck smelled exactly as it had in the 1980s. Gasoline and musky age. The seats were cloth, worn from time and use, with three generations' worth of stains. A pack of Juicy Fruit, empty except for one piece, burned hot by the sun. A long braid of sweetgrass lay on the dashboard, faded from sunlight and time. A dirty Denver Broncos hat and a large plastic black toolbox rested on the passenger side floorboard.

Grandma had always said that objects absorb a part of their owner's essence. In my father's truck and surrounded by his things, the truth of her words settled heavily in the back of my heart.

The sudden need to see Woody's face hit, urgent and strong. While keeping my eyes on the road, I stretched to reach the glove compartment, where Woody had always kept his wallet. Just like his keys under the seat, the wallet in the usual place.

When I was eleven years old, a year before he moved away, I'd asked Woody why he kept it inside the glove compartment rather than in his jeans pocket, like all the other dads. *I don't need some goddamned billfold bulking up my ass*, he'd said, his eyes crinkling at his joke. I'd teased him that yes, he did in fact need something bulking up his Indian ass. Good one, *Hakaayu Banit*, he'd said, rubbing the top of my head. It was Caddo for White Bird, what he'd called me ever since I was born with the fair coloring of my non-Indian mother.

The wallet felt heavy in my hand, its faded black leather worn and stretched. I let it rest against the steering wheel and carefully opened its plastic flipbook. The first page held his driver's license. Woodrow Hank Baker, five foot eleven, 184 pounds. His hair, long and gray, was pulled into a pony-tail, and his face wore a half-smile. Permanent lines creased the corners of his dark eyes. I hoped those were the lines of a man who had laughed often.

The second page held a picture of the two of us at Jimi Hendrix's grave. He had surprised me by flying in for my college graduation—his first time on an airplane since Vietnam, and the first time we'd spent significant time together since he'd left. We hadn't talked much during his four-day visit, both coping with the awkwardness of feeling like strangers by staying behind the lenses of their matching Nikon cameras. For this particular picture, he'd set up a tripod and timer, insisting he get at least one shot of us together.

I'd been surprised by our similarities. From the way we motioned with our hands while talking, to the way we ate our eggs—over easy, mashed, and each bite placed atop buttered toast—we mirrored one another.

On the morning of graduation, Woody had presented me with an eagle feather. *This is for courage and honor. You're the first in our family to finish college, Hakaayu Banit.* There'd been pride and a sense of wonder in his eyes.

I'd turned away, conflicted. I still wanted to know why he'd left us. Sure, he'd gotten sober, found himself. Many times, he'd looked at me with a pained expression and opened his mouth as if he wanted to answer my unspoken questions, but each time he'd closed his mouth. Still, the feather became my most cherished belonging.

I counted seven dollars in the cash slot of the wallet. I closed the wallet and let it fall onto the seat beside me, next to the Juicy Fruit. Through the truck stereo, Roy Orbison's voice rose above those of his bandmates. My chest was heavy, my mouth full of sand.

I hit the power button, cutting off the Traveling Wilburys' song mid-sentence. I concentrated on my breath and coiled a finger around a piece of my hair. As a young child, I'd loved to play with Woody's long braids.

There were only two times when he'd worn short hair: during his service in the Army and following his grandfather's death. Woody's own father was often away, working on oil rigs, and his grandfather, Willis, had been a stand-in father for him.

I had been in first grade when Willis passed. A day after the funeral, I'd found Woody and Grandma sitting on the porch talking over cups of Folgers, and Woody with freshly cut short hair. He explained that it was meant as a show of mourning. *It's the Indian way*, he'd said, wiping tears from his eyes.

I slipped out of my sandals, one at a time, and kicked them to the floorboard on the passenger's side. They landed next to Woody's toolbox. His words reverberated through my head: *It's the Indian way*.

I downshifted gears and let the truck slow to a stop on the side of the road. Inside the toolbox, amongst a half-dozen other items, was a small pair of all-purpose shears. They were heavy, with faded red handles and more rust than their original silver color. I held them in my right hand and stared at my reflection in the rearview mirror. It was a face everyone said was beautiful, but I knew was merely that of an average small-town girl. *I can see it in your cheekbones*, men liked to say, after I told them of my Native American heritage. It was bullshit, something they said to get what they wanted, but I always let it go.

I held a small section of my hair in my left hand and raised the shears to a spot just above my ear. My chest heaved with short, shallow breaths, and my arm shook, causing the shears to tap against my head. I took a deep breath and closed my eyes and squeezed the shears together. When my thumb and middle finger, inside of the scissors' loops, met, I knew I'd faced the scariest step. I opened my eyes and saw a bundle of seven inches of hair resting in my lap.

Too late to turn back now. I took the next section of hair and slipped it between the scissors' blades. As I squeezed them together, I thought about Woody, and what must have been on his mind when he lost Grandpa Willis. Had he, too, been unable to cry in the immediate aftermath? Would he understand why I couldn't cry?

The third and fourth handfuls of hair were easy to cut, and with the slicing of the fifth, I no longer worried how it would look, or what people would think. I cut, methodically, clipping my hair until it looked like that of a young boy who'd cut his own hair. Could I still be called beautiful? Not likely. But the process of cutting, of repeating a ritual my father had performed, calmed me. The scissors slipped from my hands and onto the truck's floor.

There were seventeen miles left to go. With my elbow resting out the open window, I started the truck and eased off the clutch, steering the vehicle back onto the highway.

Once it was in fifth gear, I released the clumps of cut hair out the window. Through the corner of my eye, I saw them take flight and scatter, first straight up, and then out into a dozen different directions. My hair had always been the type to look either blonde or brown, depending on time of year and the way it caught the light. Now the strands reminded me of the eagle feather Woody had given me, and I watched them dance in the wind, shining like medals, like little feathers of courage, sacrifice, and love.

Thomas Hrycyk

BLOOD OF A DIFFERENT COLOR

Laura Horn would have believed you a fool if you called them cords because anyone who knew anything about the business referred to them as folds. But they weren't folds, rather membranous tissue that vibrated to create noise and in her line of work that noise was often guttural and coming from a dark place. Frankie Maul, her newest client, believed crowd surfing caused people to fall onto their heads and crack their skulls. He also believed, for the longest time, he had been screaming correctly into a microphone in front of crowds of hundreds of heavily made-up and ravenous fans. It was only after he suffered a vocal fold hemorrhage that he learned maybe deathcore metal was about more than anger, passion, fire, and fury. Often, life called to be disciplined.

Laura Horn was gentle, in her late sixties, sweet, and proud of her German heritage that called her to duty. With a broad chest, straight back, yet forward-falling shoulders, she had the appearance of an enduring working woman. Laura had wondrously thin eyebrows that were pencil black and spread across her beautiful face above blue eyes that were simple and vast. She had been a vocal coach since her forties and a dance instructor before then, and she believed her German patience lent itself greatly to her skill set. Laura spent her summers traveling between Midwestern music festivals and had found employment from every possible metal band with dollars to spend: sludge, grindcore, thrash, industrial, drone, crust, and black gaze metal. They all screamed in some form or another.

With a high voice calling out, Laura would knock on the tour bus doors and sing to the band members in the morning, when they were still recuperating, her singsong as soothing, smooth, and delicate as one could imagine. She would stand by the empty driver's seat as men with mohawks and tattoos and naked torsos searched for pants, calling to the drummers, bassists, and groupies to get up and get out. Laura loved to see these dark and moldy places. She always loved to watch and talk and listen with men who were extreme.

It was her sixth day working with Frankie Maul, the lead singer of the deathcore metal band, Icarus Smicarus, and she had hoped to see some sort of improvement a week or so in from the man who, when healthy, believed that his voice alone could advance the Dark Night of the Apocalypse, that the chill of his song depended on this as did the filth of his deep, gravelly notes. He was a foul-mouthed freak and he accepted it head on. Frankie Maul was a large man with long, black hair and dark clothing. The mixture of fat and muscles was deceiving; he was all mass and he was by nature slatternly and careless but could be trained by Laura Horn into a superficial neatness which would eventually deepen over time.

They were on the tour bus working on their morning exercises. There were tomato stains on the carpet, cigarette smoke soaked into the ceiling, and thongs strewn about. The bus was cramped, smelled of mold, and for Laura Horn often felt like home, bringing her back to the days when she and her husband followed the likes of David Bowie, Faces, and Donna Summer when they were on tour. No matter the genre or type of crowd attracted to these events, they all stank the same: some mixture of fear and anticipation in their sweat.

Laura sat at the table, Frankie across from her. All the nooks and crannies of the chair were filled full of his soft and spreading body. His beard was leaning on his chest as he played with a pencil Mrs. Horn had given him.

"The *oh-oh-eee-oh* hasn't been working," Frankie said, spinning in his chair. "It hasn't been working in here." He pointed to his chest. "I'd been repeating the same dried-out verses—you know, the whole incantation of the rapture stuff. My lungs feel too tight when we get to the blood hymnal part." He began to scream the chorus from their latest song, "Bulfinch's Bitch."

"Do you have new lyrics for me to look at?" This was not a probing question; it was to be stimulating, to distract him. The time would come later for more noise and more singing. "You're not a noisemaker, Frankie. You're a vocalist. Enunciate and maybe you won't hemorrhage."

Laura knew he would make a great student, though he was a bastard, and possibly a drug addict playing bass notes on what appeared to be track marks on his arms. She had put him through the gamut. He screamed the letters of the alphabet while doing jumping jacks, shaking the whole bus. She put him through every exercise she had learned when classically trained. After a few sets of vocal stretches, he handed over a notebook with lyrics to a new song.

She sat adjusting her glasses on her pointy nose and she read them and shook her red head.

Frankie Maul, who wished he could have even more of her attention, that maybe she would have been a better mother to him than his own, not that he needed another mother now, bit his lip and said nothing but continued to make monkey noises in all the keys as she asked of him.

"I'll see videos of us and it's like every step, every bounce, I'll run over here and fucking jump into the drum set and it's like *uh, uh, uh, uh, uh* when I scream across the stage. You're not gonna nail it. You know? When you're out of breath? I'm just a fat, lazy fuck."

"Well, when you can't breathe, you can't deliver. You need to impact *them* out there while absorbing impact." Laura reached into her bag and twisted open a water bottle and placed a straw in Frankie's hands. "Impact me by working out those lungs. Scream bloody murder, dear."

Frankie craned his long neck and blew bubbles into the straw.

"Not so sharp at first. See that rise? You don't want that. Scream and enunciate into it."

He screamed into the straw.

She was impressed to see him doing well. "Yes," Laura said. "Impact me. Impact me harder."

He made profound use of his face. His Adam's apple protruded as he pushed out a song.

"Keep going. C'mon, Frankie, I have longer sneezes than this."

He was immersed in himself and his work, his pupils white as a stream.

"Put that down now. Let's go outside." She stopped herself. "Notice how I said that, with the sharper intake. Use your ears, Frankie," said Laura, rubbing the outside of her own. "There are secrets to them. Fold them flat to the head, like a dog, to hear yourself."

Outside was hot, even their spot parked on the side of a galley of trees in the shade was stifling. A branch quivered with the shadow of a bird flying off.

"I'm going to punch you in the stomach," she said to him. "And you're going to ignore me and project your voice. I want you to send it off, Frankie. Send it off across the fields. Drown out those damn cicadas." She gave him a gut punch and he caved in. "Go."

He began to shout and looked down, noticing the little cross around her neck that drowned in her cleavage.

She gave him a harder slug. "Look out there! THERE!"

He shouted it out. "Are you a religious person, Mrs. Horn!?!"

She gave out a sigh as if annoyed. "My god is the wind, Frankie, the one that lends its mouth to us." She gave another punch and he folded over. "So we might sing. At least better than you are now."

***

Laura would perform good hard work every morning with Frankie Maul
and on the pleasant, sunny afternoons she would call her husband so as to
speak with her two grandchildren who would visit Grandpa for a period of
two weeks as her son and his wife went on vacation. She was upset to miss
her grandkids if the work had pulled her too far away from Chicago, and it
did this time, but it was good money and she had enjoyed it often enough. It
really was a hobby more than anything else.

The other girls, the raucous, young ones Laura was surrounded by,
were lazy, and lounged out on sunny afternoons until it was night, but
treated her well enough, like she was a cool mother who knew how to cook
a decent meal for them. They all called her the scream tech. They all, too,
liked to tease her, for it was so easy to make her laugh it off, and seem all
helpless, for she would appear to not be able to learn just what these girls
meant by the queer things they said, but Mrs. Horn knew very well what
they meant and what they were doing. The four or five girls here to see the
members of Icarus Smicarus, the ones that Laura was sitting with, worked
together to tease her and play with her. But still, it was pleasant, all this
life, for Laura.

"What do you have on your finger there, Mrs. Horn?" Tenny, one of the
girls she always sat outside the bus with, one day asked her. Tenny was good
natured, quick witted, intelligent, and terribly bored by everything.

Laura had just finished visiting the forest trails on her lunch break and
sat down across from Tenny. She fingered at her necklace while she waited
to start the next lesson.

"My wedding ring?" she asked her back.

"No. That dirt spot right there?" Tenny pointed to a smudge above the
ring on her hand. "Were you picking berries?"

Laura put the dirt spot to her mouth and tasted. "I was picking a rose.
I pricked myself. Just blood is all."

"No. That's awful poison. That's not a prick, don't you know there's a
berry bush by the roses?" said Tenny. "That red splash of juice you just tasted."

"Well, I had to push aside some the bright red berries to get to the most
beautiful flower, yes," Laura Horn said, looking hard at her finger. She did
not know just how much Tenny meant by what she said.

"Isn't that poison, Aubrey, that Mrs. Horn just sucked off her finger?"
asked Tenny, consulting a girl who was busy rolling a joint in a phase of
intense concentration. "We aren't messing around. Right, Aubrey? That's
poison on your finger right now. Go wash up."

Laura was a little troubled. She looked hard at her finger where the juice stain was, and she wondered and looked at her finger and thought, was it really poison she had just tasted?

Aubrey smiled and did not answer. She was dark, thin, and without most of her clothes. She had a large mass of black Italian hair and she wore it high rather than across the small of her back. It was like Aubrey to smile, maybe laugh, but not to say much, and often she would look at Laura to perplex her.

And so they all sat with their weird little feelings in the sunshine an awfully long time until Frankie was back. And Laura often looked at her ring finger and wondered if it was really poison that she had just tasted and then she rubbed it against her pant leg a little harder to see what hurt.

Both the girls often looked queerly at her.

***

Since it was now the summer tour season and they had warm light to wander, Frankie and Laura walked the grounds of every Midwest festival they visited. They went along rushing rivers where they could see themselves from head to toe along with naked fans floating along in tubes. Some nights they'd stay up extra late past the parties and watched the moon execute itself out of the sky. Mrs. Horn never wandered around unless she was with Frankie Maul, whose real last name, she had learned, was Beaumont. Sometimes they wandered a good deal together around the festival grounds to the forests' edges. Frankie Maul liked to talk and talk and talk and he had not, even over the weeks, got over his way of talking to her all the time about all the things he was always thinking. They were surrounded by such doom and death and narcissism and drugs and fake blood that only the cicadas hidden in the fields across from the highway spoke rather persuasively in praise of life. Sometimes they maneuvered through the cars of fans that were pastured along grassless lots along the highway. Some were having sex and ignored them as they took their stroll.

"My friends told me when I was twelve that having sex made you walk differently," Laura told Frankie one night out wandering. "They said it changed something within your elbows when you walked and that everyone would notice it."

"When did you lose your virginity, Mrs. Horn?"

"What about you?" she said, half jokingly, doing a dance around the shock of it. "I bet you came out of your mother a ladies' man." Mrs. Horn did not make him any answer, and Frankie, without looking at her, after a little while, went on with his talking.

"I certainly, for sure, once really did believe, Mrs. Horn, I knew something about all kinds of women. You'd see all types here and there on the road. I certainly know now, how I don't know a damn thing at all about you, Mrs. Horn, though I've been around you so long, and so many times for hours and hours, and I like so much to be around you and with you, and I can always say anything I am thinking to you, which is great. I really do wish, Mrs. Horn, I was really more understanding of you though."

Laura was most beautiful, to Frankie, and at the moment, it was the posture she took, when she hesitated—when her hands and head rested against the air as if she were an angel, or rather, to him, some sort of lovely demon. With a force akin to that of a fastball to his groin, Frankie Maul, of the deathcore metal group, Icarus Smicarus, formerly known as Euhemerism, was falling in love with a sixty-something-year-old grandmother.

***

For Laura, there were three types of screams: fry, false cords, and death. She believed the best scream had both a high and low overtone. It was neither scratchy nor squeaky—something more like a dinosaur who smoked six packs a day growling into a wood chipper.

They were on the bus in a new town, somewhere just north of the Tennessee border. Frankie was back to blowing bubbles, this time, into a cup of whiskey.

"So you agree with me?" Laura asked, in reference to how Daedalus probably loved Perdix, his nephew, more than his own sons and instead desired to push Iapyx off the edge of the Acropolis.

"Yes, I agree with you." Frankie was back to looking at her chest and to her eyes as if there were bouncing basketballs in his head.

"Do you always agree with me?"

"You know I always agree with you."

"Then that seems fairly satisfactory."

"To me."

"To me too," Laura said, and then smiled.

"Do you have a picture of you when you were younger?" Frankie asked. "I'd like to know how punk you were in the '70s."

"I was part of the bowling team," Laura said, laughing. "I can name off on these ten fingers all the concerts I'd been to back in high school." Let's talk about old music I listened to was an easy conversation for Laura Horn to hold with Frankie. It was a way around this impending feeling of uncertainty. "Back to your work."

Frankie went on with his exercise and his head went moving up and down, as it shouldn't have been doing, and sometimes he was blowing through the straw, and other times he was thinking about all the things he wanted to be doing, and then he rubbed the back of his dark hand over his forehead to remove the sweat, and in between breaths he began to frown with all his thinking. And Laura just sat still in that tour bus and watched the lights flicker and sometimes she'd turn the lights off, afraid the bus's battery would die and all would get to smoking around them, bursting into flames.

What's going on in that head of yours? she wanted to ask him.

And, when they passed within a hundred miles of her house, Laura Horn would go home and see her family, happy to sleep in her own bed. Her husband would be glad to see her. He was no fan of her work.

How could she possibly trust these freaks, junkies, racists, and thugs? he'd ask her. He wanted her to retire. Her husband had even driven down to see Laura the past week, disrupting the whole vibe the band had going.

Frankie could not see what Mrs. Horn could find good in that fat, old husband of hers. It had made Frankie physically sick to see him kiss her cheek before a big show. The incoherent goop of adrenal syrup built inside him and Frankie tried to begin again with his thinking, and he could not make it come clear to himself, with all that thinking, and he felt everything all thick and smoky and bad, inside his guts. And he went to look at his hands—they were weak. His mouth was too small to utter what he needed to say to her. So he got up and sat outside. There was a flame in him now that did his thinking and a wind in him for his fire and for his sails.

Mrs. Horn joined him on the back side of the bus. A branch quivered across the creek. A family of birds danced on the branch. The setting sun ignited the matchless colors of their feathers. Despite security, the concert-goers threw rocks at them. Not for game, but to see blood of a different color.

"Frankie?"

Nothing came out. His voice felt as if it had congealed into a knot of steam.

"Something to say, Frankie?"

"There is and yet, I don't know how to say just what I mean, Mrs. Horn, but there was something awful hard about your instruction to me, so different from the way I'm always used to seeing people treat me. Like to prove that they're better," he said. And for an instant, Frankie felt completely happy, as he took Laura's hand, and caressed it as if he knew, for once, exactly what to do with this world. He took her hand to his lips, kissed it gently, and put her fingers into his mouth, when he got to her ring finger. He sucked a little longer and took off her wedding band with his tongue.

The excitement and strangeness stopped her breath, and made her words come sharp and with a jerk.

"Frankie! No!" she said, not entirely sure what she meant to do when her face warmed and turned red. Mrs. Horn's feelings spread her breath out, making her words now come out slow, but more pleasant and even more easily than a moment before. "No. That's not right." Laura Horn knew then, Frankie could never know what it was he really wanted with her. She knew then he never could know really what it was he felt inside. All she knew was that Frankie Maul very badly wanted Laura Horn there beside him, and she wanted very badly too to throw him away from her like a boomerang; there would be a joy in expecting him to return.

He tried to say something to her, but the words in his mouth felt as chewy as old caramels. Maybe, she thought, he did not know anything he could do, now that his advances had been rejected, to set himself right in his acting and his thinking toward her. Her time with him now would have to come to an end, though she was, or became increasingly, a woman with nothing to lose. She thought maybe either the world was mute, or she was deaf, but perhaps they were both doomed to their sort of afflictions, therefore they should have, arm in arm, gone blindly toward new horizons together but what happened here could never happen again.

She was sixty-something and he had eight gallons of pig's blood in his tour bus.

***

One night Laura Horn was lying in bed, her husband on the couch snoring into a dream, with her thinking, and that night she could not do any sleeping for her thinking made her sit up in her bed, and it had all come clear to Laura Horn, and she picked up the pillow and smashed it against the headboard, and she almost shouted out alone to Frankie there that maybe this was what she needed, to be able to appropriately age and let go, to embrace the aches and the feeling of welded joints. Though she felt she wasn't exactly nearing a time of spontaneous naps, forgetting keys and phone numbers, heavier breaths, and more, she had been told that all beings as they age leak like a loose gutter when it rains—that all old people that leak dream of love as a new gutter.

A week later in a chilly room, her throat tight, she received a phone call from Tenny; in this call, each word stood apart like a loving heart. Tenny said that Frankie suffered from something called arteriovenous malformation and that he was in the hospital and that he might die.

***

Tenny, Laura had heard, as pale and fiery as always, on her way to the hospital, passing by some roses, decided to fling herself onto the bush, mutilating her flesh with her short shorts and tank top. She wished to stifle the beauty of the world which gushed from the ground as from a wound.

***

Laura Horn was staring out the window as they brought Frankie Maul back from surgery. The clouds outside were the color of beaten eggs on a scalded hull of blue. He was unconscious, wearing a helmet, and breathing through a tube. She wanted him so badly to utilize the air pressure in his lungs.

"Guess he will want you to stick around or whatever," said Tenny, picking at her fresh scabs.

"Folds," Laura Horn corrected her. "They're called vocal folds." She could not take her eyes off him, or the big, swollen, bursted veins in his great big shaven head.

It would be days before he was conscious and able to speak. Laura made sure to show up right around dinner time, knowing the other girls would be out with the bandmates, partying as if nothing had happened to their lead singer, thinking that that was probably what he wanted. But she knew him better.

"Where are your parents?" asked Laura, looking out the dark window.

"They won't come," Frankie said.

"Guess there was a weird little tangle of blood vessels in your brain. Caused an aneurysm. A quarter of your skull is currently in your stomach, feeding off your blood," said Laura, smiling up through her crying. "That's so very metal of you."

Frankie laughed and he wondered whether it was wrong to move without fear now, because anything could still happen to him. Even if he was to have brain damage, the crucial thing was that his heart was powered by heavy, thick blood when it should have been filled with air, should have been given wings by her instruction, something both Frankie and Icarus could not accept. He was careful not to hurt Laura Horn, when he knew she would be sure to feel it badly in her mind a long time after this was all over with. He hated that he could not now nor ever be honest with her. He wanted to stay away, to work it out all alone, without her. He was afraid she would feel it and suffer if he kept her away. He felt uneasy, beyond the fact that part of his skull was in his stomach; he was uneasy when he thought about her.

His face changed as if he was disgusted with what he had been thinking. He laid there a long time, quiet, and then, slowly, somehow, it came strongly to him that Laura Horn, there beside him, was trembling and feeling it all, very much in the moment. He sat up in the bed as best he could, this man, this treasure, this honeycomb Laura had learned to make glisten, and he put his arm around her like a brother.

Beth Uznis Johnson
WILD TURKEY

The smoke traveled across the yard like a cloud rolling in with a thunderstorm. It morphed into thin and wispy fog as it hit the kitchen window with as much force as an angry sigh. More smoke billowed from the fryer. Flames gasped from the edges of the pot in search of oxygen and light. Soon the whole view had the appearance of a hazy winter morning, though not quite thick enough to hide Rick and Jesse, who had leapt to the side and were involved in some strange, ritualistic dance of the drunk and entertained.

Lori scanned the yard for kids, her heart an angry thump, praying they were all far enough away to avoid smoke inhalation and oil splatters. The two boys were swimming through the fog, a slow and deliberate breaststroke as they ran across the grass. The girls waded within the protective confines of the inflatable pool. The little ones stood next to the pool, leaning on tiptoes to reach over the edge and dip sticky fingers into the water.

"Christ!" Angie said behind her, reaching around Lori to set the shucked corn on the counter. She brushed her hands together and tried to snap the remaining threads from her fingers onto the floor. "What the hell are they doing out there?"

"The more Rick drinks, the more his brains turn to shit," Lori said, punching the handle of the faucet to fill the stockpot.

"We may as well have our fun, too," Angie said, lifting her watery Jack and Coke and tipping it toward Lori's cheek. Lori turned off the water and reached for her white Zin. She watched Rick through the window as Angie walked out the screen door into the fog. The fire had subsided so he used a long branch to lift the heavy lid from the dirt and guide it, wobbling, back onto the cast-iron fryer. The sharp angle of his cheek came back into view as the smoke lifted and it went back to being the humid summer day with children playing in the late-afternoon sunshine that slanted through the tree line at the edge of the property.

His face was the only thing that looked the same. The rest of him looked like a bloated sausage. Rick was always built, a big guy in general, but the fast food, snacking, and endless beer drinking gave him the tendency to sweat, a persistent gleam on his forehead and biceps. She wished he'd wear a regular T-shirt so she didn't have to see the fleshy roll under his armpit.

And maybe it would mask his body odor, which reminded her of ketchup packets at Burger King. His face was still the same, though, and it made her wish they could go back and do things over. She noticed the fat fingers, lazily clawing the top of the beer can, and wanted to swat it to the ground with a splash of golden piss and foam.

The boys ran close to the fryer. Lori froze. Rick hadn't even moved. He stood with his head cocked talking to Jesse and Angie, who had sauntered up to her husband and wrapped her arm around his elbow. She was well aware of how Jesse looked up every few seconds and threw a glance toward the pool to check on the little ones. They'd spent nearly three years trying to get pregnant with those twins. Unlike Lori, who seemed to get pregnant every time Rick's dick got hard. Four kids—two boys, two girls—in six years. She hadn't expected to feel hatred this fierce.

Now, Ricky was ten and Max nine. Brittney was seven, Angel five. The girls splashed in the pool. Lori admired their lean arms, their taut stomachs. But most of all, she admired their carelessness. That ability to leap and jump and laugh and play, to get angry and get over it, to laugh again and grab each other around the waist and sink to the bottom of the pool in perfect sync: let's just say her jealousy of her own girls was shameful.

"Watch those boys," she called from the screen door. "Last thing we need is a trip to the ER with no insurance."

Rick acknowledged her with a quick raise of his eyebrows. He didn't check for the boys, didn't call a corrective warning. Not that they listened to anything he said anyway. Lori knew how it was; it was beyond changing anything. Moments like these made her want to scream to stun him into submission so he'd know she had a lot to say, and she'd say it, goddammit, and she'd ruin him right then and there in front of everyone.

He'd blame the scaffolding. That was the cause of everything wrong in the world. The one time he'd actually gone into the city for a job, it had to go badly. She'd never gone herself, despite years of hinting that she'd love to see the shopping and maybe a show. They could stay in one of those hotels on Michigan Avenue. There was even a Days Inn. But Rick always said no, it was too expensive and anyway, who would watch the kids? *Angie*, she'd thought. Or the neighbor, Mrs. Park. But the kids weren't the point. Rick was too intimidated to go to the city. People in Chicago would lean into each other's arms on the busy streets, whispering with hushed laughter about the hick in the too-tight shorts and wife beater. Rick had half a brain, but he was smart enough to know that much. He watched TV, knew that people didn't dress like that anymore.

So they'd never gone to Chicago. Years went by until the day Rick came home from work and said they were taking a crew to the city to help with reconstruction of that skyscraper with the big office fire. Lori remembered the exact moment: despite the state of her family room—all toys and crumbs and an empty juice bag on the carpet—her breastbone fluttered with hope. Maybe she could take the train down for a night! They could go to dinner, maybe at the Hard Rock or that place where the waitstaff treated the customers rude on purpose.

But that idea hadn't gone over.

Rick had snapped that they were going by van, all eight of them, and wouldn't be staying overnight anywhere. The morning he left, he'd worn his best T-shirt, the one with the pineapple and fancy logo that his brother had sent from Florida, instead of the ratty undershirt. He wore his khaki shorts, along with workboots and socks, instead of the hacked-off sweatpants. Lori didn't have to lift the T-shirt to know the waistband strained against his belly, if they were buttoned at all. He walked out the door, shoulders tight with nerves, and climbed into the van with his mini-lunch cooler packed with sandwiches and Fritos.

Lori brushed her blue jean shorts and fingered the jelly stain on the front of her oversized T-shirt. Her husband was crossing the Illinois border—actually leaving Michigan—and going into the city. At least he got to do that. All she had to do that day was keep four kids occupied during summer vacation. She hadn't meant to shout so loud when Brittney and Max began fighting. They started crying and she ordered them to their bedrooms and kicked the door shut with a bang. The other two eyed her nervously from the couch and were silent, pretending to watch the TV commercials.

"You better stay quiet," she hissed at the two who were behaving. "I can't deal with any bullshit today."

The call came right after lunch when Lori cleared the table of plates, napkins, and cups and realized that Ricky had pushed his carrots under the edge of his plate, a haphazard halo of sticks on the table. She considered making the boy come back inside and eat the carrots. You had to let some things go, otherwise insanity prevailed. So she sat down on his chair, her thighs grinding into breadcrumbs and potato chip shrapnel, and ate one of the carrots. She'd clean up later. The phone was clipped to her shorts so she picked up on the second ring.

"It's me," Rick said.

"Hey, how is it?"

"Hell if I know. I got injured five seconds after I walked onto the site. I barely got to look at the skyline."

"I take it you're not in a coma?"

"Piece of plywood fell off some scaffolding when I walked underneath. Landed on my shoulder. Hurts like a bitch and ruined my shirt."

"You're lucky it didn't hit you in the head. Are you at a hospital?"

"An urgent care place. The foreman is kissing my ass. Even took me into Macy's to buy a new shirt and shorts before we came. After this, he's sending me home in a cab on his own dime."

"Why?"

"So I don't sue his ass!"

"Do you at least get today's pay?" Lori said.

"I better. I'll ask. I'll make sure."

"Are you OK?"

"Yeah, I'm fine. Feel like an ass, but I'm fine."

Lori hung up, half disappointed he was coming home early. It was nice to have time alone in the house. She sat back on Ricky's chair and wondered what it would be like if the foreman had called, if he'd said that Rick was struck on the head and was in a coma. Or if Rick was dead. She'd collect the life insurance money. She could probably sue the construction company and get enough to buy a bigger house in a better neighborhood. She could buy a car. She'd sell Rick's pickup and buy some new clothes for a job. She wasn't stupid. She had an associate's degree in finance.

Rick got home three hours later. The unfamiliar sounds of approaching tires on the gravel road and harsh squeak of the cab door should have warned her that things had changed. She opened the front door and he hobbled into the house, clutching an ice bag to his shoulder. How the injury had affected his back, she still didn't know. Yet, here they were two years later and he still wasn't working. Still home every damn day, stretched on the couch eating pork rinds or beef jerky or fruit snacks she bought for the kids' lunches. The construction company had given Rick a lot of time, a lot of leeway. After his worker's compensation claim was rejected, they fired him. He insisted he'd win on appeal, with a new lawyer they couldn't afford. His shoulder was fine; it was his back that was hurt. It hurt when he was supposed to mow the grass or help carry groceries. It didn't hurt when he played tackle football with Ricky and Max in the front yard.

"Move, Mom! I have to poo."

Max jumped around on the other side of the screen door, waiting to dash to the bathroom. The tender juices of frying turkey filled the air, a soothing reminder of childhood holidays when life wasn't so fast. Max slipped a loud fart and jumped again so she scooted to the side and he ran past.

"You don't need to be rude!" she called. "And flush the toilet this time."

"I'm hungry, Mommy," Angel said, sliding through the door. She leaned her head into Lori's stomach.

"I know, Angel baby. Have some chips. Dinner won't be ready for a little while."

She poured a fresh glass of white Zin and followed Angel back outside. All it took, she knew, was a sweet moment with her daughter to make things seem all right. It could still be a fun night, even though she always did most of the work. The cold wine was refreshing against her lips and the sun had melted in the sky so it wasn't nearly as hot. She wrapped her arms around Rick's neck. She pressed her body against his and kissed his mouth, still wet from the snappy carbonation of the beer. She let her cool mouth linger against his. Whatever it was that worked between them woke like a wild animal roused by hunger. He wrapped his arm around her back.

"Get a room!" Angie cried. "And use birth control."

"Listen woman," Rick told her. "It's not my fault God wanted to spread my greatness around the earth."

"They're not going to be so great if they drown each other," Angie said.

"Watch and learn," Rick said to Jesse, handing him his beer and ambling over to the pool.

"Hey," he barked at the girls, whose shrieks and whines had grown in intensity. "Hey!"

He reached into the pool and lifted each girl, dripping and confused, by the armpit and dropped them on the grass. He leaned close.

"Stop fighting!"

Lori heard the echo of his words over the tops of the trees. The girls stood, stunned and silent.

"Hug it out. Now!"

They stepped toward each other and wrapped long brown arms around the other's neck. Rick picked up Brittney first and tossed her back into the pool. Angel knew she was next so she raised her arms helpfully.

"What would you like to play?" Brittney asked Angel with forced friendliness.

Rick dried his hands on the front of his shirt. The wet finger marks stuck against his stomach.

"Now that's some fine parenting," he said, heading back to the fryer.

Jesse put his arm around Angie. She clutched his arm even tighter.

"I'll remember that when the twins are big enough to fight," Jesse said.

"You better not!" Angie said.

Lori laughed and drank her wine. It wasn't funny, she knew. Rick was way too rough with the kids, and even more so on the rare occasions he chose to discipline them. She had talked to Angie about it a million times. She fought back the prickly humiliation. *These are your friends*, she told herself. *They know Rick doesn't abuse his kids.* But did they? Lori saw the quick glance between Jesse and Angie. They'd talk about this later, probably about how lucky Rick was that neither girl ended up with a dislocated shoulder. The wine had warmed from the humidity, but Lori drank it anyway. Rick used the branch to lift the lid off the fryer. The aroma of steaming turkey flooded the yard.

"Damn, that smells good," Angie said.

"See honey," Rick said to Lori. "Told you I could fry us a turkey. This fryer won't be a waste of money after all."

He was right. They sat down an hour later with plates full of crisp hot turkey meat and corn on the cob dripping with butter. Lori looked up at Rick, across from her at the picnic table, and watched him pick at the fried crust around the edges of his turkey. This was good, right? They had friends over. Rick cooked a meal. Well, he cooked a turkey anyway and no one got hurt in the process. Families all over the world did this—had friends over and entertained. The children played and no one got hurt. It was worth the hundred dollars. Even the kids were eating. She watched Angel pick up her ear of corn and lick off the butter. Ricky gnawed at a turkey leg. His lips glistened.

Lori decided it was enough. To think a few moments ago she nearly lost her temper and played her hand. That would have been a mistake.

Sure, Rick drank too much and needed to get back to work, but at the end of the day, wasn't family all that mattered? She thought of her own father, a salesman who traveled most weeks, and tried to pull forth a memory of a family barbecue. She came up with nothing, but instead saw her parents sitting at the kitchen table, silent, while she picked at the meatloaf in front of her. No one talked. No one laughed. So when Brittney leaned over and licked Ricky's corn, and Ricky laughed and cried, "That's disgusting," Lori did all she knew how. She laughed until Rick, Jesse, and Angie joined in. The clouds above were wispy white against the blue, like the feathers of the swans in the retention pond outside the kitchen window of her childhood home. So pure, those swans in the murky water. So beautiful.

And why shouldn't they laugh? They had a roof over their heads. They were a family. There was love. But dammit if Angie didn't give Jesse that look again; Angie wouldn't laugh if one of the twins licked the butter off another twin's corn. Lori was a bad mother. And if she was a bad mother, what else in life did she have to show for herself? She pissed away her own dreams of a career to have babies with this man who didn't want to work, who wanted to sit on the couch and watch *Jeopardy!* and eat Chex Mix even though it wasn't a holiday.

Lori finished her plate and went back for seconds, stabbing a thick slice of meat with her plastic fork and covering it with gravy. It shouldn't go to waste, even though she was full already.

"What kind of lawyer?" Jesse was asking Rick.

"Workers comp."

"So this guy doesn't take money until you win?"

"That's right." He looked across the table at Lori. "You hear that, baby? I saw an ad on TV about a lawyer you don't pay until you win."

The turkey and gravy in Lori's mouth turned to gelatin. The rumble in her insides pushed a ball of gas through her system, a hot pressure against her ass. She wanted nothing more than to let it escape and poison the air. She shifted on the bench and clenched.

"I thought you were feeling better," she said.

"It's the principle of the thing!" Rick cried, scanning the table for support. "A goddamned plank fell on me."

"It was over two years ago," Lori said. "Can't we just forget it?"

Jesse and Angie busied themselves with Cheerios, which they passed to the little ones in their bouncy seats on the grass. They'd heard all this before, at bowling nights and card games and holiday potlucks.

Max reached across and picked from Angel's plate. She shrieked.

"Dammit, Lori!" Everything on the table bounced as Rick let his thick arms fall with a slam. He pushed himself to standing.

"Get a job," she mouthed slowly, looking past his looming figure at the strands of clouds. "Wouldn't it just be easier if he got himself a new job?"

"We're leaving," Angie said. "We're not having this talk again."

Jesse stood and began scooping Cheerios back into the plastic storage containers.

"Angie!" Lori said.

Friends were supposed to support each other. In private, Angie agreed with everything Lori had to say about Rick not having a job. She'd even called him a deadbeat.

"Screw this," Angie said, tossing everything into the diaper bag. She lifted one of the bouncy seats by its legs, the little one still strapped inside. His soft mouth worked a Cheerio as he waved his arms. Jesse picked up the other chair and they left, not even going through the house, but walking the perimeter.

"Way to go," Rick said, sitting back down and lifting his beer.

"Screw you," Lori said. "Our friends can't stand listening to you talking about it for another minute. You need to get your ass off the couch and get a job. You're not even hurt."

"Oh no?" He reached across the table and clamped his fingers around her shoulder. He squeezed hard, his fingers digging into the fleshy muscle.

"Rick!"

"Does that hurt?" he shouted. "Don't tell me how I feel!"

"Let go of me!"

He did. Lori rubbed her pulsing shoulder and stared venom across the table. Rick's face was purple, sweat beads along his forehead, and his nostrils flared. She hadn't seen him this pissed in a long time.

"Go play," Rick told the kids.

They got up and went into the house.

He stood up and approached Lori. He grabbed her breast and squeezed her nipple with his fingertips.

She shrieked and cowered. "Let go!"

"Does that hurt?" he shouted.

"Rick, don't!"

He let go.

"Yes," she told him. "Yes, Rick, you hurt me. Are you happy now?"

She stood up and went into the house, one hand rubbing her breast, the other her shoulder. Behind her, she heard the rattle and rage as Rick lifted the picnic table and tossed it over.

What an idiot, wasting all those leftovers.

"You go to bed now," she told the kids, who were watching TV. "Dad's angry and you want to stay out of his way. Do as I say."

"But Mommy," Brittney whined.

"Now!"

All four retreated down the hall into their rooms. Lori turned to the sink, her throat burning, so she put her lips to the faucet and slurped cold water.

Then she poured a fresh glass of wine and started the dishes. She didn't look into the backyard. If you could flip Rick's damn head open you'd find putrid shit rotting and festering inside his skull—a stink so bad, like when the crown on her tooth fell off and it smelled like the juice in the bottom of a garbage can. It didn't seem like there was anything good going on inside his head anymore.

The telephone rang as Lori finished the dishes. She pulled the phone to her ear as she mopped her forehead.

"It's me," Angie whispered. "Don't be pissed. It's just that Jesse and I had agreed we'd leave if it came up again."

"I know, Ange."

"Are you OK? Everything's OK over there?"

"I'm just stuck. I don't know how to change things."

"That's not true. You know."

Lori cringed in that inward way that always happened when she confided in someone. She didn't want to get into it. Not tonight.

"What's he doing now?" Angie said.

Lori squinted out the window. The sun had dropped far below the tree line so the sky had gone gray.

"He's smoking a ham, I think."

"Now?"

Lori laughed and Angie joined in.

She watched her husband open the smoker and pour from the bottle of bourbon. He took a swig from the bottle.

She reached into the kitchen drawer and pulled out a pack of Camels. "Now I'm smoking, too," she told Angie, lighting it on the gas stove.

"Weed?"

"Cigarette," Lori said.

"Listen, I have to run. Did he hurt you?"

"Nothing big."

"Just remember, you're in control. You can pull the trigger anytime you choose. You've got the resources. You did the homework. We're with you on this," Angie said.

Lori hung up and leaned against the counter, watching Rick adjust his T-shirt over his belly. She reached for the bottle of wine. Such a cool contrast after bending over the hot sink for so long. The pile of bills inside the plastic basket teetered over the top, leaning so far to one side it was hard to figure out how they hadn't fallen onto the floor.

"Mommy?"

"For Christ's sake," Lori muttered.

She went into Angel's room and snapped on the light.

"I told you only one cup of Kool-Aid."

Angel was already out of bed, peeling off the wet nightgown. She pulled on dry underpants and a new nightgown and sat cross-legged on the floor. Lori leaned across the bed. The wine and her dinner pressed into her esophagus. She yanked the sheets free and tossed them on the floor. The Barbie blanket was folded on the dresser so she snapped it open and laid it on top of the plastic mattress cover.

"Sleep on Barbie."

Angel climbed back onto the bed with the nightgown bunched around her waist so Lori could see the pink bears on her underpants and the smooth skin on the back of her thighs.

"Mom?"

"What, Angel?"

"Are you mad at me?"

"No. I just wish you could change your own bed so I didn't have to do it."

"Sorry, Mommy."

Lori leaned forward and brushed her lips against the smooth cheek that smelled like chlorine and butter.

"You're my Angel," she said.

Angel snuggled into herself and closed her eyes.

Rick was poking around the kitchen cupboards when Lori came out of Angel's bedroom and softly pulled the door closed.

"Did she piss again?" he said.

"What do you think?"

"She was probably drinking the pool water."

"Whatever. Is your ham done?"

"No, still has a couple hours, I think."

"Will you be awake?" Lori said.

"Yes!" The indignation rose to his cheeks. "I just need more bourbon."

"We don't have anymore," Lori said.

"That's why I want you to go get me some, baby. This ham will feed us all week. Sandwiches tomorrow. Pea soup."

The clock above the microwave said 11:37.

"I've had four glasses of wine and I'm tired. I cleaned everything up and changed a bed full of piss."

"Come on, baby!"

"Rick. No. Jesus."

"That's real fucking nice, Lori."

"You're real nice to me, too." She pulled up her shirt and yanked the bra to the side, revealing the red tip of her nipple, which had throbbed and pulsed since he pinched it.

"I'm sorry, baby," he said. He came to her and caressed her breast with his palm. "I'm sorry," he mumbled, leaning down to kiss her nipple. Hot pain rifled through her collarbone, across to the ache in her shoulder.

"You're always sorry, that's for sure," Lori said.

"Fine." He stood up. "I'll go get it myself."

"Yep. That sounds like something you'd do."

"We're fucking when I get home," he called over his shoulder. "You shouldn't show them to me if you're not planning to fuck me."

"Whatever, Rick. You think what you want."

She heard him rev the engine of the pickup before he backed down the gravel to the road. The house seemed larger without him. Cleaner, too. Lori scooped her glass from the kitchen counter on her way into the family room. She sat on the couch to watch sitcom reruns, propping her feet on the coffee table even though she shouted at the kids when they did it. She pulled the chenille afghan from the back of the couch and draped it across her lap. Her grandmother had knitted it, just a month before she died. She knitted the whole afghan even though her knuckles were knotted and swollen from arthritis.

And Rick couldn't muster enough motivation to accomplish a load of laundry. Tomorrow, she'd do it. She really would. She kicked a mostly empty bag of Doritos with her foot, the crunching rattle startling her as it slid across the glass and sent a shower of orange crumbs onto the carpet before it fell to the floor. She sank deeper into the couch and closed her eyes; if she could get the apartment soon enough, she might not even have to vacuum that mess. She'd been saving the money from the bottle deposits for two years now, hadn't even imagined how much money she could collect from the heaping pile of glass and aluminum next to the garbage cans on the side of the house. It almost made her happy when Rick cracked open another beer, and another.

"Keep drinking, asshole," she said to the empty room. She'd be up to six hundred dollars pretty soon, enough for over two month's rent in the apartment complex. She'd already talked to Mrs. Park; she'd watch the kids after school every day for just seventy-five dollars a week. Even if Lori had to start out as a bank teller, she'd be able to make that much plus rent. When Rick was forced to sell their piece-of-shit house, the only thing his parents left him when they died, she'd get half the money. At least half, Angie said.

Lori stretched out on the couch and pulled the afghan around her shoulders. Maybe she would fuck Rick when he got home, one last long fuck that would leave his head spinning when she told him she was moving out and taking the kids. She'd fuck him and fall asleep, leaving him alone with his bourbon and his ham in the dark.

When she woke up, the clock above the television said 1:03. A hard rap on the door, and she leapt to her feet with her heart pounding in her ears. Red flashed on the trunk of the tree in the front yard. It flashed blue and went back to pink. Another rap on the door. She ran to it and threw it open so the knob banged into the wall, but the damage had been done years ago.

It was Douggie Schwartz. She'd never gotten used to seeing Douggie in his uniform. The image of a nervous teenager with pimples, red and lumpy on his face and neck, was forever ingrained in her mind. The pimples were gone now as he stood on the cement slab outside the door. His flashers lit up the night. He looked startled, as though he had forgotten she lived there, in the same house she'd lived with Rick since they moved in together when she was nineteen.

"Lori Pierce," he said.

"Gunther," she corrected him.

"Right, sorry," he mumbled. He extended a paper until she saw the registration certificate for Rick's truck.

"Oh God, what happened?"

"He didn't have a wallet," Douggie said. "But it was Rick."

"Yes, it was Rick."

"His truck hit the tree around the curve..."

Lori grabbed her jean jacket and purse from the doorknob of the closet. She threw keys into her purse.

"Let's go," she said.

"No," he said. "There's no rush."

"What are you saying, Douggie?"

"Lori," he said.

"Just let me run next door and get the neighbor to watch my kids," she said.

His hand on her shoulder stopped her. She winced as he grasped the bruised flesh so he removed his hand and held it in the air.

"His body was thrown from the car into the tree. He went by ambulance to the hospital in Cleary. Take a moment to gather your thoughts. Make some calls. You need a ride there?"

"I don't have a car."

"I'll get a car over here within the hour to take you up."

"I want to go now, Douggie. He's not dead. He's hanging on."

He pressed his lips together, but the sigh still softly escaped through his nose. Lori knew Rick was dead from the sound of it.

"He went through the windshield. His head went into the tree. I'm sorry."

"He fried a turkey tonight," she said. She didn't mention the wasted turkey leftovers or the ham. Or the bourbon, but they probably smelled that on Rick.

Douggie leaned forward onto the balls of his feet and back to his heels. He stuffed both hands into his pockets and stared at their family portrait on the wall from when Angel was barely old enough to walk.

The curve wasn't far. She slid her arms into the jean jacket and ducked her head under the strap of her purse. She left Douggie standing there and went through the garage and hoisted the door. There were two options: a bicycle or the motorized scooter Rick insisted they buy that summer. Fun for the whole family, he'd said.

"Lori?" she heard Douggie call from the front porch.

She started the scooter and pulled onto the road, the night air a fresh slap on her face. The purse bumped her leg so she pulled it around her body until it rested on her hip. There were no cars on the road this time of night. She wondered what she'd find on the side of the road—perhaps a crew of firefighters and police and investigators with glaring flashlights and little placards with numbers on them placed next to all the evidence.

Eventually she heard Douggie's police car behind her. He pulled alongside and rolled down the passenger window. She kept her eyes on the road ahead. Finally, Douggie passed her. He flipped on the flashers. No siren. Her first police escort, so slow she nearly laughed at how ridiculous it seemed to hear each grain of gravel crunch and explode beneath the four tires.

The curve ahead stretched dark and silent. Douggie pulled over and cut the lights. Lori pulled the scooter next to the heap smashed into the big willow tree. The hood had crunched to an angular teepee. Shards of glass outlined the front of the pickup like glimmering jewels. Lori took in the wreckage and turned off the scooter. The only sound besides the crickets was the occasional click of the engine.

I let him drive. I made him drive.

She tried to track the trunk of the willow to find solace in the sweeping canopy of leaves. Fear embraced her in the darkness. She flipped the headlight of the scooter back on and recoiled when the stain illuminated. It was dark and tinged with crimson, and dripping and textured with fluids or flesh or tissue. It was Rick on that tree. She clenched her eyes and batted until she found the switch to shut off the headlight.

"Christ almighty," Douggie exclaimed. "Lori, get in the car and let me take you back."

Lori used all her strength to push the heavy scooter in the arc required to turn it. She got on and flipped on the light. As she powered the engine and pulled away, she ran over something. She stumbled back to the black square on the earth. She squatted down and picked up Rick's wallet. It was slick and cool. She pushed it toward the headlight and saw a thick strand of white hanging over the top corner and wrapping underneath. She threw the wallet away and ran to the edge of the road to wipe her fingers frantically on the gravel.

She stood and looked both ways, avoiding Douggie's gaze, then turned onto the road and started walking home with her chin pressed to her chest. She expected to hear the police car's engine start, but it didn't. Douggie had been shy in high school. Only in a small town could someone so meek become a policeman. She couldn't remember having spoken to him one time in four years. When brisk footsteps scratched behind her—purposeful, confident footsteps—she almost believed it was Rick catching up, not Douggie. Rick had been the only guy who could keep up with Lori.

"We'll walk back together," Douggie said.

Fresh air gradually took the place of the burnt rubber and exhaust Lori hadn't realized until now. When the house came into view, she smelled cooked meat. The ham. It would be nearly done.

"Rick and I had our problems," she said.

Douggie nodded.

"We have four kids."

"I'll get that neighbor you mentioned to sit for them tonight."

"Mrs. Park. She's going to watch my kids from now on after school."

"I'm sure your ride to Cleary will be here soon."

"I have to get the ham from the smoker first. So it doesn't go to waste."

Douggie said nothing, but what did he know about having kids or taking care of a family? She tried to ignore his footsteps and the swing of his arm—the blue uniform shirt, so official—in her peripheral vision. Tomorrow, for something to do, she'd make soup with the kids. They'd do it for their dad. She'd do it for Rick.

A lump rose in her throat because she knew she would have fucked him when he got home. Amid the lingering smells in the house—turkey, ham, the fresh corn husks, the drip-drying dishes in the rack—he'd have brushed her arm with the back of his hand. That's all it took for her animal to wake up to his. Together they were wild.

And she knew she wouldn't have left.

Stephanie Joyce
NOS MORITURI

"**Y**ou're going the wrong way." Mabby gritted her teeth as Helen turned the Buick—Mabby's Buick—in a swaggering right. "The funeral home is on Longwood."

"That's Pinelli's. We went there last week. Jen McCauley, remember? Heart attack." Helen waved vaguely toward O'Donnell's and the departed Mary Donnelly. The car wobbled. "We're going to O'Donnell's. Right, Sister?"

"Right, Sister!" In the front next to Helen, Juley lifted the box holding the cake and straightened the habit across her lap.

Mabby, stuck in the backseat, hugged her elbows and glowered at the back of Helen's head, which barely poked up above the headrest. She hated the smell inside the car. Talcum powder and the aging bodies of the three surviving Riordan sisters and Cousin Marg. Helen was driving too fast. Night fell so fast this time of year, the cars swooshing through the slush.

"No," she said. "That's not right. The...the *thing* that came in the mail said..." Helen just ignored her; Mabby silently cursed her and cursed the gaps in her words. She'd been sure it was Pinelli's. Her fingers itched to take the wheel. Helen just loved driving, but back at the convent they usually took buses, and so she didn't get much chance to practice. Mabby knew that these three had always envied her her car. They didn't know she'd envied them, going into the convent while Mabby stayed with her aging parents until everything was too late.

Helen swerved one-handedly onto Archer Boulevard and fishtailed across a pool of half-melted snow. This set off an orchestra of car horns and slid Mabby along the backseat into the blue-habited haunch of Cousin Marg, known outside the family as Sister Miriam. "Ooh! Control yourself there," Marg squealed, and Helen barked, "Seatbelt, Mabby!"

Mabby smothered an urge to open the door and jump. Twenty years ago she might have. Twenty years ago—even 366 days ago—she'd have been doing the driving.

"Headlights, Helen!" Juley said. "Cake, Juley!" Helen replied, and the three nuns went off, spouting commands at each other till they choked with laughter and the car wobbled again. Something was nagging at the back of Mabby's mind. Juley turned in the front seat and made a mock-scared face at Mabby, eyebrows nearly vanishing into her veil. That veil was looking too big for her these days. "If she crashes she'll make me drop the cake. Pinelli's won't let me in with cake all over my habit."

"Just say the Dominicans are working on new habits," Marg said. They all thought this was terribly funny, and Marg reached over to poke Mabby. "Get it? New habits!"

Mabby frowned. Pinelli's... Helen had sounded so sure of herself, but hadn't the... *announcement*, that was the word, hadn't the announcement said... Just as Mabby opened her mouth to say something, Juley piped up. "Wait, Hel! It was O'Donnell's last week. But this one's Clanahans. They always use Pinelli's."

"That's right." Marg nodded, her whole body quivering with certitude. Helen nodded. She'd take *their* word for it. Surprisingly, she passed up the thrill of a U-turn, instead making a ladylike detour around the block, and headed the car to the other side of town.

Mabby had wanted to drive. It was nearly a year since the stroke and everything was just fine. If she'd been driving, they wouldn't bother asking where to go, where to turn. Helen insisted on waiting the full 365 days. For your health, she'd said, but Mabby thought it was because she'd been an Abbess for ten years and an overbearing bully for sixty-five. Juley always liked it when Helen drove, because then she got to sit in front.

Mabby looked down at her hands, clasped in her lap, and noted with irritation that Marg's and Juley's hands were clasped in their laps too, that their legs were all crossed the same way, left over right. She uncrossed her legs, spread them like the little boys she used to teach, and rolled down the window. They were on the overpass, the only place in the city where buildings didn't obscure the sky.

Light and cold air sliced in. Marg started, but pleasurably. She and Mabby gazed out at the sky. It was heavy and pink and smelled of snow. Juley turned to help them look.

"Ooh! Isn't that fresh!" she said. "It'll be snowing when we get there."

Marg leaned over Mabby and rolled the window back up, leaving the car full of the smell of gasoline and snow. The seat creaked as the cousins recrossed their legs. "I'd rather have a clear night for a wake," Marg said and lit a cigarette. She thought of herself as a rebel, the only one of them to smoke.

"Poor Edgar," Juley said. "Fifty years we've known him."

"Remember how he used to chase us up the stairs in the house on Loomis?" Juley said. Helen laughed. Juley sighed. Mabby looked at her hands, upturned in her lap. A small tic was jerking her little finger. Fifty years didn't seem right.

"Falling asleep, Mabby?" hollered Marg in her ear. Mabby jumped. Not the way Helen drove, she wasn't falling asleep. She wanted to bite Marg's nose, but she kept her tone even.

"I was remembering," she said. "When we all lived on Loomis."

"Ah, Mabby, Mabby," Juley sighed. She had opened the cake box and was snacking on the icing. "Those grand old days."

"Remember the Thanksgiving when all the Clanahans came?" chimed in Juley. Sometimes Mabby thought Juley recalled every meal she'd ever eaten. As if they all didn't know the story, she began to explain. "Fifteen at the big table, and so many kids that the grownups had to put a table on the porch."

"Seventeen," said Helen. "And Min Clanahan got drunk and lay down in the grass."

They all started coloring in the scene, specifying menu items, quarreling over which kid had crept under the table to look under the ladies' dresses, arguing over who had thrown up cranberry sauce on Marg's new wool coat. Mabby stared out at the colored lights that blurred by as the car swept westward. It wasn't fifty years that she'd known Edgar; it was seventy.

Mabby was five. It was the Fourth of July, and the Loomis Street neighbors were jammed into the Fortune Park picnic grounds. Riordans, O'Malleys, Clanahans, Caseys, mothers, fathers, grandparents, cousins sprawled in the brown grass waiting for the fireworks. The evening smelled of charcoal and dust and beer.

Mabby had eaten three hot dogs and two pieces of chocolate cream pie and was nearly asleep on a blanket near the edge of the park when someone twitched her ear. She blinked up into a freckled face and white-lashed, bottle-green eyes. Seven-year-old Edgar squatted next to her to whisper, "Come on. I've got sparklers!" He pulled up the tail of his shirt to show three iron-colored tips sticking out of his shorts. "And matches!"

Mabby stifled a shocked giggle. Sparklers were strictly forbidden to kids under ten. They darted away from the Loomis Street neighbors, to the edge of the park to where an old pine laid its branches down almost to the ground, and in that darkness Edgar lit the first sparkler. Pink rockets spat out from the tip. Edgar swung the fizzing sparkler like a sword, thrusting and zigzagging, making circles and triangles. Right before his sparkler sputtered out he lit one for Mabby. She squealed as she flourished the wand;

Edgar instructed her and she spun it faster and faster until it made a blur of smoking gold loops. Edgar lit the third one. Red sparks fountained out.

"Look! I'll write your name!" His hand moved so fast that Mabby couldn't see, leaving a golden squiggle glowing in the air. "See? M...A...B!" said Edgar. The glittering scrawl cutting the darkness looked like the name Mab, but the name burned into her heart that evening was Edgar's.

As the smoke drifted up into the pine branches, cheers and clapping floated down from the crowd. "Come on!" said Edgar and pulled at Mabby's hand. The first orange stars were blasting off as they pelted back to the picnic ground. All of Loomis Street was looking up at the exploding sky. In the fiery light, Edgar grinned at her. "Nobody even knew we were gone."

Mabby held his hand as they watched the fireworks, green circles of flame, crackling white banners, silver rockets, yellow suns raining down on a hundred upturned, wonder-filled faces. The scene was so clear in her mind; she started counting the faces, the numbers soothing even as their growing total alarmed. Her brothers, her sisters, her parents, aunts and uncles, six O'Malleys, eight Riordans, four Caseys, eight Clanahans—no, Edgar was the last.

Now the only ones left were here, in this car.

A blast of air made Mabby jump. Marg had rolled down the window and lit another cigarette. The survivors of the Loomis Street picnic were still talking about food.

"That canned cranberry sauce," Juley said. "You remember the name, don't you, Mabby dear?"

Juley looked back at Mabby. They wouldn't let her drive, but they always looked to her for the names of things. They were looking now, even Helen peering at her in the rearview mirror. They looked to her for everything—loans, dinners and pitchers of forbidden Manhattans, the authority of their collective virgin status, rides to and from their convents, and now the car itself. In the cigarette fog they looked pale and wavery, while Edgar waited for their last visit, laid out solid and real in his coffin—arrived, finally, at his destination. And all they could talk about was cranberry sauce. Edgar is in the real world now, she thought. We're all ghosts. The thought frightened her so much that she giggled.

"What is it, sister dear?" said Juley.

"Edgarberry sauce," blurted Mabby. Puzzled frowns appeared on the faces around her. Mabby let out a ghastly chuckle. Nobody else laughed. She appealed to Juley, always her staunchest ally (except for escaping into the convent). "Edgarberry sauce, isn't it, Juley? By Del Monte. You liked it on your toast. Edgarberry toast!" Juley's mouth opened but nothing came out. "Edgarberry wine!" Mabby heard herself saying.

Everybody went quiet. Helen turned completely around, craning her neck to look at Mabby around the headrest. Cars honked behind them. Helen started off again with a jerk, and Marg filled the car with a cough of smoke.

"Jesus, Mary, and Joseph, Mabby!" she said. "This is a *wake* we're going to."

Exactly, Mabby thought, but she smiled at Marg and folded her right knee over her left. Now they all matched. In a minute the nuns were reminiscing again. They were like a batch of starlings twittering away before the winter flight, remembering the only place they knew to go back to. Mabby's pinky was twitching again, and a voice in her head chanted over and over, "Edgarberry wine, Edgarberry wine."

At the door of the funeral home Helen skidded to one of the screeching stops she so loved. They all piled out. Mabby dawdled at the curb looking at Pinelli's. It was getting to be like a home away from home. Discreet yellow light leaked from the doors and fuzzy shapes drifted behind the windows. She looked at the houses beyond Pinelli's, at the hard cheery light streaming from the windows, and started to edge away. Marg took her firmly by the left arm and Helen flanked her on the right, with Juley, bearing the box of nibbled cake, blocking escape from behind. They lofted Mabby up the steps and through the great oaken Pinelli doors.

Inside, they released her. "Home again," said Mabby. Marg looked at her. Glaring, probably, but it was hard to tell. What did these funeral people have against light? Candles burned everywhere, yet their flicker barely illuminated the throng of mourners. Mabby could smell them, though—wet wool, hair tonic, soap. Age. How could there still be so many?

A shadow emerged and solidified. "Ah, Father Dan," Juley said.

Father Dan Murphy advanced upon them, hands extended. "The Riordan ladies," he said, clasping their hands in turn.

"Paying our respects," said Juley.

"The last from Loomis Street," said Father Dan, taking Mabby's hand in a grip that was dry and a little too firm.

"We're the Loomis Street Death Squad," Mabby heard herself saying. Oh, God. Father Dan's warm professional smile froze, and Mabby couldn't stop herself from adding, "Sweeping up the souls." Even in the dim light she could see Father Dan's red face grow purple. Helen, behind him, frowned and shook her head.

Mabby backed away, almost forgetting to let go of Father Dan's hand. "I'll just have a drink," she said. "To raise my spirits. Ha, ha." She wasn't supposed to drink yet, but so what. As she turned away she felt all their eyes on her, scorching her back.

Familiar faces flicked on and off in the dimness. She pictured each face as she first knew it: disheveled pigtails, mouths smeared with jam and chocolate, scabbed shins and elbows, eyes shy and shining under straw Easter hats. Mabby had taught math for forty years. She started adding up the years she had known each mourner. The gray hall behind her filled with the images of toddlers and impish children, and she was close to two thousand years.

"Mabby Riordan!" Pale, jowly, her wispy pink hair flying out like fading firecrackers, Sal Grady (freckled tear-stained face, forty-seven years) embraced Mabby. The green tweed jacket prickled. Since when was green a color for a wake? "Oh, Mabby, isn't it sad?" Sal slipped her arm into Mabby's and peeped up at her. She had been Mabby's height, but years of secretarial work had hunched her into a question mark.

"Two thousand and three," said Mabby.

"What?" said Sal. "Let's have a glass of punch." She hauled Mabby to the bar where somebody's nephew (she didn't count him; he seemed to have sprung into being full grown) poured a ladleful of the spiced wine into Mabby's plastic cup, then poured two into her own.

Mabby looked into her cup. The drink looked like blood. She crossed herself with the cup and raised it like the Host. "The Body and Blood!" She grinned at Sal. Sal looked scandalized. Mabby drank the punch in one swallow.

"Mabby, are you sure you should...?" said Sal. Mabby was pretty sure she shouldn't, but hell, it wasn't as if she was driving. Anyway, everybody in this crowd knew all about everybody else's strokes and heart attacks, all the stuttering, inevitable stages of decline, and they repeated the knowledge like holy liturgy at every encounter, which was about once a week now. By tomorrow they'd all be blathering about Mabby's "drinking problem." They'd say they'd suspected all along, don't you remember when she...

Sal herself polished off the punch in two gulps. Her eyes immediately grew misty. She breathed a long winey sigh. "Poor dear Edgar. I used to tease him and call him Eddie. He'd puff his chest out and say, EDGAR, very proud. So dignified." She wiped her eyes. "Such a gentleman."

"Dignified to death," Mabby said. By the time her parents died, Edgar had entered the priesthood. "Good oooold Deadgar. Beloveeeeed Deaddy." Wine was no help at all really.

Sal reached for Mabby's cup. "I think you..."

Mabby turned away, murmuring numbers under her breath. The room tilted. Was she flying? She was falling. Mabby thought that was fine.

"Whoa, Nell," said a scratchy male voice. Bony arms eased Mabby up onto her feet. "Well, Mabby!" Mabby looked up into a face with watery blue eyes, a faded yellowish mustache, the goatee hiding the weak chin. "Queen Mab. How are you?" Pat Kirby. A near stranger; only thirty-three years. Not a regular at these shindigs. He had wanted to marry her.

Pat left his hands on her shoulders. His touch was firm but light, just as she remembered. It had always been too light to hold her. "I'm sorry to see you *here*," he said, in his new, scratchy mouse voice. "But I'm never sorry to see you." He smiled, his face opening like a wrinkled curtain to reveal gleaming dentures.

Mabby missed the gold eyetooth he'd had when they met, but she kept that to herself. She didn't want to laugh at Pat. She took the arm he offered. "Shall we go in and see the show?" she said, and bit her lip. But Pat was already talking in his reedy old man's falsetto, a long, detailed story of Edgar in the old days. His hearing aid emitted squealing noises (Mabby's hearing had remained very acute) as they wove among the bereaved. Mabby held Pat's skinny arm and trailed him like a balloon, muttering and tallying as the faces wafted past her, and all at once he was looking right at her and they had stopped.

"...Very traditional, Edgar was."

"Very *stiff*," said Mabby. *Three thousand thirty*.

Pat didn't blink. "Wanted a traditional funeral with all the fireworks." He gestured, like a maître d'. They stepped past the fringe of the crowd.

The cherry-colored coffin stood at the edge of the room. The lid was flung open as if someone had just scurried inside and hadn't had time to close it. No one was near. Twin squads of candles stood guard, their flames shimmying in the polished wood. Mabby pulled her arm free of Pat's and went over to the coffin. A feeling of numbness replaced her dread. The body lay against a blue velvet pillow wearing Edgar's black suit and notched collar. There was Edgar's brush of silver hair–gleaming in the candlelight as if still alive–and there was a mask of Edgar's face, trapped at the true turning point, the invisible wall at the end of every road.

Mabby fumbled in her purse for her compact and lipstick–Killer Krimson, it was called. She watched in the mirror as the color stained her mouth like blood, watched as behind her, the shadowy crowd seethed. Then she stepped to the coffin, bent over, and mashed her lips against the cold wax that had been Edgar's lips, leaving a smiling crimson smear. "Three thousand thirty years, Edgar," she said.

Beyond the circle of light around the coffin milled the gray, blurred forms of her friends and relatives. Mabby pictured them falling like dominoes before an army of tidy headstones. She took Pat's arm again, smiling into his startled face. Like queen and king they walked toward the throng of ghosts.

Karan Madhok
NEW MUTINY

Verona Point was a rare ledge of flat land in the otherwise jagged topography of Dharamshala. An even aberration in the consistently odd Himalayas. It used to be an old colonial home, long, thin, and rectangular, with an open-air porch serving as the verandah outside the building. In front of the structure was an open square patio, which ended on a ledge from where residents and visitors could see the entire expanse: the deodar-rich lower hills in the valley and the North Indian plains farther below.

A century ago, Verona Point had been a single, uninterrupted block, where a retired British viceroy lived the last of his days. But when the viceroy passed away and the rest of his countrymen left India, each room in the block was partitioned into five smaller blocks, and each partition became a small establishment with outdoor seating on the verandah. For visitors, the very first establishment was the Best Stop Tea Shop, closest to the partially pucca motorable road that ended up on the hill.

And on the farthest end of this property was Sanjay's Café, alike in dignity to the Best Stop, but carrying an ancient grudge that would soon spill into new mutiny. Sanjay lived in his two-bedroom home above the café with his son Momo. All day, Sanjay worked behind a partial glass window on his four-burner gas stove, making chai and his famous egg fried instant Maggi noodles for customers. "Sanjay Style," it was called. He shouted orders to Chhotu—his young helper—to serve the guests and keep the metal napkin holders stacked, and to chase away those little grayish-red monkeys that dug into the trash bin when the humans weren't looking. When he cooked, Sanjay hummed old filmi songs, tunes that would have made his customers nostalgic for the '80s had he had a better voice.

When someone engaged with him, he talked back. He talked about his father and the history of his café. He told tourists that the owner of Best Stop Tea Shop had been stealing his recipes. Often, he also created fictions when they asked him about Verona Point's origin story.

"Verona is the most beautiful peak in England," Sanjay told one couple from Bengal who shriveled together in the breeze, unfamiliar with the cold of the mountains.

"Verona was the viceroy's lover, whom he kept hidden from his respected wife," he said to a group of young monks from the monastery in McLeod Ganj above.

And in between his fictions, he occasionally stumbled across the truth. "The viceroy liked to read many books," Sanjay said to a teenager, a student from that expensive boarding school nearby. "His favorite book—his number one book—was about Verona."

"Oh, is that true?" the boy smiled from cheek to cheek. "This Verona?"

"Some Verona."

The boy was about Chhotu's age, but he wore a clean black jacket and tight narrow jeans. He had shiny black hair that made Sanjay conscious of his own shiny bald spot. He wanted Sanjay Style Maggi and a cup of chai, and Sanjay got to work. Behind his window, he poured a cup of water into a pot and set it to boil. It got smoky quickly in his tight cubicle, but he sniffed and continued without pause. On the wall to his right, he had three rows of plain wooden shelves stacked with the essentials: packets of Maggi and Wai-Wai noodles, slices of processed cheese, little bowls filled with green and red chilies, one plate each of peeled tomatoes and onions, and a loaf of sliced bread. He reached up to grab a square, yellow packet of Maggi and ripped it open. "Chhotu," Sanjay said. "Get me an egg, quick."

Chhotu was nimble on his feet and crept up behind Sanjay. On a separate frying pan, Sanjay heated some oil, cracked open the egg, and splashed it with a gratifying *thissh* sound, letting the yellow sun rise on the pan proudly in the middle of its white orbit. Once his noodles were soft and stringy, he drained out the water from the pot and transferred them to the frying pan, carefully displacing the fried egg to flip it back on top of the noodles. He added chopped onions. He added freckles of tomato. And even when nobody asked for it, he added some red chili.

"Ready," he grunted and placed the dish in a plastic white bowl.

"Aah, wonderful Sanjay ji," the boy smiled. "You still have the best fried Maggi here. Better than Best Stop, even."

Sanjay scoffed. "These are the original and best, boy. Bhaskar there," Sanjay pointed, "Bhaskar is just a fraud."

The Sanjay Style was the simplest of dishes; even an adolescent could master it in a matter of minutes. But at Verona Point, the most popular items were the easiest, the type of food that tourists would feel less guilty about gorging on their holidays. Sanjay—the master of instant meals—was proud of the minute complications of his creations.

Sanjay looked past the young customer. He looked past Himal's Dhaba next to his café, where coolies and taxi-*wallahs* huddled in a tiny, dark space, eating Rawat's simple rice and *daal* and *sabzis*. He looked past Ravi Kaka's cassette-recording shop—the store with no name—where the only sign of life, as always, was old Ravi Kaka himself, staring contentedly out into the world from behind his thick square-rimmed glasses. He looked past Kumar and Sons, owned by Bhaskar's brother, where other students from the boarding school purchased chips and Kur-Kures and sometimes, even cigarettes.

Finally, his gaze settled on that very first establishment. Bhaskar's Best Stop Tea Shop, right next to the little parking ground, which got especially crowded on weekends and school holidays. The Best Stop was crowded today, too, with customers eating noodles and bun omelettes and *aloo-parathas*. They were men and women, young and old. A family with boisterous children spilled ketchup all over their table. A young couple from that boarding school nearby shared a waffle between them. Those foreigners in their Tibetan shirts sat around the third table.

From the smoky, open kitchen of his café, Sanjay saw Bhaskar behind a glass window, just like Sanjay's, manning his kitchen. Sanjay hadn't realized it because he had seen him every day for the past four decades, but Bhaskar looked plump and heavy, fatter than ever before, with his rosy cheeks breaking out into bloated smiles at every customer.

Next to Bhaskar in the kitchen, however, was a familiar young face, a young woman. Devina. Bhaskar's elder daughter; the younger one was still too young to help around the café. It had been months since Sanjay had seen Devina last, maybe even a year. She was back to Verona Point. She had grown up so quickly, Sanjay thought. She didn't have any of Bhaskar's features. That sharp nose, those big eyes—they all came from her mother. While other local women wore simple *salwar-kameez* and saris in various shades of dark mustard, Devina was a splash of Technicolor in their sepia world, dressed like one of the tourists from Delhi or Chandigarh, in a tight blue Western-style T-shirt and a pair of black trousers.

She laughed at something, and Sanjay could now see her resemblance to her father. It was an over-exaggerated, full-teethed gurgle; fifty percent real amusement, fifty percent pretense. It seemed to work. The tourists in the front table—foreigners in Tibetan toethung T-shirts—all smiled back, charmed by the young woman's boisterousness.

Sanjay frowned to himself. She was only back in town for a few months, he knew. Just for her summer holidays. And then she would leave Verona Point again.

Devina wore that bubbly smile as she carried dishes from the kitchen to the table. She really looked grown-up now, Sanjay thought again. Momo and Devina were the same age. But she looked so much older than him. Sanjay knew that this was the thing with girls: teenage girls became full-grown women, with big eyes and long hair and full lips, even while teenage boys—like Momo—continued to look and behave like little children. One of the young men in the table full of foreigners smiled at her, in a way that men smile when they want to talk about something other than chai and Maggi. Sanjay knew that look.

"Sanjay ji," he heard the schoolboy's voice, buzzing him back to his place. "My chai?"

"Oh, yes, yes," Sanjay shuffled in his slippers back behind his kitchen counter. "Oh yes."

"Devina is back, Papa," Momo said.

"I know," Sanjay replied.

"She got back last night, Papa," Momo's chubby cheeks were glowing now. "Did you see?"

"Yes, yes, fatso. Are you going to help me clean up or just stand there smiling like an idiot?"

It was near sunset, the time of day when Momo usually returned to Verona Point. School was off for the summer, but Momo spent these days taking extra coaching classes in advance of his 12th board exams next year. At school, he was known by his *real* name, Vinod, the kid who sat in the front of the class and knew from memory all the important dates of Indian history and could easily memorize complicated chemical formulas.

He spent entirely too much time in his books, Sanjay thought. Too much time at those classes. It was as if he wanted to avoid the café.

When he returned home in the evenings, Vinod became Momo, a nickname he earned from his father after his penchant for fried-*momo* gluttony down in the bazaar. Sanjay had begun to think that the little dumplings had turned Momo's face into a *momo* itself: endlessly round and greasy, with a little glint of piggy pink every time he smiled.

"Papa…" Momo returned to the kitchen, still smiling. "She looks so…"

Sanjay put down his pan. "So what?"

"So grown-up."

"So," Sanjay grunted and laughed, in the way he did when he was angrier than he pretended to be. "So, then, did you talk to your old friend? Did you ask her why her father is making Sanjay Style now, too? Did you know that?"

Momo's smile evaporated off of his face. "I don't... I don't know, Papa."

There were no other customers that evening, but Sanjay wanted to stay busy, so he put some water to boil for another cup of chai. "He's a bastard. And his daughter is—" Sanjay stopped himself. "You just need to stay away from them, OK?"

"Papa," Momo sighed. "Not again—"

"He steals all my recipes. Lies to the customers. They all sit there and line up for his noodles and omelettes as if his food is something special. And all he does is smile at them. All his wife does is smile all day. That's all they've taught that little girl of theirs, too."

"Papa."

"Look, you start cleaning up now, I need a break," Sanjay moved out of the kitchen and nudged Momo into the narrow space.

"Papa... Devina, she's a good friend. She's nice, and—"

"Close up."

Sanjay took the water abruptly off the boil and spilled it down the sink next to the stove. He walked out behind the shop to the staircase that led him upstairs to his home, and into his bathroom. It was dark up here, except for the last rays of the setting sun through a glass window.

She *was* a nice girl, Sanjay thought to himself. If his wife had still been alive, she would have said so, too. She had always wanted a daughter. Sanjay had been happy with Momo, but his wife had always talked about having a daughter.

Without turning on any of the lights, Sanjay stared at a reflection of his face in the bathroom mirror, lit only from the faint ray of sunlight filtering through the blades of the exhaust fan above. He was growing old, he knew. Everyone was. Bhaskar was old and fat, and Bhaskar's daughter was not a child anymore, and Momo wanted to go to college next year, and every holiday season, more tourists showed up to Verona Point with new cars and new touchscreen phones.

Sanjay had a new phone, too, one of those Chinese ones that could store thousands of his favorite songs. Only old Ravi Kaka remained stuck in time, recording cassette tapes that no one listened to anymore. But soon, he, too, would be gone.

Sanjay lay in bed that night and worried about his son. He knew that Momo wanted to move down to Kangra for college. He saw the way Momo talked to his friends and cousins who studied and worked in bigger cities, who got management degrees or joined the army reserves. He could see that his son wasn't here, even when he was, in his hesitation to wash dishes, to make chai, to flip omelettes at the Café. There was no life in their small towns anymore.

Momo had wanted to leave ever since Devina left. Separated by less than thirty meters of verandah, Sanjay and Bhaskar had done everything to avoid looking eye to eye for decades. But Little Momo and Little Devina had been exempt from their cold war. The kids would run together on the patio, all the way to the edge of Verona Point. Back then, they had been too young to see over the protective railings, and dared each other to climb up the lower railing to look down at the valley below. Sanjay's wife would shout out, "Be careful, Vinod!" or Bhaskar's wife would shout, "No, Devi, *beti!*" and the kids would giggle at each other and run back, overjoyed that they had conspired together to annoy their elders.

Sanjay was the sole parent in charge now, and under his command, Momo was told to stay away from that girl. It wouldn't be right, Sanjay thought. Not after things had gone from bad to worse between Bhaskar and him. After Bhaskar spread rumors among the tourists about rats in Sanjay's kitchen. After Bhaskar stole his ideas to make pancakes and waffles for the tourists. Bhaskar hadn't even sent anything—no money, no gifts, no offer of chai, not a "sorry, old friend"—after Sanjay's wife passed away.

Sanjay had seen the Best Stop Tea Shop grow busier every year, and now Bhaskar had printed and laminated his menus, and hired three small *chhotus* to work alongside him and his wife. He could afford to buy his wife nicer *salwars* and send his elder daughter to a better school in a different town.

Sanjay shuffled over his hard mattress. It wasn't the girl's fault, he told himself. She was a nice, polite girl. Bhaskar had been blessed with two daughters. Sanjay knew that his wife had always wanted one.

Every weekend that summer, tourists drove up to Verona Point in scores. Families from the plains stopped on their way to McLeodganj and shuddered dramatically at mellow wafts of wind. Young couples came on honeymoons where the brides still hadn't washed off the intricate *mehendi* temporarily tattooed on their palms. Large numbers of leather jacket–clad men on motorcycles zoomed together higher up the Himalayas. Everyone did good business on the weekends. Everyone except Ravi Kaka and his cassette-recording shop, of course. Only the occasional grandparents peered into his store, geriatric couples who drove those old cars equipped only with cassette players under their dashboards.

Sanjay's Café had been crowded from lunchtime till late in the evening—late, in Dharamshala was any time after eight p.m.—and Sanjay and Chhotu had been busy cooking and serving and sweating and running. But Momo had gone to play football in the afternoon and hadn't returned yet.

"Where's that *motu*?" Sanjay asked Chhotu. Chhotu—in his ever-silent way—only shrugged.

Just as Sanjay had served his final customer, he heard the sound of his scooter rumbling up the road. He saw Momo, and sitting behind him on the scooter, Devina.

Momo dropped her in front of the Best Stop Tea Shop, and Sanjay saw Bhaskar and his wife glare at the young couple. Momo gave the girl a rosy-cheeked smile, that "good-boy" smile he used whenever someone offered him *golgappas* or *momos* from the market. Then, he parked the scooter and walked back to Sanjay's Café.

"Where were you all day?"

"Football, Papa," Momo casually swung the scooter keychain around his index finger.

"Football? You call that football?" Sanjay felt his voice getting louder, loud enough for the entire verandah to hear. "What were you doing with that girl?"

"Papa, I was just dropping her back. She was down in the market, too, buying vegetables. I asked if she wanted a lift and I—"

"No, you listen to me now, fat boy: you are not to spend time with that... that type of girl, you hear me?"

"But Papa, I—"

"They are dirty people, you understand. Dirty people from a dirty family." Another voice interjected.

"Hey," Bhaskar said. "That's my daughter you are talking about."

Sanjay stopped. For the first time in a decade—or more—Bhaskar stomped across the verandah that separated them.

The two brothers who ran Himal stepped out to take a look, too, and so did Kumar and his wife and his two sons from Kumar and Sons, and so did Chhotu and the three *chhotus* who worked with Bhaskar, and Bhaskar's wife, and both his daughters.

Under the clear, starry sky, Bhaskar met Sanjay on his turf, next to the unoccupied tables of Sanjay's Cafe. "Why was your son giving Devina a joy-ride? Keep your family away from my household, you understand?"

Sanjay laughed. "My family? You didn't worry about me or my family when you stole my dishes, did you? The egg *parathas*! The waffles! And now...and now..." Sanjay could barely get himself to say it. Perspiration formed on his forehead as he spoke. Momo crept up behind his father and held his arm gently. Sanjay pulled away to point an index finger at Bhaskar, hovering it close to his flaring nostrils. "And now, I hear you've been making Maggi Sanjay Style, too."

"Papa," Momo pleaded behind Sanjay.

"Papaji," Devina appeared behind Bhaskar.

Bhaskar moved closer to Sanjay's outstretched hand, as if daring to be touched.

"Please, my friends," Kumar, Bhaskar's brother, intervened. "My friends, please calm down. Calm down." He grabbed Bhaskar's hand and pulled him back. "This is not our way. Please, please, what if we had customers here? What would they think?"

Sanjay looked at Kumar first, who had a thinner version of Bhaskar's red face, but with a fuller head of hair and a proud black moustache. Then, he turned back to Bhaskar, who was still fuming.

"Tell your fatso son to stay away from my daughter," Bhaskar said.

"Tell your daughter to stay away from my fatso," Sanjay replied.

Bhaskar turned around and left, and his family followed him. Only Devina looked back, and only Momo saw her look, and all the rest of the occupants of Verona Point went back into their respective homes. Sanjay closed up and walked home upstairs, and Momo followed him. The lights went off in each shop at the downstairs verandah first, and soon enough, in the upstairs homes, too, and for the rest of the night, the dark Himalayan jungles forced their world into a peaceful silence.

Ravi Kaka, the cassette-*wallah*, was the middle shop at Verona Point, equidistant between Sanjay and Bhaskar. The two corner cafés had a silent arrangement to alternate making chai for the old man every day: Sanjay's chai came with breakfast and Bhaskar's was served after dinner.

Ravi Kaka sat wordlessly behind his counter, barely seeing through his thick square-rimmed spectacles, smiling with his few remaining teeth when Sanjay handed him a cup a few mornings later.

"I have something for you," the old man said in a croaky whisper. He reached under his counter and pulled out an audiocassette, a blank gray tape under a blank square glass cover.

"What is this, Ravi Kaka?"

"Your son," he said. "He got this recorded two days ago. Give it to him, will you?"

"My son?" Sanjay flipped the glass case back and forth. It felt archaic between his fingers, like an artifact from another age.

"Yes, yes," Ravi Kaka said. "Vinod. He ordered it."

Sanjay continued to flip the cassette in its case over and around. This was a mystery, he thought. He felt confused and curious. Momo got a cassette recorded?

"Watch the shop, Chhotu," Sanjay shouted before stomping up the stairs. It was a weekday and Verona Point wouldn't get crowded until lunchtime. Momo had left for his coaching class, and Sanjay was soon alone in the silence of his room. He crouched down on all fours to look underneath his bed. There it was: his steel rectangular storage trunk, silver all over under a layer of dust. He grabbed a handle on the short side of the trunk and pulled it out, making a terrifying sound as the metal screeched against the wooden floor. Still down on his knees, Sanjay pulled the bolt up and opened the lid. A smell of moth balls and old damp clothes wafted up to him. He dug into the trunk to fish out a number of items of women's clothing: *lehengas*, saris he had refused to sell or donate to his neighbors, *chunnis*, even old shoes, too, including his wife's favorite pair of black sandals—never worn—with pink ribbon tied to their toe-loops. "I'm saving them for a special occasion," she used to say, but that day never came. He pulled out an old, empty picture frame with the glass cracked, old pairs of socks he should have thrown away, and phone chargers for phones that didn't exist anymore.

And uncovering it all, there, he found it. His wife's Sanyo cassette player. It was a relic of another time, like Ravi Kaka and his shop. The small black box had a cassette deck, with large, clunky buttons, and an empty spot where the radio antenna had once been. A dusty wire twirled up around it like a whimpering tail.

Sanjay wiped the dust off the square buttons on top, pressed "stop" hard to eject the deck and blew into the dust inside. When he was ready, he plugged the old machine into a socket behind his bed and a small red light brought it to life. Sanjay softly moaned to himself as he popped in Momo's tape. He pressed "play."

After a brief second of static, a sudden explosion of happy synthesizer music played out of the crinkling speakers. Sanjay faintly recognized the tune, and then the lyrics kicked in. "*Angrezi mein kehte hain ki* I love you/ *Gujarati ma bole tanne prem karoon chhu.*"

He smiled. The music immediately conjured a flashback to his own youth, of seeing Amitabh Bachchan dancing around in that red jacket and white trousers, of a film he had seen when he would have been only six or seven years old.

He stopped the tape and pressed fast forward for a few seconds, and then a few more, till the song changed. Asha Bhosle's voice started singing over a persistent alarm beat: "*Dil ki maya puchiye to jara mujhko kya chahiye.*" It was another romantic song from his youth, maybe around the time he was Momo's age. He was laughing out loud to himself now, not caring who might hear him below.

The next song was a *ghazal* of love and longing and pain. Sanjay got up and walked to the bathroom, now singing along in nostalgia, "*Marke bhi hum na tumse juda ho...*" and only when he saw his reflection did he understand, and it dawned on him why Momo had gone to Ravi Kaka.

He stopped singing.

Sanjay rushed back to the Sanyo and brought the music to an abrupt halt. Enough, he thought to himself. That is enough. He changed his usual tracksuit bottoms for a thick pair of trousers and exchanged his sandals for his walking boots. He ignored the trunk sitting dormant in the middle of his bedroom and rushed back down.

"Momo!" he shouted when he got to the café downstairs. He brandished the tape—now naked without its cover—in his hand. "Momo, what is this? Momo—where is that *motu*?"

"He's at his coaching class, Sanjay ji," Chhotu said.

"Coaching my ass! I know where he is. He's taken my scooter again and gone out with Bhaskar's daughter. I'll find him."

"Hello Sanjay Uncle—who are you looking for?"

It was Devina.

She was there by herself, smiling, wearing a light-blue T-shirt and denim jeans. Her deep black hair was untied, cascading halfway down her back.

"M-Momo," Sanjay said, and he could feel his voice losing a bit of its earlier fizzle. "Have you... Have you seen him?"

"Oh, I'm looking for Vinod, too. He's not home?"

"He... He's probably at his class."

"Oh, yes, of course," Devina slapped her forehead in an animated gesture. "He told me he goes to the Sardarji for physics on Tuesdays."

Her voice was sunny and happy, as if the drama of last week had had no effect on her. Sanjay looked beyond her towards the Best Stop Tea Shop. There were a couple of tables occupied by some tourists already. The *chhotus* were at work, but neither Bhaskar nor his wife were there.

"Chhotu, you get out," Sanjay looked into his kitchen and commanded. "Go, play somewhere. Do something else. Come back later."

Chhotu nodded and scurried out to the patio, towards the railing that overlooked the valley.

They were alone. Sanjay turned back to Devina. "Where is your thief father, then?

"Uncle," her voice fell a little. "It's not like that. Papa never—"

"Your papa *did*! He stole my dishes. He stole my customers. He sits there with his wife and his family getting fat and healthy while I'm here..."

"Uncle, it's not like that. I don't understand why the two of you—"

"And he is stealing Sanjay Style. *Sanjay Style*, too?" Sanjay's breath got heavier as he spoke.

"Uncle—Papa talks about you so much. He said the two of you used to be best friends when you were little. This is all so silly, isn't it? Our families are so alike. We should stop all this and—"

"Our families are *not* alike," Sanjay interrupted her. "He is stealing everything. What will be left of my café when he steals *everything*? My noodles, my customers... My son, too?"

Devina didn't reply. Her face had long lost its bubbly smile, but she was still calm, composed. Suddenly, Sanjay felt her seeing him, seeing a crazy man, rambling away at an innocent young girl. He allowed himself a few deep breaths until his voice became stable again.

"Go back home, Devina," he said. His shoulders slumped down, tense no longer. "Take this," he said, passing the cassette over to her. "This is Momo's. I think..." His voice dropped. "I think he got it recorded for you."

"For me?"

"Yes, yes, take it."

"Wow, thank you, Uncle," she said.

Sanjay stepped back into the kitchen, but Devina remained in her spot, motionless, holding the cassette in her hand.

"What do you want now?" Sanjay asked from behind his glass window.

"Uncle, there must have been a misunderstanding about the Sanjay Style. Papa would never copy anything without your permission."

"My *permission*?" Sanjay laughed. "That bas—that papa of yours *should* have asked me. His Maggi tastes like trash."

Now, Devina smiled again. "Trash? No. Uncle, Papa is a wonderful cook, and—"

"Your papa and I were very close friends, yes. Did he ever tell you that?

Best friends in school. We used to play with marbles here all day and throw rocks at the monkeys. One time, one of the monkeys bit him. I took him to the doctor down in the market. We were very young. Did he ever tell you?"

In the kitchen, Sanjay pretended to busy himself, setting up a pot of water to boil, even though there was nobody at the shop to feed.

"Uncle, you can be friends again."

"*He* should come to me. I can teach him some things, you know. Everyone here knows I'm a better cook. I can teach him." Sanjay hesitated and looked up at Devina. "I can teach you my Maggi style, too. Proper egg fried Maggi." he added.

Devina laughed. "Uncle, it's the easiest thing to cook in the world."

"No, no, come in, come in. I watch Bhaskar from here. He does it all wrong. You have to wait till it's just right before adding the masala, you know? Till it's just right. Not when it's too soupy or when it's too dry. Go, go in." Sanjay beckoned Devina into the kitchen, moving back to give her room. "You show me. Make it the way you know. Then I'll help you."

Walled around three ends like a gulf, the kitchen was cramped. Devina hopped in ahead of Sanjay and stepped up to the stove. Sanjay came back in a few feet behind her.

Devina looked around till she spotted the shelf with a dozen packets of Maggi stacked above her on the right. She lifted her hand. Her shirt rose up with her, and for a quick half second, Sanjay saw the naked skin on her waist, between her shirt and her tight, dark-blue jeans.

Then the shirt came back down. She was only a few inches shorter than him. Momo, Sanjay had seen, always had to go on his tiptoes to reach that higher shelf. Sanjay handed her a frying pan from behind and Devina lit another burner next to the boiling water.

"Where are the eggs, Uncle?"

"I have seen your father work, Devina," Sanjay said. "He is always distracted. Always doing too many things at the same time. No, no, he should learn to focus. Slow down. Do everything properly, you understand?"

Sanjay reached out to the shelf behind him and pulled out an egg from a carton of twelve—the cleanest, whitest one he could find—and handed it to her. Her cold, smooth fingers touched his.

He moved back a step and watched from behind as she cracked the egg on the side of the pot and released the yolk into the frying pan. It began to sizzle. He watched her thick hair run down her shoulders and her back, spreading out in curls near the tips. He looked at the bit of fair skin visible on both sides of her neck, between her hair and the parts of her T-shirt that covered her shoulders. His eyes followed down her T-shirt to where he had seen that bit of flesh, where her clothing stuck close to her slightly chubby waist. He liked that she wasn't too thin, he thought to himself. Too many young girls these days barely ate anything.

His wife had always wanted a daughter. Momo was supposed to have a sister. That bastard Bhaskar. Sanjay hated his fat face, and the way he fixed his spectacles when he noted down orders as if he was an educated man, and the way he smiled at tourists as if he was genuinely happy. And now his daughter was here. And Momo was in love with her. Sanjay knew it. He knew it for sure. Momo loved her, and maybe she loved him back. Well, that would destroy Bhaskar, wouldn't it? That bastard would never recover. Imagine— Sanjay thought—my son and his daughter. He smiled.

"Look, Uncle," Devina said. "So easy. Even a child could do it."

That bastard would never recover, Sanjay thought again. If something were to happen to her, he would never recover.

Sanjay moved back closer behind Devina to take a look. The noodles sat in a perfect cobweb of pale yellow, intertwined strings, with a fried egg—white and yellow—sitting neatly on top. He could hardly have made it better looking himself. Even Momo hadn't learned to do it after all these years.

"Just add some red chili now," Sanjay said. "That will complete it. Just a little bit of red chili."

"Not everyone likes the noodles to be spicy, Uncle."

"Those idiots don't know what they want."

Devina laughed out loud. Sanjay moved up even closer behind her until he could smell the lemony scent of her shampoo. He reached to the shelves to the small plate of chilies. He leaned in, till his chest rustled against her back, till his breaths were close enough to ruffle the hair on the back of her neck.

Devina flinched.

"Oh!" she said and turned around, wearing a look of surprise in her large, round eyes. Sanjay moved back a step.

"Papa?"

Momo. Momo was out on the verandah, looking in at them.

Sanjay froze in his spot.

Momo was there: shirt messily untucked, bookbag hanging off of one of his shoulders, mouth open wide, eyes glaring. He dropped his bag on an unoccupied table on the verandah and stomped away, back towards the parking spot.

"Vinod!" Devina called out. She moved backwards, brushed past the space between Sanjay and the kitchen counter, and ran behind Momo. "Vinod, wait!"

Sanjay looked down at the food she had prepared and then back up again, out to his right past the Best Stop Tea Shop and the parking space where Momo jumped back on the scooter.

It will be fine, he thought. It will all be fine. With a chopping knife, he cut a piece of red chili into smaller bits and sprinkled it over the noodles. It was ready.

It was the last day of the summer break and Sanjay was ensuring that Momo stayed busy, that he helped out as much as he could before he would have to restart school. A half-dozen of those boarding school kids sat at Sanjay's Café; each requested a bowl of Sanjay Style. They made a racket, blasting English music from a mobile phone and talking loudly around their plastic table. It had been a busy weekend, so busy that Sanjay realized he had run out of those cheese slices that the kids liked on their noodles.

"Momo," Sanjay said. "Get started. I have to get something from next door."

Momo nodded and replaced Sanjay inside the kitchen. Sanjay stepped out onto the verandah. The kids' music annoyed him, but he thought to himself that, perhaps, he could do the same, that he could play his own music at the café. He could go back to Ravi Kaka and ask him to record another cassette just like the one Momo had gotten made. He could play all of those old songs *he* liked.

At Himal's, Sanjay asked for a packet of Amul cheese. While he waited outside, he couldn't help but glance towards the far end of the verandah. The Best Stop was busy as usual. All three tables were packed, and twice as many groups loitered outside the café, waiting for their turn to sit. Devina was cooking at the stovetop while Bhaskar stood around the tables talking to an old couple. It was her last day in Dharamshala before she was to return to Solan. Nothing would be different after that, Sanjay thought. Nothing was ever different.

Momo was almost done with the noodles. Behind him, he reached for an egg and knocked it against the frying pan, but the shell didn't crack. He tried again, and this time, the shell broke hard into his palm, sending the yolk flying onto the stovetop.

Sanjay came up behind him into the kitchen. "You fatso," he smacked Momo behind his head. "Can't even do the easiest things. Move, move."

"No, Papa let me—"

"Move," Sanjay pulled his son out of the way. "I'll do it myself."

Ryan Masters
EVERYONE NEGOTIATES

I was riding an antiquated transport into the anus of the universe, a god-forbidden hole called the Carcine Archipelago. My only company was a half platoon of Millennian soldiers who drank and fought and gambled as the bus creaked, groaned, and hissed, month after month, across the Great Plains.

Why waste six months traveling to a cyst like the Archipelago? Money. More than I'd ever seen in my life if my employer could be believed. Lady Silkwood Frank, heir to the SpecMod fortune and the richest woman in the galaxy, had hired me back in the Aldeveans to negotiate for the life of her son.

"These new friends of Lenny's, they aren't good for him," Lady Frank said. "I'm afraid he's being taken advantage of."

"New friends?"

Lady Frank's personal assistant, a stiletto heel of a man named Sonny Vitro, handed me a dossier. "A clique of arty extradimensionals calling themselves El Cid. Wildly pretentious."

"Equally dull," sighed Lady Frank.

"El Cid traffics in exotic pharmaceuticals, SpecMod's specialty. That can't be a coincidence."

"We have reason to believe Lenny may be experimenting with a highly classified substance," Vitro said.

"Or being experimented on," Lady Frank interjected.

"A substance that, as you so astutely surmised, is the sole intellectual property of SpecMod Incorporated."

"So what's your priority here, the property or Lenny?"

"Lenny hasn't worked a day in his goddamn life," Lady Frank said. "He's a middle-aged child. These people have taken advantage of his frailties."

"Given that it's highly illegal for humans to ingest extradimensional narcotics, someone would have had to alter SpecMod product to accomplish it. Who has access to your proprietary code?"

"Not even God can bypass SpecMod encryptions," Vitro said. "I know. I oversee the security. El Cid used Lenny to steal his mother's IP. Now his usefulness has run out. Instant hostage."

"What exactly did this transmission from the Carcine Archipelago say?"

"Might as well show him everything," Lady Frank said. "He needs to know what he's getting into."

Vitro unscrolled a screen that flickered alive. A paunchy man with a web of broken blood vessels on his face sat naked on a ratty brown sofa. A large, two-headed black slug hung around his neck like a glistening boa. The slug's twin mouths suckled Lenny's nipples like horrible infants, obviously stimulating him. Drool oozed from his mouth.

"Mommy? You need to pay these people," Lenny murmured. "You need to give them whatever they want. You pay them. They are wizards from another dimension, Mommy. Ha ha ha ha. Anything they want" He nodded off mid-sentence and enjoyed a minor seizure. El Cid's videocameraman lingered on one of the slug's mouths. It slurped the nipple luxuriously.

"Your son into this kind of stuff?" I asked.

"He most certainly is not. This is coercion. Sadism. Terrorism."

"Yes," said Vitro. "Yes, he is into this kind of stuff."

"Their demand?"

"Seventy-four pounds of uncut Tessier 14."

El Cid was not fucking around. Tessier 14 was one of the rarest minerals known to civilized space. Seventy-four pounds was enough to buy a solar system.

"What makes you think I'm the guy they'll listen to?"

"You're the only negotiator in the Aldeveans willing to travel to the Archipelago," Vitro said. "We've checked."

They knew I'd do it, of course. If I didn't, they'd simply turn me over to my creditors.

"Congratulations. You got yourself a negotiator."

Spend six months on a transport with a bunch of soldiers and you start acting like a soldier. I'd been doing my fair share of drinking and gambling. Unfortunately, my lousy luck followed me on board this rustbucket and I owed a couple soldiers some money. Not much in the my grander scheme of debt, but grunts made a big deal about small debts. As a precaution, I took to sleeping in the reactor room. It was always a good place to lay low. The danger of radiation poisoning was highly exaggerated, but most soldiers didn't know that. When the ship docked today I was hoping to slip unnoticed off the transport and into the busy city. Again, rotten luck. I was packing my haversack when they found me.

"Looky here. We found the ship's rat," Blaylock said as he stepped into the reactor room. His big dumb companion, Middlebrook was his name, I think, blocked the door as Blaylock stood over me. "Been looking for you for weeks, rat." Blaylock's teeth and mouth were bright red from chewing binglang. "Should've known you'd be hiding all the way down here."

"It's nice and warm." As I turned to face the intruders, I drew my blaster from the haversack and liquefied Blaylock's torso. His head slumped into what remained of his thorax, the face creased with incomprehension.

"Hold on now," Middlebrook said, his big meaty hands raised between the muzzle of my blaster and his face. "It's only five hundred credits. It's only five hundred credits!"

"Sorry, buddy. In for a penny, in for a pound."

I let him have it, and the lummox joined Blaylock on the reactor room floor. As their quasi-liquefied bodies leaked down a grate at the center of the room, I fished through their pockets for cash and valuables, found nothing, and made my unobtrusive way to the disembarkment zone upstairs.

I walked through the concourse, down the port's double staircase, and into Carcina, the Archipelago's rat-trap capital city. Ash shrouded the distant, gray sun, bathing the city in a pallor of death. An alarm sounded, screeching from the port's public address system. Inevitable, considering the mess I'd left. I pulled the brim of my hat down over my face and blended into the dense mass of organisms inhabiting the main square. Vendors sat and stood before tables and blankets filled with scrap parts, collectibles. As I approached the square's energy well, I found Barlaagan priests harassing the poor, who were forced by circumstance to queue at the well to charge their various machines. I tried to skirt the whole scene, but a younger priest spotted me, peeled off from a less desirable target, and fell in step beside me. "You appear to have a noisy soul, brother."

"Not me, friend," I assured him. "Easy like Sunday morning."

"The soul's eye cannot be painted shut like a blind harlot with false and prideful words."

"If you say so."

"Beware, traveler." The priest paused but continued to clock my progress as I slipped down a crackling and steaming alley of fried food stalls. "Lies are an affront to Barlaag. Heresy is no small crime here in the Carcine," he cried as I left him behind.

"Welcome to Hotel Echelon, sir. Reservation is under...?" asked the concierge.

"Sunshine Vasquez, NCCRA."

"We don't see many negotiators in Carcina these days. It's a shame. They can be handy in a pinch. How long will you be staying with us, Mr. Vasquez?"

"Indefinitely."

"Very good."

In the lobby bar, spindly insectoid entities with pincers for hands pushed pieces around game boards. Guests and hotel employees flowed through the grand interior. Echelon's architecture was based on a Carcine cross. Each of the six arms divided into three wings and sported its own dome with one large dome above the crossing. The marble floor of the lobby spun with tessellations in geometric patterns and alien designs. Bright mosaics containing a wide variety of colorful minerals covered the upper order of the lobby. I turned back to the concierge. "You know where a guy might find a little XtraD?"

Eight limbs paused midstroke. Thick hairs bristled erect in a wave of keratin switchblades from tarsus bone to spider paw. The concierge's eyes glistened wetly as he smiled, revealing a pair of long fangs iridescent as scarabs. "Room 1465." I took the key and tipped him a hundred credits. The money disappeared trapdoor-fast into his vest pocket.

"There's a phantom box beyond the wall to the west. Ask there." He leaned across the desk to me and lowered his voice. "Listen here, stranger. El Cid does not negotiate. Never. Ever. Ever."

"Everyone negotiates," I said with a wink.

Carcina was a city of canals. Neither aesthetic nor functional, the canals oozed with a sentient, mucus-like slime: the Vandersloot. An ancient species of indigenous alien, the Vandersloot was poorly understood. When the earliest settlers arrived to the region in search of rare minerals, they found the Zeboym, an indigenous race of rubbery black katydids living among the canals. The Zeboym were rumored to communicate telepathically with the Vandersloot. Over the ensuing two thousand years, Carcina grew around the Vandersloot. Now city and creature were inextricably linked. In hindsight, a regrettable decision. Fall into the Vandersloot and be consumed slowly in its gelatinous mass for all to see. A humiliating, torturous, and highly public fate. The digestion process lasted roughly seven hours. The victim remained conscious for four of them.

After six months on the transport, I needed some action. The phantom box could wait a few hours. El Cid was aware I'd reached the Archipelago. No rush. Besides, there was the red-light district of the Cloud Palace to investigate. The Cloud Palace purveyed depravities so grotesque they had cracked open the minds of strong, decent men like rotten eggs.

As I walked west from the Echelon, the architecture of the city devolved from high alien Mughal to a chic-but-seedy artists' district, then I passed into a densely populated world of degraded concrete and jagged, exposed rebar. I spotted stores, homes, offices, and other societal outposts, but many of the people on the street appeared drunk or tweaking on speed. Derelicts reeled and ambled about or lay passed out where they fell. I followed the canals until I eventually mingled with the sleazebags funneling toward the Cloud Palace. Before I passed through the district's ominous black gates, something caught my eye and I paused at the sight of a leathery four-legged creature, likely someone's pet, in the Vandersloot. From the pearlescent slime, a pair of horrified and pleading eyes looked at me. I didn't look away, didn't move on.

"You have an appreciation for suffering, Negotiator."

Zeboym, this being suddenly beside me. Female, too. The Zeboym were in some ways morphologically analogous to humans. The Zeboym was gloss black, mostly katydid in face and form, yet blessed with tentacle arms that shone like obsidian. Sensual antennae as long as riding crops undulated from her forehead, waving luridly in the air between us as she moved or spoke.

"You'd think the city would build a railing around this thing," I said. "Real safety hazard."

"Carcina loves the Vandersloot. It's the oldest life form in the Archipelago, and a reliable municipal waste disposal system. It cleans our streets of garbage like a cleansing storm. It is God-like."

"Form and function," I said, studying the pet trapped in the Vandersloot. "Very elegant."

"Carcina herself is much like the Vandersloot. Tumble headlong into her pleasures and risk quivering forever in her dirty hold. This city *uses*. She injects men such as you like drugs, then sucks the cum out of them in one long pull through her proboscis."

"Now we're talking."

"The doomed, the ones that will never regain their souls, spend the rest of existence wandering the Carcine Archipelago like rotted-out husks. Things like that."

A sallow creature with an onion-shaped head passed by. It appeared to be carrying its genitalia in a shopping bag.

"Avert your eyes, bitch, or I'll eat them," Onionhead hissed.

"Come, walk with me, Negotiator. What a coincidence we should find ourselves here at the edge of the Cloud Palace, no?"

"Some kind of shakedown, eh?"

"Nothing so dull as graft, I assure you. It's simply my business to notice men like you and...help them."

"Men like me?"

"Men with the vigor necessary to experience XtraD."

"I have no idea what you're talking about."

"Your mind ejaculates like an anus weeping maple syrup at the very thought of it." She pulled a hand mirror from inside her breastplate. "Breathe upon this." I did as instructed. When the mirror cleared, another man's eyes peered back at me from within it. *Do not enter the fold inside the fold*, the eyes said. *Nor the fold inside the fold inside the fold.* My consciousness hiccupped. For a moment I thought I would vomit. I regrouped.

"No tango, sister. My dealings with XtraD are business related, not personal."

"Of course, Mr. Vasquez." She unfurled a gelatinous tentacle and wrapped it around my shoulder "Please, come with me. You must not leave Carcina without seeing the Cloud Palace. It would be an affront to Barlaag himself." I allowed her to push me gently toward the palace gates. Her appendage was warm, black, and bulbous, hefty and pendulous as a sow's breast.

Beyond the gates, the Cloud Palace rose to meet us in variegated stacks of scaffolding. Complex and baffling warrens of sin clambered crazily into the ashen sky. Each floor showcased every manner of carnal delight. Hundreds of simultaneous exhibitions. Thousands of raging, screaming, moaning fornicators. Every morphology and evolutionary peccadillo imaginable. For a moment, my mind traveled through these many beasts, their own minds bent to the task of coitus, and I nearly erupted.

"Steady there," said the Zeboym. "Magnificent, is it not?"

"Where are the walls?"

"Walls are banned in the Cloud Palace."

"Wild."

"Purely functional. It guarantees the Brotherhood receives its cut of every throat and dick in the alley," she indicated a pair of heavily armored Barlaagan priests lounging against a post. Streetlights popped and hummed, casting the scene in a jittery blue light. "Come." My guide strode on her powerful hind legs. They looked better suited for leaping than walking. Her femur muscles flexed impressively with each step. The hinge connecting femur to tibia pumped behind her head with each stride.

"You are aroused by pain."

"Not my own."

"True. You are a connoisseur of others' depravity and agony. Of their ultimate humiliation."

"Warmer, lady. Definitely warmer."

"I will bring you to the Carp."

The Carp worked the roof of a building near the dead end of the Cloud Palace's main drag. It was a long walk down this gauntlet of shuddering climax, slurping ritual, and open-faced horror. The din alone would drive a decent man mad. Displays so savage they no longer resembled sexual congress. As I climbed, the unholy cacophony enveloped me, strangled my senses. The Cloud Palace was all one great, horrific orgy. The most ungodly was saved for last.

At center stage lolled the Carp. Once a whole man, all that remained of him was a jug-bald head atop a sack of swollen meat. The Carp's arms and legs had been surgically removed at the hip and shoulder. Perfect, scarless nubs characterized his obliterated joints. The rest of his body was shaved hairless. I felt and suppressed a compulsion to mount and ride him like a bouncy horse. A tight brass collar around his fat neck connected him to the wall via a chain. Also, he was not alone on stage. A tall, funereal figure swayed seductively beside him. This figure stripped off its black frills and fishnets, and revealed herself as a luminous, white tapeworm. Naked, she fell to the floor and slithered toward the Carp, who moaned in horror. Rearing up, the tapeworm pierced his anus, driving toward his prostate and intestines.

"Enough!" my guide shouted. The tapeworm withdrew violently from the Carp's body, picked up her costume, and stepped offstage for a cigarette. The room began to clear. My guide pointed at the Carp, who was now slumped over in exhaustion, and said, "I could sell you an hour alone with it. Or I could sell it to you."

"All of it?"

The Carp cleared his ragged throat and spit, breathing shallowly. His flaccid penis poked from beneath the belly fat, crushed like a tiny witch beneath a house.

"For certain clientele, we provide a premiere luxury service. Le Liège. The Carp here has recently been placed on the menu. It is an extraordinary, once-in-a-lifetime opportunity, as you no doubt recognize. Of course, the price reflects this. You would like to hear more? Perhaps a closer look?"

"No need. I want it."

"But you have not heard the price."

I didn't care. I lusted to Le Liège the Carp. "I want it *now*."

"So be it," the guide smiled.

Rough hands restrained me. A hood was thrust over my head, blinding me, right before I was struck conscious and awoke.

A door opened and the Carp part-hopped, part-slid through it, surprisingly graceful. Dignified. With every lurch, the Carp crushed his genitalia against the floor.

"That's a hell of a trick," I said.

The Carp gained a large floor pillow and leaned back with a sigh. "What do you know about the expansion of your universe, Negotiator?"

"That would be nothing, pal."

"Your universe is riding an expanding bubble of dark energy that sits within a fourth dimension—"

"I don't know anything about that."

"—the 'extra' dimension."

"Strictly business."

"All matter in the universe exists in strings that reach into another dimension, and dark energy strengthens as it grows. Thus, the expansion is accelerating." The Carp casually rolled over on his side, the aperture of his anus blinked open, and the tapeworm emerged.

"Hey there, hot stuff," the tapeworm said, but it was too late, I was falling out once more.

I came to in a subterranean cavern. Bioluminescent lichen carpeted the stone walls and ceiling, washing the surrounding priests in a murky blue light. As a radical political cult, the Barlaagan Priesthood had been operating on the edges of the universe and sanity since the middle of the last century. Until they kidnapped me, I'd generally disregarded their worldview and mission as absurd and dull. A regrettable oversight. I now stood bound and helpless before the local Barlaagan headman, a human loon by the name of Christ Alhaywire.

"Murderer!" Alhaywire roared. His voice echoed through the cavern, an impressive basso profundo.

"I didn't do a goddamn thing," I sneered.

"Your intention was to defile and kill the Carp, Negotiator, and if a deed has been *considered* in this string, it has surely been accomplished in another. The facts have been established and stand submitted as evidence."

"Ridiculous. Even if I did think it, how would you know?"

"Thoughts are not just thoughts on XtraD."

"For the last time, I am not *on* anything. I am at work here. This is a business enterprise. Commerce, plain and straight."

"Here is our offer."

"OK, good. Now we're getting somewhere."

"Repent and the butcher will remove your troublesome arms and legs. You can help us reset our Carp, just as our Carp did for you."

"Go fuck yourself."

"Open the Gloryhole," Alhaywire replied in a bored tone.

A team of child slaves, naked except for sharp, thorny crowns, swarmed in from a series of small tunnels. Each slave grabbed a ring at the edge of an enormous iron disk, heaving and dragging it from its resting place on the floor. Within, the Gloryhole writhed—a dense carpet of blind, pink tentacles swaying across its collective surface. A sea of tiny mouths gaped at each appendage tip. The Gloryhole was hungry.

"Do you see, Negotiator? They sense it is time to feed," said Alhaywire.

The slave children moved with caution near the Gloryhole, but one slave had suffered a crushed foot while removing the iron lid from the pit. He struggled to flee to a safe distance. The tentacles, sensing the child's vulnerability, leapt from the pit, stretching to the width of a human finger. The tentacles found the slave and snatched him, dragging him headfirst into its many-mawed face. His life ended with a horrifying screech as a buzzsaw of teeth shredded him into little pieces. I vomited. Chunks of curd and meat splattered the edge of the pit. Lightning fast, a brace of tentacles whipped forth and consumed my vomit. The mouths made a horrifying noise, a slurping hum as they ate. I lurched back from the pit, crying, "No, no, no, no, no—"

"Nerve, Negotiator. Gaze upon your hard fate," said Alhaywire. My knees wobbled and a dark blossom of warm urine bloomed at my crotch. The high priest grasped my shoulders. Firm, but not without a certain paternal kindness.

"I want to repent. I repent," I croaked.

He whispered into my ear now. "Oh, the time to repent has long passed." The tentacles inched toward my cold toes, each tip with its own exploratory tongue, its own circular blade of teeth. "Now there is only the Gloryhole."

"I can bring you El Cid," I screamed.

"You can or you will?" Alhaywire roared.

"I WILL!"

"And the serum! What of the serum?"

"Yes! A thousand times yes. I swear to you," I blubbered.

"Swear it to the many mouths of the Barlaag!"

"I SWEAR!"

Alhaywire embraced me and I wept in his arms. Sobs wracked my body. He patted my head softly, affectionately. "There, there, Negotiator. After all this time, you are finally on the path to righteousness."

After I fucked the Carp, it rolled over and plucked a cigarette from the bedside table with its lips.

"You coming down yet?" the Carp asked.

"I'm sober as a priest."

"The hell you fucking are," the Carp laughed.

"Those drugs have scrambled your brain, buddy," I said, standing up to go.

"Quite the opposite," the Carp said. "It's your brain that should concern you."

I was halfway to the door when my brain folded. An infinite, perfect enfolding, each pinprick a universe, each sound a radio wave breaking through a black hole. When I recovered, I was looking up at myself. I was smiling down on me. I was placing a hand on my head. I was saying, "You should have been more careful. You took way too much your first time."

I followed the western branch of the Vandersloot from the city limits into a chalky white desert. Huge flocks of pollinator bats leapt from one salt crystal tree to another. Here in the wild, eels swam with the Vandersloot. Some kind of symbiotic relationship. I captured a bat using my shirt as a net and tried to lure an eel to the surface with it, but the Vandersloot merely gobbled my bait, burning my fingertips badly with a noxious chemical.

Small kiosks run by families of Zeboym lined the road to the phantom box. The Zeboym sold cheap manufactured goods and salted snacks. The daughter of a grilled-eel salesman caught my eye and for the briefest of moments, I imagined stopping here, taking this girl as my bride and living forever outside Carcina on the banks of the Vandersloot. But the father shooed me away. Instead, I continued toward my uncertain destiny.

Built atop a bridge, the phantom box served as both extradimensional communication booth and toll gate to the far side of the Vandersloot. The only other way to cross was to buy a pole and vault the canal, yet this mode of transportation required more upper-body strength and steadier nerves than I currently possessed. In short, I was a wreck. I hated to admit it, but this job was beginning to look like it might be too much for me.

The wall of the phantom box shimmered as I stepped through. Inside, a structure of flat, polished surfaces rotated in constantly shifting directions. Disoriented, I reached out, seeking something to support me. I fell into someone or something and an unseen hand steadied me.

"Keep your eyes closed until you put these on, son."

Someone strapped a pair of goggles to my head. I adjusted them over my eyes and the endless prisming clarified. Now I stood within a magnificent Ottoman chamber. Sofas, carpets, and pillows littered the marble floor beneath an expansive gilt dome. Flames danced in a plume-shaped bronze fireplace. Water gurgled from a series of intricate and interconnected marble fountains. Iznik tiles covered the walls. Amidst it all stood Sonny Vitro, impeccably dressed in Turkish leathers.

"Playtime's over, Lenny," Vitro said. "I expect your mother any minute. You will need to speak with her, give her assurances." He appeared to be speaking to me. I considered the possibility that the phantom box's wires were shorted or on the wrong channel. "Well?"

I looked over my shoulder to make sure no one was standing behind me before speaking. "Lenny isn't here. It's me. Sunshine Vasquez. The negotiator hired by Lady Frank."

Vitro rolled his eyes. "Please, Lenny."

Before I could reply, Lady Frank entered the phantom box. She wore şalvar pants, thigh-high boots, and held a riding crop. Without hesitation, she crossed the room and beat me with the crop again and again, grunting from the effort. Welts bloomed on my face, neck, and shoulders. When I tried to grab the crop, she broke my left pinkie finger. Cowed, I retreated behind the fountains of water. "Why are you doing this?"

"You insolent brat! You sold me out. Your own mother! We're ruined!" She attempted to strike me again with her riding crop, but I ducked behind the fountain, and the crop's tip found only stone.

"My name is Sunshine Vasquez. You hired me in the Aldeveans six months ago to find your son and negotiate his release."

Lady Frank looked to Vitro for an answer. Her assistant merely shrugged.

"This is uncharted territory," Vitro explained to her. "The serum had limited clinical testing and no human trials before he broke into the SpecMod labs and stole it. It's impossible to tell how much he took and how much he sold."

"So what does that mean?"

"It means he may very well play this particular string out to its conclusion. Leonard Frank, for all intents and purposes, disappeared from this dimension when he ingested the SpecMod serum."

"For fuck's sake," Lady Frank said, tossing the riding crop into the fireplace. "Let's go."

With relief, I watched her and her assistant depart.

"Does this mean I'm not getting paid?" I ventured.

Vitro paused at the door. "You have bankrupted SpecMod Industries and put the known multiverse in jeopardy. No, you're not getting paid. Later, *Sunshine*." He disappeared from the room with a shimmer.

I found a bar cart in the corner of the room, made myself a drink to steady my nerves, drank it, and made another. I studied my face in a wall mirror. Multiple bruises colored my face. A goose egg was forming above my right temple.

"I sensed you had an appreciation for suffering, Negotiator, but, bravo, you have mustered a tour de force." The Zeboym slapped bulbous tentacles together in mock applause.

"El Cid, I presume."

"If you wish," she said.

"I've come for the serum."

"You have the serum. You are the serum. Or more accurately, you have spilled the serum across an enormous landscape of possible universes and, in short, doomed hundreds of years of work. Now string theory might never be unified."

"If that's the case, it sounds like my work is done here. Of course, there is still the small matter of payment."

Propelled by powerful hind legs, she crossed the room at an alarming clip. With her final step, she attained full extension and leapt at me, tentacles reaching, antennae aquiver. I turned back to the bar and pounded the last of my drink.

It's true that if you lose your arms and legs, spirit versions of them remain. You can almost feel them. After El Cid had finished with me, they threw me into the Vandersloot. I tried to swim. Of course I could not. Instead, I remained still, suspended in carnivorous gelatin, arms and legs severed, immaculately shaven, all my holes and sutures plugged with camphor and lit on fire. It was the most humiliating high of my life, and I fucking loved it. As I slowly died, I caught the eye of a young man, a negotiator by the looks of him. He gazed down at me, an expression of horror and lust on his face. Yes, he understood. He understood. In the end, everyone negotiates.

Hannah Moloney
THE WATER

asically, no one lives here. Even the people who come here don't stay long. Why would they stay here? Most of the time it rains—not lately though. Most of the time there're bugs; spiders like you've never seen and cicadas so loud in the summers you can't sleep. But we do; we live here. Ever since I was born. Even before Mama was born.

Mama rings the bell. My head turns instinctively in the direction of the sound. I unstick my feet from the splintering wooden dock over the marsh and run.

"Sasha, let's go." I scoop my baby sister up from the dirt. She is still clutching some long grass in her tiny fist. She's too big for me to carry now, so I hold her chubby wrist in my hand and walk quickly, hunched so I can reach her. We scurry up the hill to the house, which is squat like a mushroom but dried up like it's long since been picked. The porch across the front is its wide smile, with bad, rotting teeth.

"It's getting dark out; you know I'll be needing your help." Mama stands on the front porch, hands on her hips, a wrung-out kitchen towel in one hand. Her hair is long and clay brown, with strands of gray that zigzag off of her head and promise to take over someday. Her eyes are the color of dark beach water. My brother has his skinny arm around her leg and his thumb in his mouth. "Change out of that smelly bathing suit, will you?"

The house smells like earth and burning wood. Some kind of air machine beeps and clicks in Daddy's room. I can hear him cough from the kitchen. Sometimes it sounds like he's drowning.

"You stay right here, little girl." I leave my sister and she sits back in an invisible chair and tumbles to the floor. She doesn't cry. Across the house is my room. Our room. Small piles of little clothes in every color, clean and dirty, are in the corners and the middle of the floor. I close the door behind me and take off my old one-piece bathing suit, adding to one of the piles. I sit on the mattress that I share with my sister and put on some clothes.

"Get out here, Shane," Mama calls from the kitchen.

"I'm coming."

"Bring this to your daddy." Looking away, she shoves a plate of food into my hands. Microwaved corn, slices of beef, and bread.

"Sit at the table, Joe," Mama instructs my brother as she picks my sister up off the floor. The baby has just put something in her mouth.

"Daddy?" I say, pushing open the door to the room that my parents used to share.

"Sweetie." His voice is raspy from wailing and screaming all morning; that's when Joe and me and the baby know to go to the water.

"Here you go." I set his plate on the tray table in his lap and see his face, skinny and gray. He sits propped up like a doll on his pillow against the wall.

I remember him strong, when he could walk and work and was only mad sometimes. He can't chop firewood now. He can't hold a hammer. He loved Mama then, even though she wasn't so beautiful. Maybe she was before the sun dried her up, and before my brother and sister and me wore her away like water on a riverbank.

"You know Daddy's not mad at you," he says, "or your mama. Never was. I'm just hurting, you know."

I nod, looking away. I don't really know this person anymore.

The night is hot and the air hangs heavy and motionless. The white sheets on our mattress stick to me. My sister kicks her tiny legs like she's dreaming of running. Mama is half sleeping on the couch. She hasn't slept deeply in years, and you can see every hour in the pockets under her eyes.

Dawn explodes with a deep, tormented yell. Daddy's cries drown out every bug mating call and fox's scream in the woods.

Mama runs to Daddy. On the way she yells, "Shane! Get up! Get Joe, get out now, hear me?!"

Getting out of bed I knock over my cup, spilling water on the floor. I want to clean it up but I have no time. I step on toys scattered around and grab Sasha. The dim light of the sun about to rise shines timidly through the window.

"You stupid bitch!" I hear Daddy yell. He cries out again, convulsing in pain.

Mama says, "Easy, I'm right here," but it never helps. She pets his head, smoothing back his hair.

"Shut up! Ah God!"

Flailing, thoughtless, he grabs her neck and her face with his weak hands. His skinny white fingers wrap and squish her skin like it's playdough. His pain travels through him, rushing out of his fingertips, as though he is strong again. Mama is stronger and could pull away, but she is stuck. Daddy screams in her face.

"I want to fucking die!" he yells.

I hear him. Joe and I rush across the porch and down the steps, our bare feet slapping the concrete floor. As I run with a sloppy grip on the baby, my long T-shirt holds taut against me. The air is damp and salty.

Joe runs a few paces behind me. He is whimpering again.

"Mama," he keeps saying. I know she means to protect us but I don't see the point anymore.

"Here it is," I coo to Sasha who is grabbing at my collarbone. I turn to look at Joe who is watching his own feet travel over the grass and stones, like if he doesn't watch, he will have to stop. Sasha never cries when she wakes up like this. I lower the baby to the ground and sit next to her, facing the water. This low stream feeds the marsh. The marsh, Mama told me, feeds the ocean. It hasn't rained in a few days.

"Do you think it'll rain soon, Joe?" I ask, trying feebly to distract us from the wailing in the distance, and I know the answer.

"Yeah. For four whole days, prob'ly," he responds, handing a rock to Sasha and then throwing one into the stream. I know he's made a wish. We make wishes on the rocks we throw into our stream. I've stopped wishing for Daddy to get better.

Sometimes I come to the water, look out over it, and imagine that I'm a fish. I have a school of fish like me; we glide through the currents and breathe underwater. Sometimes I'm a heron stalking through the tall reeds and flying over this place. I catch the fish in my long beak and flap my big, glistening silver wings. Sometimes I think I'll be just like Mama and stay here forever. Sometimes I know I will leave.

Alastair Murdoch
THE CHALET

The coffin-dodgers sit at tables in the far corner, staring down into their half-empty pints. Across the room and a swathe of carpet that lost its color, pattern, and pile well before they banned smoking in Scottish pubs twelve years ago (and yet somehow still reeks of stale fags), under-age lads in football jerseys and acne stand by the fruit machine at the door, daring each other to go up to the bar and order. Not that Big Alan would refuse them. He always served Tommy and me when we were their age, and God knows he needs the sales. It's dead in the Castle Hotel public bar. I'm only here now, on a Sunday evening, because Tommy, my oldest and best friend, is back home on a flying visit to see his ma, and nowhere else in town is open.

I watch Big Alan polishing glasses he won't be filling this evening. Or tomorrow. Behind him, framed team photos chart the lows, lowers, and lowests of local football and young men's skin care and hair styling. I look back at Tommy, whose stare I've been avoiding.

"You know, Dougie—the girlfriend you were telling me about on the phone? You could bring her," Tommy's saying. "I'd love to meet her."

"Och, it's just a lassie—nothing serious."

"Well, I'm sure Susanne would love to see you again."

I pounce on the chance to deflect. "Well I'm sure she would," I say, adding a lascivious wink. "And I assure you it's mutual."

Tommy doesn't take the bait. He's playing me: Now I can either come clean about my girlfriend-who-isn't, or I can dig myself an even deeper hole. What was I thinking? Why do I still try to make Tommy jealous? Can I not just accept that he got away from here, with the girl, Susanne, and that he's living the life, working for a bank in Switzerland of all places, while I... I should know better, but as Mrs. Urquhart once told our class from inside a cloud of chalk dust as she beat the crap out of the blackboard, "Douglas MacCready, you are incapable of learning!" Mrs. Urquhart hated me. She'll be laughing now, even as her Shetland sweater singes in the fires of Hell.

"Think it over, anyway," Tommy says, glancing at his watch. "Look, I've got tae go. Flying back to Zurich first thing tomorrow. It was good catching up, Dougie. Even in this dump."

"Oh, come on!" I say. "Your ball and chain's back in Switzerland, man! Are you no up for getting trollied wi' your oldest pal, just for auld lang syne?"

Tommy shakes his head. "Sorry. But do think about coming over, aye? A guy at work has a chalet in the Alps we can borrow for a weekend. It's massive, so I mean it about bringing your girlfriend," Tommy pauses. "If she exists."

Damn you, Thomas Patterson!

***

But here's the thing: A month later, there I am in the chalet, sitting next to the gorgeous Morag. The leather on the sofa where we're sitting is butter soft, the carpet pile's so deep I can't see my feet, and the walls are covered with a silky fabric I don't dare touch. Every door and every window in the chalet opens and shuts silently, and every appliance functions noiselessly—never interrupting the soft music being piped through speakers so small and inconspicuous I'm buggered if I can see where they are. I don't know how Tommy can even relate to his old life back at home, if this is what his life in Switzerland is like now.

Susanne's just put the children to bed, and is pouring wine. Susanne and Tommy's four children were supposed to have been just two. First came Ian, seven years ago, then two years later the "two and done" turned out to be the twins, Graham and Yvonne, only for Katriona to surprise everyone another three years later. *The best-laid plans of mice and men gang oft agley!* That responsibility's one thing I don't envy Tommy.

Now Katriona's come back down to the living room in her pajamas. She's a little darling, with her golden curls. I call her Wee Bobblylugs, laughing. She looks confused, unsure, maybe even about to cry, but when she sees her parents smiling and nodding she decides she likes the name and asks me for a good night song. Me? Where Tommy and I are from, men only sing and get soppy about football, or when someone puts some maudlin crap on Big Alan's jukebox at closing time. Everyone's looking at me though, so I pull Katriona up on my knee—awkward's not the word—and I sing her this old Johnny Cash song about a guy who hangs for a murder he didn't commit, rather than provide an alibi, because he was away with his best friend's wife at the time. Haven't a Scooby why I pick that one, Spoon that I am. Oh, Scooby's rhyming slang: a Scooby Doo's a clue. And a Spoon's just someone too stupid to be given a knife and fork.

Katriona heads back upstairs to bed after the song, happy and seemingly undamaged, and I take a glass from Susanne. It's a white with a name

I can't pronounce. I'll bet it cost a packet; it's nicely chilled, and I hammer it. Katriona's left me red in the face, and Morag's not even trying to hide her amusement.

Morag's even more gorgeous than the latest girlfriend I invented for Tommy. She's bewitching—she's my Nannie Dee, my Cutty Sark—and she's not just up for this whole mad adventure, including our fake romantic history; no, she's relishing it, with a wicked grin stuck on the most kissable mouth ever. She's got the long red Highland curls down to the small of her back, and her skin's more powdery white even than Mrs. Urquhart's chalk cloud, though she's already freckled up from sitting out on the terrace earlier, admiring the Alps in the early autumn sun. The freckles just make her even cuter when she wrinkles her nose. Then there are her eyes: they're the deepest, purest cobalt, and they make even the cloudless alpine sky look a wee bit shabby. And she has the body of a champion dancer because, well, she was a champion dancer. West Lanarkshire Schoolgirls Highland Dancing Champion two years running. That was a while back, mind you.

"Och, you two look lovely together, so you do," coos Susanne. "How long's it been now?"

Tommy leans forward in the armchair that engulfed him after dinner. His eyes are wide open, and his ears are pricked like a gun dog's. I'm no dead duck, though.

"About six months," Morag and I reply in perfect unison, like creepy twins (unlike Graham and Yvonne—they're bonnie). Maybe a wee bit over-rehearsed there.

***

I only met Morag two weeks ago, while working. I do promotions for a distillery I won't name, driving around the Highlands all summer, dishing out whisky samples, and I'm very good at it: I turn on the charm, and I look pure gallus in a kilt because my calves are shredded. Not that you need charm or good calves to hand out free booze on a dreek Tuesday night in Inverness. I like my job, even if my despairing Presbyterian parents, who always break the silence over Sunday dinner by asking how my "nice friend Thomas" is getting along in "the world of high finance," don't. Tooling around from Highland Games to golf tournaments, to bagpipe competitions and ceilidhs, flirting with the lassies and the old ladies, having my picture taken with the tourists, and getting all coy when they ask what, if anything, I wear under my kilt, may not be a career, and it's only seasonal, but it's a good craic. Sorry, parents.

Morag was teaching tourists to dance at a ceilidh in Drumnadrochit where I was pushing the liquid gold. That's her job; like me, she spends her summers peddling Scottish culture. We got to talking, and went for drinks in a wee pub after, where she tried teaching me a few steps. I lost my balance and fell. She tried to catch me, lost her own balance, and landed on top of me, laughing. I could feel her body convulsing, and I wanted that moment to last, even if we did look like proper pair of eejits, sprawled across the middle of the pub, kilts all asunder.

"Do you fancy coming tae Switzerland for a long weekend?" I asked as casually as I could, lying there on the pub floor underneath her. "A friend has a *chalet* in the Alps." Note the French accent on *chalet*, there. Real smooth.

"Sure," she said. "Sounds like a laugh."

Oh my God.

***

So back in Switzerland, Susanne's showing Morag the village the next morning. We went over our story again before breakfast, because I know Tommy will have primed Susanne to do some digging. Tommy and I are back in the chalet with the kids when he asks me to watch them while he pops down the shops. What's he bloody thinking? But he's out the door before I can say anything. I go back to the guestroom bed to enjoy Morag's scent on the pillows.

Of course I fall asleep, but I wake to screaming and shrieking from the living room just a few minutes later. I rush over, expecting a massacre, only to find the twins have dragged a plastic sled in from the mudroom, and built themselves an indoor toboggan run using cushions from every piece of furniture in the place. Little buggers must have even snuck into the guestroom while I was asleep, and nicked the cushions from there. Whee! Bang! Laugh! Whee! Bang! Laugh! Repeat. Repeat. Repeat. Never gets old when you're five, I guess.

"Stop it, you little—" I check myself. "You'll get yourselves killed! Think of the wallpaper! Oh, your Mammy and your Daddy'll kill me!"

The twins giggle, and talk to each other in German. I guess that's what they speak at school, the wee show-offs. While I wonder what to do, a drop of water lands on my head. I look up and see another drop already forming on the ceiling. I realize it's not some soothing New Age babbling burn soundtrack coming through the music system, but the sound of actual water running above our heads. A quick expletive, and I'm away up the stairs, taking them two at a time, to the bathroom, where Ian's sitting on the cludgie playing his video games. The washbasin's overflowing because he's left taps running, and a lake's already forming under his feet, but the wee fellah's oblivious, happily wiping out entire armies and burning down enemy villages, or whatever it is.

I haul him off the toilet and out of the flooded bathroom. I turn off the taps, and I take him downstairs to join the twins in the living room, where the wee buggers aren't just at it again—no, they've added to their toboggan run by going out and taking the cushions off the terrace furniture, too, and now they're giving it laldy again. Whee! Bang! Laugh! They've left the terrace door open, and... Shit! Where's Katriona?

"Where's Wee Bobblylugs?" I scream. "Oh, Jesus suffering fuck!"

The children stare at me wide eyed and open mouthed. I don't suppose Thomas curses much nowadays, but they should have heard their Old Man back in the day.

Nothing out on the terrace, except the denuded furniture, and then I see the railing. I walk toward it. Shaking, ready to throw up, I grasp the rail and make myself look over the edge. It's a forty-foot drop—but thank God there's nothing down there.

I stumble back into the living room, a shaking mess. Ian and the twins watch me in silence. There's just the soft music and the steady drip-drip from the ceiling and then a faint, muffled "Mama!," followed by a distant sob.

I set off again, tearing from room to room, calling Katriona. It's not until I get to the main bedroom, by which time I've searched every other room in the chalet, and even found the damn music system speakers, that I hear another "Mama!" coming from the closet. I open it, pull back the hanging clothes, and there's wee Katriona in the back, sobbing. Mrs. Urquhart loved that bastard C.S. Lewis—this is all her doing. I start crying with relief.

Scooping Katriona out of the closet, I cover her in tears and kisses, assuring her that her Mammy and her Daddy will be home soon, and that they will have missed her more than she's missed them. What I don't say is that I've missed them even more. What I also don't say is how good it feels just to cuddle her, to feel the warmth, the softness, the trust of a small child, to be able provide such simple comfort, and to be hugged in return when she puts her wee arms around my neck. I squeeze her without saying anything more—not because it'd be daft trying to express what I'm feeling right now to a two-year-old, but because I can't process it. I'm just tears and snot.

I carry Katriona down to the living room, and close the door to the terrace. It self-locks. Silently, of course.

"Now none of you move. I'll be right back!"

I race back up the stairs, to the cupboard where Susanne showed me the towels. I rip out a couple of armfuls. They're soft, fluffy, perfectly white and probably brand new, but I hurl them around the bathroom like old rags to soak up the worst of the flooding, before shooting downstairs again to the children.

"Right!" I say to the kids. "We're all staying together, where I can keep an eye on you, and if you don't tell your parents what just happened, then I won't either. You know what? We're gonnae build a castle out of all these cushions—a haunted Scottish castle—and I'll even tell you a ghostie story. OK?"

The children are up for it, so we break down the toboggan run and we build this brilliant castle, just like the ones Tommy and I used to make at home, as I rehash one of the stories I remember us making up all that time ago. The kids are in the castle, and I'm just finishing the story when the chalet door opens and Tommy, Susanne, and Morag spill in, laughing. They stopped off to get coffee while I was here playing Mrs. Doubtfire. My guilt and terror are about to turn to moral outrage when Susanne points to the sled.

"What's that doing in here?" she asks.

"It's... It's the castle drawbridge," I reply. I put the sled in place, and use its rope to pull it up like a drawbridge, securing the children inside. Not bad, eh?

"Oh, that's lovely! So creative!" Susanne says.

"Well," I say, "I just thought we'd do something fun together."

"No just putting on the telly or letting them play their video games?" Susanne shoots an accusing look at Tommy. Tommy cringes, and I shrug, all aw-shucks like.

"Aye, but I'm afraid I flooded the bathroom, and I haven't had time to clean it up properly. I'll go sort it out now, eh?"

"Och, you didnae try giving them a bath, too?" says Susanne. Got to love Susanne—she's streets ahead of everyone else in the room on this one. "Oh, Dougie, I'd never have thought!"

The children look at me from inside the castle, but say nothing. Bless!

"Well we're glad you grownups had a nice time, too," I say. I pluck Wee Bobblylugs out of the castle, partly as a prop, though mostly because I just fancy another wee squish.

"Wow!" says Tommy, looking at me. "You feeling all right there, Dougie?"

Tommy and Susanne grin approval and delight, though all of a sudden Morag's got a face on her like a bulldog chewing a wasp. What now?

"Oh I see what's going on!" she says. "You just set this all up to make yourself look like Captain Domestic, didn't you, Dougie? I'm thinking it's just a weekend away. But you, Dougie, you're trying to convince me to... well, to settle down, aren't you?"

My stomach drops. Everything drops. Not Katriona, though—I clutch her to me.

"I'm no that kind of girl, Dougie. What were you thinking? We've only known each other for, what...?" says Morag. I don't believe this—she's throwing me under the bus, with my oldest, best pal at the steering wheel.

Wait! There's a spark in those cobalt eyes. The corners of her mouth twitch and her freckled nose wrinkles. Oh, you beauty! You've just had me at my own game there, didn't you?

"Six months?" she says. "Don't rush me, Dougie, just don't rush me. OK?"

She's a keeper is Morag, and I'm not talking about goalies.

Donají Olmedo
BETWEEN AUTUMNS

Early autumn 2006

I didn't keep my word. Admittedly, I'm only flesh and blood. Oh, I also have thoughts. I have no reasonable excuse—here's the proof.

After you were gone, I swore I wouldn't think about you, and with my characteristic cynicism, I must admit that you penetrate my mind with the same force that you thrust your cock into my pussy. Now I look around and my gaze gets lost in the lime trees in the ritual of shedding leaves.

My memory creates forms in certain places: in the bed, in the solitary corner where I always read, in the forest with gigantic trees guarding our steps, whispers, and sunken knees during battles. A story of two got lost in that forest of limes and acacias.

As autumn begins, I keep caressing you for hours, without letting go of your hand. You keep me company during my visits; you sing me our song, sticking to my back. There are days when the color of my mood is army green and I decide to scold you. Furious, I mistake your actions for affronts, taunts, and conceits. Then I answer with images of irony.

I'm sure that autumn isn't time to stop thinking about you. I worry about your baseless logic, your faith, which I think needs glasses. I want you to keep my thoughts, then, sit on the edge of the abyss and repeat them nonstop. They, these quibbles, are the only irrefutable proof of my walk that was going from a corner toward you and not staying quiet on the way back.

It's autumn and melancholy is present, caused by the absence of light. I look for it in the territory of your body: attracted to your back, my tongue savors it and gets stuck in the place where your back ends and your rear begins. I love feeling your gaze on me and breathing in your sweat.

This autumn I accept taunts and snide remarks that make me vulnerable. I will use fantasy and imagination to make up for your absence. I will be a manipulator of letters, words, and sentences. With them, I will love you, you will love me. Naked, we will watch videos, drink coffee, you will read to me, and I will recite poems to you—crazy, surrealist, and meaningless ones.

One more autumn for this impulsive woman who sometimes uses words to touch your eyes, lips, and skin, knowing that you will never read what I write.

Late autumn 2006

It occurred to me to write to you. I began in the upper right corner of the sheet and let truths slide one by one until they were scattered through the paper. In the middle, I spread a considerable number of lies; the most cynical ones settled in beside the truths to defy them.

As I write, the hidden door of a mirror opens so that the one who reads leaps toward the other side. I think that's why I thought about writing to you.

"I'm so happy." That's how I began. Then I took great pains to explain my happiness: every night I tell the moon that I'm a red rosebud; I don't care if others see me as a rose, not as a bud; you met me and breathed in my scent.

I say to myself in front of the mirror: "What a beautiful rose dressed as a bud!" They say I'm not old-fashioned, of course, because I'm a red rosebud. I fell into ripeness and my mouth was filled with strange sounds. I'm sure it happened when I learned to gather some fragments of emptiness and stuffed them with letters. Now I arrange and classify pieces of soul. I don't do it as if they were spoils of war. What I do is to sing and write down feelings. In every word, every sentence, and every paragraph, there is me.

The horizon looms in the distance. The leaves fall from our acacia, and I kneel down to pick them up... Tomorrow is another day.

Winter 2006

Today I won't tear myself with the useless exercise of remembering. Skins and shadows are awake; it just so happens that I don't feel like desiring or whimpering. Smiles are placed on the blank sheet of paper; the lines dance to the rhythm of a cheerful tune. The glaciers thaw to the sound of my bright eyes. I keep my imagination well fed with the daily portion of dreaming, watching, and reading. I needed a platform to let go of the enormous discourse I carry in my soul. Here is the place, and this is the story.

Early spring 2007

When I decided to write about you, I wasn't finding a suitable place. I walked several streets, and with sore feet, at last sat in a bar, and ordered a beer. The Eleventh Commandment—Thou shalt not smoke—had not reached those streets; so I lit up a cigarette. I started smoking when I was twenty and enjoy every cigarette I smoke; this time was no exception, and in the place with wooden chairs and metal music in the background, I let go of the foam from the heart.

I recounted the even-numbered day we spent together with the help of tamed sparrows. I wrote down the odd-numbered days with the thrust of guitar scratches. I was there writing about you: the place became filled with wings and lightning flashes. Some sculptures appeared, then soon disintegrated, leaving sand piles. The wind messed up my hair and blew through the bar, scattering napkins and table runners. A tablecloth ghost appeared over my shoulder and read words, including the ones that remained hidden between the cracks of haste, in the impunity of what it reads and what it doesn't. I was leaving in letters our story, the exact moment you arrived, unmet expectations, and mistakes. The cold froze some moments; determined, I thought about redefining them and managed to do it. Smoking two packs of cigarettes, I finished the story and left eight empty beer bottles on the table and twenty pages in a thin hand.

I went out again for another walk. Fog accompanied the splashing rain. I took my shoes off and felt the cool cobblestones under my bare feet. Seated on the ground outside an inn, I buried my head into my solitude. Like a lost bird, I knew it was the time to break free.

I possess many treasures, I sustain myself with them, and nothing escapes through a crack of memory. I will keep writing them.

Still early spring 2007
I can't help but talk about you. When I finally stop doing it, my skin will burst open and your sap will be found in my tired joints; then, I will have no other choice but to talk about you.

You entered me thousands of times, spewing your essence. Where else had you entered with your maddening juice? When did you stop fighting, allowing it to be replaced by resignation? Maybe the day when we dreamed awake and, defying destiny, made a chordless, soundless song. Doubts and fears crept in. The demon came down, dragged me by the hair, and planted me in the garden of lies. Resigned, I walked along one side of the abyss. About to fall, I saw you at the bottom. You were singing, but your music didn't light the blue flame of the dream. Where on the street did you stop looking for me? Where would the good and evil we put through our asses be? Because that is where they play life, sanity, dignity, and, ironically, love as well.

Hours and days pass, and I don't move forward toward the other side where we weren't telling our story. You will see me with open arms and my hands spilling words filled with doubts. Moods, skins, whispers, and different shadows; if I go back to the smell of your steps and I breathe in on your body.

Filled with sensations, I go from one side to the other. At times I want to know who lives in me because I have gotten lost in some of the traveled paths, and the person who moves, talks, eats, and thinks is very different from the one who took her first step toward the adventure with her left leg.

I have seen myself lost many times, hitting my head against the wall of indifference. I try to control this other me; then, my hand shakes the shoulder of my confused self. When I manage to get its attention, I understand its boring routine of catching birds; not daring to walk outside the established line; taking out the same garbage; seeing a crack in the sculpture of solitude. But my pride is wide, in comparison to humility. I'm stubborn like a circle because I hate the squareness of resignation.

You don't tell it to anyone. The truth is that some days I seat myself in the armchair and memories come back: I sing in your ear; I tell you adventures; I caress your eyes; I savor your tongue; I let you bite my breasts, and then I swallow the moment.

And who could have told me? I worry, not knowing if you're alive or dead... but in me.

Still summer 2007
Eternity. That's what solitude that floods the streets is like. I form a part of what fills the space. I'm solitude. An eternal dreamer believing that I invent myself each day and with each passing day I don't stop thinking about you. When I say something, I draw a mental image of your listening to me. This lie, however, is also my reality. The reality of being alone, the reality of keeping thinking about you. In search of company I find myself in front of solitude. I touch it, caress it, and lay it on my bed. Today I woke up alone again; I deceived myself, imagining you. Wrapped in the sheets, you whispered: "I love you."

Between the sheets lay a letter I wrote, which ended with "I'll never forget you..."

Autumn 2007
I'm the result of absences and fears. That's why I write. I devote myself to filling spaces with letters. I drop them again on the white background and now black paragraphs will come out. Today a few thick-lipped, tough sentences beat me in a race. On a curve they penetrated my defenses and suddenly knocked me down. I was busted up and wounded. So I doubt writing, filling spaces, is my thing. While I think about it, miserable ghosts make fun of my

insecurity. I put on some music and lie down on the floor to think. I hope it will rain and someone will heed my desire and fulfill it.

Now, while the sky, stones, ideas, names, and scenes slip away. A beginning appears, and as it always happens with me, I have no idea how it will end. Without warning, you appear, caressing the waist of a guitar. You smile at me. I run, and before the idea flees from me, I write it down.

I need leisure, time, absences, love, letters, and a blank sheet. I need the rain. Shit, I need you, damn it.

Winter 2007

I belong here. I'm learning to live in spite of your distance. I sit in the place of dread and watch it go by. I hear life shooting up around me and the voices we knew sing our song.

I don't let the color of our bodies fade. I don't allow love to become transparent. I don't pluck daisies anymore, nor do I allow the river to rob the petals that indecision let go with tears through the confluence of solitude.

I decipher the gazes of ashes, fire, water, and wind. I translate words, embellish them, and blend them to give them meaning. When I finally give shape to a birch branch to cling to, the noise in the night, or the humidity of spilled seeds, traps me. I get lost among the leaves; I find birds and join their flight. I also interpret sounds. At times I get tired of accepting my weakness that appears as a tremor on my lips.

Here I stay, taken up again by past love affairs. Damn it.

Spring 2008

Will there be paths that lead us toward oblivion? If that's the case, the journey is wide.

I accept that nostalgia tortures me. It shows up to taunt me and manages to fill my eyes with tears. It's not a longing, but a disagreement; it's an open confrontation with facts. In the distance I hear others who, like me, suffer, cry; some others heal their wounds. An amazing spectacle of musty customs. As I assimilate them, I manage to nuance displeasure little by little, snatching a pathetic version of bad luck from the corner of my lips.

In those difficult times, I'm approached by men with black and white silhouettes, like images from vintage photos, without contrast, without relief, figures that have not arrived yet because they haven't left other places.

Summer 2008
"And Mariana wants to be a song..." To be a song is not a fleeting desire, but rather an ambitious one. To be a song you need several things: an encounter and then...

His eyes lock into mine. Our gazes ricochet between us. He reads my biography on my skin and leisurely takes the long road in the line of my legs. He kisses me and pulls the words hidden behind the layer of pretense with his tongue. He dismantles my defenses, injecting imagination, creativity, and tenacity. As he piques my curiosity, he's compensated by the game of desire. He possesses me as a lover, Lolita, whore, and friend. He touches me at any time, for any reason, anywhere on the planet and anywhere on my body. He sniffs me out among thousands of women and, with his eyes closed, runs his hands over my valleys, taking an outlined image between his palms. He doesn't want to take control of my skin, but of my dreams and his. He's not here, but he arises. He accepts that nothing is certain with me. He talks with his body, sings with his gaze, and sows with his words. He writes about me, because of me, and for me; each letter is the color of my skin; his conjunctions have the sound of my voice; his verbs have the reflection of my actions; my adjectives arise in his texts, in his dreams, and in his memory, becoming a part of his consciousness.

Being a song is similar to being history, tales, or short fiction; even it's like a true lie.

I was and I am a song. I can also be writing.

Someone will read my story and get to know me.

Autumn 2008
I can write nonsense, make up crazy stories, and speak frankly, without sleight of hand. Many days no letter comes out. I don't know how to do it.

I look over my old writing and smile. I'm the same and the other; I read myself and say no and then think yes. I keep going like that.

I know about disturbances, hurricanes, and turbulences. I know the sound of kisses and tears.

There are difficult days. I get bored. I spend time reading books, listening to music, and watching movies. At times I feel that the typewriter has stopped me, that my hand forgot how to turn on the computer, and that I had a screw loose. And like this, confused, I dare to place words. For weeks, time has enclosed me, because I need it, and then I disappear. I get bored.

Suddenly there seem to be too many windows. Through one of them I saw you again hiding from everyone and wanting to come back to me. I have moments when I love everything, or most, or nothing. Memories arrive and grab me so hard that my skin hurts when I feel them. As I surrender to them, they melt with desire, and burn. Hugs I receive are also spiritual, emotions have forms, and desire keeps alive.

I'm tempted by freedom. I'm going to the country for a few days. I'll pick up giant arum lilies and pluck heaps of ashes. The river of convictions will show me several paths. I'll float in the river of tranquility.

On my return I'll solve two problems: the fitting of the mask and the knot of ribbons in the nape. I have to settle down in the nonstory to put up with living it, or maybe to enjoy it.

Spring 2009

I read and write with my misplaced ego. After three years of crying over your absence, I found your emails and websites. It was a stroke of luck: if luck is what hurt my ego, and fortune has been the cause before being broken and with bruises before being lost.

In the morning I ask the mirror if my ego is hiding in a dark corner. It answers, showing my reflection, as always. Then angry, I spit at its patronizing attitude. As if I hadn't had enough millennial words of consolation. Haven't they come up with anything else? What poor imagination!

Don't they realize? Darn it! I lost my ego. But before it got lost, I felt it distracted, restless. One day it woke up, cursing. It declared that life was fucking meaningless. I'm sure that my ego is looking for its trace, if it has left some behind.

I deleted some of your love notes for other women. Well, now I'm another woman.

Summer 2009

Where will the words written by your heart live? You would think that they're in dark places filled with oblivion. Because you watered them there, in emails, in websites, at the expense of sticks and screams. At times brushing against anguish and madness. I imagine you alone, dragging your emotional miseries, your fragmented feelings. Looking for everything in many months without finding the center, where thirst, happiness, and love sprout and overflow. That day, loving green eyes; another week, in the yearning of that young body, unrepeatable, in any month, trickling down the mature womb of another man's wife; the next year, swearing eternal love, allowing eternity.

I hate you and sum up this sensation when I read loving words you gave me and that were not directed toward me. Wretched, ill-bred, lying bastard! I'll curse to free myself from the pain provoked by this heartbreak.

Early autumn 2010
Once again you're packing your luggage somewhere else. Nine years here, two years there, one year there, and your suitcase is still the same size. You're not another man. I read your letter many times. Your words arrived slipping through the rug at the entrance. I found the envelope when I was arranging a chair and a small table in front of the TV: I was going to watch *Cinema Paradiso* over dinner. There lay your letter. How much uncertainty does fit in two pages, waiting for the stab? You addressed me as "friend." Damn, now I'm your friend! Then you talked about your dreams. For a while I didn't understand what you meant by "I saw you dreaming of me." Then I remembered you always found me riding on clouds of ideas. I'm sure you meant that. You don't like order, so you described the place you abandoned this time without it: a house with cats, without children, with books, without magic, with music, with gestures, without certainty, with cries. It's a good thing that I didn't read complaints and excuses. It ended again and you'll walk away once more. I smile, remembering your crazy associations to explain the attraction of two bodies. Now I know how you are: desire personified. A man of flesh and fire. Was it a dream or reality that inspired you in your eternal search? Because I'm more certain now than ever that you believed in your urge as an explanation for the internal vacuum. How incomplete your chest felt next to an unimaginative body? But at the same time, you made associations to respond adequately at the required moment.

I was gradually getting to know you: an insatiable seeker, someone who believed in magnetism, the mystery of death, entropy, and perfect actions; someone who was sure that happiness was found in a smile, a hair, legs, a song, a cleavage, and a balmy, simple afternoon; someone who believed being beyond good and evil.

For many years I remained in lies and managed to survive when the truth arrived. Today, your memory helps me learn to live. The day I die, I'll die old.

I didn't dream of you. I confess that before your letter arrived, the leaves rustled, announcing your new defeat...

Late autumn 2010

Human life is a fanciful, absurd knot. I met people who didn't want questions because they didn't want anyone to know they had no answers. Then I decided to go beyond what's apparent and found people who live the same way. As astonished spectators, they find these lines. Certain that they understand my desires and guess who I am and what I think. They even stare at me straight because as they read those letters, they touch me and feel me. What irony! After all, we're nothing more than a previously formed image, an appearance.

I propose something uncertain as the last entry in this diary. I suggest injecting happiness and sadness in it because love is precious that way. There they say sorrows of love aren't really sorrows.

Translated by Toshiya Kamei

Colleen Kearney Rich
WILD HORSES

Kaitlyn leaned against the porch railing, lit a cigarette, and inhaled deeply. Alice couldn't help watching the girl, this friend of her granddaughter's; she made smoking look delicious. Cigarettes were something Alice had never taken to. After watching Kaitlyn blow smoke rings into the air, she asked for one, which the girl promptly lit for her.

Alice took a puff but didn't inhale. Instead, she held it at arm's length. The long white cigarette in her wrinkled spotted hand looked so ridiculous that she almost burst out laughing.

"This is silly," Alice said, mostly to herself. She put the cigarette out in the nearby ashtray and pulled the sleeves of her cardigan down to cover the tops of her hands.

Alice had a beer, then another. They tasted so good, better than she remembered. The girls had been with them a week and the change in their routine had been good for Alice. She was sorry to see them go.

She sat there on her front porch inhaling the salt air, trying to absorb it deep into her pores. She felt young, carefree, as if she were a girl herself, with so much ahead of her and almost nothing to look back on.

A rental sign on one of the houses across the street creaked with the wind. In less than a month, she would be gone from this place. During her second marriage, her marriage to Jim, the two had traveled a great deal after her boys were grown. They decided on an early visit to Ocean City that this was where they would retire. Imagining sunrises over the bay helped Alice through many tedious days at the bank in those final years before retirement.

Now Jim's health was poor. What began with a fall, a simple misstep, had led to a litany of other disorders. She watched a robust, broad-chested man who once moved sides of beef for a living melt down into a tottering old man—and she still felt young. But Ocean City was too far from everyone and the long drives, something Jim once did for fun, now made him anxious. He didn't trust the car or his own reactions. They needed to be closer in, near the relatives, near the doctors.

"It's late," Alice reminded them.

"But it's our last night," said her granddaughter Darcy. "A little longer."

In an effort to keep Alice on the porch with them, Kaitlyn began telling stories of her own about catching shoplifters at the store and people who tried to return dirty underwear. Soon Alice was laughing so hard that it made her eyes tear.

"So the guy has this thing shoved down his shirt, and it looks a breast or a huge tumor or something," said Kaitlyn. "And he is standing there looking at me with a straight face."

They could hear it before they saw it—the vibrating wheeze of the engine, the hiss of its brakes. Conversation ceased, and the three looked down the street toward the noise, waiting to see what would turn the corner.

It was a large bus, the kind people charter to go to Atlantic City, coming down the tiny side street. With its darkened windows and earth-toned paint job, the bus looked sinister in the streetlight. As it pulled in front of the house, Alice could see that the bus had a mural of wild horses running through a tunnel of dust painted on the side.

Kaitlyn waved; Alice did the same. She felt jubilant as if she were at a parade. The bus came to a stop and the doors pushed open. Down the stairs came three men, dressed in jeans, cowboy shirts, and boots. They walked across the lawn and up near the porch.

"How are you ladies doing tonight?" asked the tallest one, smiling. He had sandy-colored hair and a reddish beard. There was something about the way the man's eyes crinkled up at the corners when he smiled that made Alice's breath catch.

Kaitlyn laughed. "We're all fine, but I think you're a little lost."

"We were trying to cross the bridge to get out of town," the man said. "But I do believe we missed our turn."

"You sure did," said Alice. "You needed to make a left at the gas station."

"Where you headed?" Kaitlyn broke in.

"On our way back to Tennessee. We just finished playing down at the Sand Castle. We played mighty good tonight, not much of a crowd though. Guess the season is truly over. You all should've been there."

"We had no idea anything so important was going on tonight," Kaitlyn said.

The cowboy nodded to the empty beer cans the girls had lined up on the porch railing. "So is this here a party?"

"It was," Kaitlyn answered. "But we're about out of beer."

"Well, we've got lots of beer and just about any other kind of liquor you might want. What do you say about your little party joining our little party?"

"I thought you were on your way back to Tennessee," Darcy answered.

"I believe we have some time to spare." The man smiled to his friends.

"We wouldn't want to hold you up or anything," said Darcy. "Tennessee is a long way from here."

"Yes, indeed," he said. "Ever been?"

"Nope," said Kaitlyn, a little too brightly. "But I've always wanted to go. I *love* to travel."

"Well, if you ladies would like to come along for the ride, we'd be pleased to have the company."

"I'll go," said Kaitlyn.

"Me, too," said Alice. She couldn't believe she said it. It felt as if the words were too big for her throat and her heart was pressing against her ribs, cutting off her air supply.

"No one is going anywhere," Darcy said and stood up.

"You know, you remind me of my ex-wife," the man said. "You even look like her a little."

He pulled a wallet from his back pocket, flipped it open to a blonde girl's graduation picture, and came up the stairs holding it out to Darcy as if it was some form of identification. "See, you both have the same kind of cheekbones."

Darcy looked down at the photo and back to his face. "I see," she said and crossed her arms. He closed the wallet and slid it into his back pocket.

Maybe it was the way the streetlight shone on the side of his face or the way he folded up his wallet, but Alice suddenly felt as if she had been waiting for this stranger for a long time, and she couldn't bear to lose him again.

"I would love to go to Tennessee." Alice stood and reached out to the man. He took her hand. "I have always loved to travel."

The cowboy smiled. "Well, ma'am, you're more than welcome."

Alice felt tears rolling down her cheeks, but she wasn't embarrassed. "Oh, you say that, but you don't want an old woman along."

"Now that's nonsense," he said and patted her hand. "We would be honored by your presence." All Alice could think of was how much she wanted to touch the man's beard. She forced her hand to be still.

"By tomorrow morning you would be ready to leave me by the side of the road. But I sure would like to go." She laughed and tried to take her hand back.

The man kissed her hand and let it go. "It's been a pleasure, ma'am."

The three climbed back on the bus, and the cowboy bowed to them before the door closed with a gasp. The bus's engine roared to a start, and it continued down the street.

Darcy was looking around at the neighbor's houses. "Jesus Christ, they probably woke up half the neighborhood," she said. "I'm going to bed."

Kaitlyn gathered up the beer cans and went in after her, but Alice felt she had to wait and see the bus go over the bridge before she could go inside. She thought she could almost make out the horses on the mural as the bus slipped out of sight.

When Alice got inside, she sat down at the kitchen table. Kaitlyn said good night and passed out of the room without pausing. Darcy sat down at the table across from her grandmother, and Alice noticed she was twirling a large piece of her hair around her index finger. It had been many years since she had seen the girl repeat this nervous habit from childhood.

"Oh Darcy, it is so terrible to be old. There's really no place for you," she told the girl quietly. She could hear Jim snoring in their bedroom. It was late, far too late. The only light in the house came from a fluorescent bulb under the cabinet over the kitchen sink.

"Oh Grandma, you know that's not true," Darcy murmured, looking out the kitchen window into the darkness.

"It is. When I was working, I felt like I was somebody. I felt like there was a reason to get up in the morning. I had some place to go. I should've never let your grandfather talk me into retiring early." Alice took a tissue out of her cardigan pocket and dabbed around her eyes.

"Yeah, but now you're free to do anything you want. That must be pretty terrific." Darcy forced a smile. It was patronizing, and Alice had to look away.

"You couldn't possibly understand. You're young. Your whole life is ahead of you. My God, if I had had your mind and the advantages you've had, there's no telling what I could've done. You could throw away your future working in that department store."

It came out harsher than she had meant it to and Alice wished she could bite back the words.

"You should get an education," she said, this time softer.

"Maybe I don't want to," Darcy said.

"You need to start making plans. When you don't make decisions for yourself, sometimes they have a way of getting made for you."

"It's late, Grandma. I think we should go to bed." The girl pushed away from the table, and Alice reached across and grasped her hand. She paused and cleared her throat, trying to keep her voice low and even. "You know, your grandfather...he's a good man. He was a good father to my kids, but I don't know that I could say I've been happy."

"Please, he might hear you." Darcy tried to pull her hand away.

"You start off doing things because you have to—your family needs the money, or someone's sick. Soon you are doing things because you should. It's expected. I don't even know what I wanted to do. Maybe I didn't 'want,' maybe I didn't dare." Alice squeezed her hand. "You have a chance, a real chance. Don't waste your life."

Darcy looked a little panicked. "I'm tired," she said. "We're both tired. We should get to bed."

"Darcy, promise me..."

"I promise, Grandma, really I do," she pleaded. "But it's late. It'll all seem better in the morning. Really, it will."

She let go of Darcy's hand and covered her face. Darcy got up from the table, but lingered at the door.

"So you'll go to bed?" the girl asked.

Alice nodded. Soon she heard Darcy's bedroom door shut and could hear the girls whispering. She didn't want to imagine what they were saying about her. She felt foolish.

She took down one of the pictures from the wall. It was a family portrait in front of a fake library. Alice looked closely at her young face and tried to decipher the feelings there. It looked like happiness, but was it? She couldn't remember. In her mind, she could picture the color of the lipstick she wore—so red—and knew that she had had to starch that blouse, but the interior of this young woman was closed to her. Still she couldn't shake the feeling that something had eluded her.

After a while, she got up and went outside. She closed her eyes and stood on her front lawn enjoying the feel of the wind in her hair and the cool dampness of the night. She walked down her block, then kept walking until she reached the bay, then she went up the steps to the bridge, where a few men were fishing. She looked out across the blackness of the bay and could make out the lights of the opposite shore. A trawler slipped through the darkness, its lights rising and falling with the waves.

She thought of the day Darcy's father was born, and how when they placed that baby in her arms she knew exactly what her life would be, the things she would have to do. It was so simple, so clear cut. There's a certainty to having children, a usefulness. She had married and had a family. There wasn't really a choice. And with that child in her arms, her fate had been decided.

Dawn Ryan
MY OWN DIVINE MOTILITY

I was nine years old. I'd bundled my few possessions inside a large hand-kerchief. I tied the bundle to a long stick so I could lug it easily over my shoulder like a bindlestiff. I was leaving. I stood at the foot of the stairs that led to my mother's bedroom. She had not left that room in many years. See, as far back as I can remember, I was a full-time liaison between my mother and the outside world. I brought her snacks, water, a comb for her hair, but lately I'd been real unhappy. I hadn't been doing my job. For one thing, I let our cat die. He dragged his thin, withered legs to his hooded litter box, pawed around with strain, then silence. He never came out. I could only assume, and I didn't bother to remove him.

I hadn't been tending to my mother either. She stunk to high heavens. She'd grown a large, matted dreadlock at the back of her head, and she hadn't done anything but whine for four whole nights. She was thirsty, she was hungry, she was in need of a scratch. I could hear her from the bottom of the stairs, but I didn't care anymore. I wanted to be out on my own. No more taking reports for my mother.

"Ma," I shouted. "I'm running away."

"What," she hollered.

"I said I'm running away."

"I need my Winston Lights," she yelled. "I need them," she whined.

"Did you hear me?" I asked. "I said I'm running away. You may never see me again."

"I can't hear you," she yelled. "God forbid you walk up some stairs to see your mother."

I walked up the stairs to my mother's room. They were old and creaky. Lately I'd grown fearful of falling through the splintering planks. I climbed cautiously, clutching the banister. Nothing could prevent me from making this final ascent. I'd scale the wall if I had to. I needed her to know I was leaving, that she'd have to do for herself now. I didn't want her waiting for me. I stood in her bedroom doorway. "I'm running away, Ma," I told her. "I'm blowing this Popsicle stand."

She took a long look at me. I had on three different flannels and four different pairs of pants so I wouldn't freeze. I had two extra pairs of tennis shoes hanging from my neck in case the pair I wore got too holey. My precious belongings were bundled in the handkerchief. I must have really been a sight to behold. My mother laughed. "You've always been so cute," she said. "I always thought that." I stood, arms akimbo. She seemed surprised for the wrong reasons.

"Why don't you take a picture," I said.

She straightened in her bed, narrowed her eyes to get a good look. She could tell I meant business. "I know, kid," she said. "I know you're mad at me. I know you have to go."

I expected her to put up more of a fight. I stood there, stunned and disappointed, but I hadn't changed my mind.

"Just remember kid," my mother said. "If you ever get tired, you come back home."

I turned around and left. It seemed I entombed a gale of dust and human detritus as I slammed the door behind me. This is the feeling I had then, that I was the forgotten living, forced to come up in my mother's decaying mausoleum.

I didn't have a plan, just a pulsing in my gut, and a deep intuition. I don't know how to explain it. I just always knew that I'd be safe, no matter where I was. The vivid world that lay beyond my mother's apartment door was filled with so much wonder. I was grateful for it, excited for whatever might happen to me, so long as it happened. I wasn't scared about leaving home. Some may think it naïve, but no harm ever came to me. The world seemed to open up its arms and let me in. I'm sure there were cold, hungry nights when I cried myself to sleep, but these are not the memories I keep, and no matter where I was, there was always the option of leaving. Wandering was in my bones.

The first people I took up with were a Jewish family not too far from my mother. They had a daughter my age who found me very handsome. I'd been panhandling outside the university where she took classes for gifted children.

She said, "Hey you're kinda cute. I like your eyes and the way you sit out here and don't care about us gifted kids going in and out."

I said, "I care."

She said, "That's even better."

I didn't know what it meant to be gifted. I assumed she had some magical sense and could read my mind. She told me it meant she was smarter than other kids her age. She invited me home for dinner and a shower. On our way to her house, I adjusted my walking style to mirror hers. And then, as we spoke, I also tried mimicking her pattern of speech. I guess I wanted to try on being smart too. I still have a certain way about me and I can't always tell if it's me I'm being or if it's her.

The dinner and shower were so nice, I felt inclined to stay. The whole family was very smart and they spent a lot of time talking, especially during dinner, which happened every night at seven sharp.

"I don't believe the earth is round," my new friend said, forking kasha and turkey gravy.

"Hmm," her father said. "I believe it's perfectly round. It's the shape of the universe that confounds me. Is it folded like this napkin?" He lifted his napkin. "Or is it but a diaphanous spilling of wine from the Great Creator's mind?" He sipped his wine.

"Well if that's the case," I chimed in, "we can't bring ourselves to worry about the roundness and the flatness of the world." I, too, forked my kasha and turkey gravy, chewed over the lumpy mysteries bouncing around my head. "We should hope, instead," I said, "that He doesn't have wandering thoughts. That He sticks to his guns. Otherwise this whole silly apparatus will spin out in chaos."

"Well, maybe that's what it's doing right now. How would we know?" my gifted friend asked, chin glossed over with turkey fat.

"What?" I asked.

"The earth," she said. "Maybe this is what spinning out in chaos looks like."

As she dabbed her face with her own folded napkin, I fell to silence, thinking of all the twisted shapes we may actually be inhabiting, thinking too of the oil that had collected around my lips. The Jewish family's wooden and warped dining room table is where I learned to have interesting conversations.

I had never heard of Jews before, but I learned from them that Jews were wanderers, and that everyone hates them because they are so good at it. I thought maybe I was a Jew, because I too was a wanderer. They let me know that I was not. They plucked at my nose, pulled at my hair, took my measurements. I wasn't one of them. "You're close though," her father said. "Your mother was, right? Grandmother?"

"I don't think so," I said, though I didn't know if this was true.

He fingered my scalp, testing for certain amino acids. "Perhaps you have a pinch of Sephardic in you," he said, "perhaps you come from a deserter clan."

This knowledge saddened me at first; I'd felt very much like part of their family. I know now that they loved me too much in some ways, too little in others. I had to leave when my breasts began to bud. No one said as much, I just knew. The family seemed too curious of my developments, and my gifted friend desperately wanted to know what color my nipples were. She was convinced they were brown, not pink like hers. Her interest in my nipples did not seem a form of adolescent bonding. It felt insulting.

"What are you ashamed of," her mother asked during an especially bountiful feast of duck and duck liver. "They're just nipples." She unstrung her apron, lifted her shirt and revealed her own pink-tipped, round breasts. We all had a good laugh, but when silence descended I knew it was only a matter of time before I also would have to undress. Things had become complicated.

∗∗∗

I set my sights for greater things after I left the home of my gifted friend. I had gotten my fill of family life, and part of me wanted to prove I was just as good a Jew as they were. I went abroad. I traveled the entire globe. I know now that I was very lucky having been given such travel opportunities at such a young age with little more than the clothes on my back. I'm sure people would like to know my secrets. If I knew, I'd tell them. All I know is that wandering is in my bones and I find a way, one way or another. Stewardesses have always taken a liking to me, as well as waitresses and cab drivers. Old men would give me things. I knew enough to refuse most gifts, but many old men would often assure me that their gifts did not have strings attached. It's not like the way things are now, where there's no such thing as a free lunch. I had so many free lunches. I remembered something my mother had told me. She said I had style. She said, "Kid, I like your style, you're going places with that style." I asked her what she meant by style, and she said, "Oh, you know," and then rolled back over in bed. It must be this indefinable quality that granted me so much freedom. I was satisfied believing this.

I was a traveler who had neither the time nor inclination to attend to the practical matters of life. There were many other people, more settled than I, who had things I needed and who enjoyed my company. I enjoyed their company too. People like this are all around the world. I stood at the edge of the Acropolis with these people. Hiked El Yunque rainforest. Ate Argentine steaks and drank Georgian wine at their tables. Discussed Derrida over espresso and digestives. Played tennis on clay courts at palatial homes outside of Seville. Sucked on cigarettes at roulette tables hidden behind noodle houses. As conspicuous as I was, I never thought to hedge my bets. Like I said, I was lucky. The day I left America felt quite similar to the day I left my mother's apartment. There was still so much of this world yet to discover, and I was not afraid.

I met a Moroccan outside of Granada, Nicaragua, at the base of the Mombacho Volcano. A fellow wanderer, he'd learned to speak English from the Nigerian missionaries who evangelized in his hometown. We filled sandbags together during the day, dug moats. Nicaragua was a very wet place. At night we bunked in shanties abandoned by the Peace Corps some years earlier. It was at night, while looking up at the stars from a hole in our shanty roof, when he taught me about motility.

"We are the happy few," he said, "who still access the drive to thrash about the universe in search of nourishment."

He told me that much of the human world has devolved, has become sessile organisms, lying dormant in one place, waiting for the earth itself to move under their bloated bodies.

"The sessile only require sustenance," he said. "They can stare at a speck on a white wall for days, nibbling at the skin around their fingernails, and this is enough for them." I couldn't help but think of my mother growing ever distant from her motile ancestors, growing rounder and less agile atop her warping queen-size bed. I wondered if she'd even bothered to change her own sheets in my absence.

We smoked hookah in our side-by-side cots. The cold, white plumes were said to repel mosquitoes. We talked of our own divine motility.

"Who's the most motile?" I asked him. "In all the world?"

He didn't have to think very long on the question. "The Australians," he said between smoke rings. "They really know how to move."

I couldn't sleep that night. I found an Aussie heading to his homeland, and I made myself a useful travel companion. And it was true, from the Down Under one could hook up with just about anybody going just about anywhere. Someone was always on their way someplace else and in need of company. I was easy to travel with, ready and willing and with few demands of my own. I went everywhere. Saw everything.

I cannot say that the partnerships I forged were always flawless, that certain expectations were never imposed on me, or that sex miraculously came and went without complications. What made perfect sense to me often baffled my companions, and vice versa. This, I learned, was a constant. What I can say is that these people, the good and the bad, showed me places I had once thought imaginary, taught me things about art and literature and the vastly complicated human condition, things that I had never thought to question or even consider. I had never worried about the human condition before, that we are all somehow burdened with an indiscernible dissatisfaction. I had never thought of my Being in such terms, had never tried to string my strange life with the strange lives of those around me.

It was in the throes of this new learning when I found myself atop the arches of Pont Royal in central Paris. I thought of how rivers had mouths. I'd learned to appreciate symbolism. I rested my chest on the bridge's concrete edge and watched the commercial riverboats float upstream. It was night, early spring, and a chill made its way up from the water and onto my flesh. In this state, bitten in reflection, I came upon Mona staring at me from across the road with a sketch pad in hand. I understood, as the cold surged through my body, up my legs, my chest, my buttocks, that I was a woman now. That, though much younger, I was like her. I noticed I had my hand resting on my hip, and that my hip was raised ever so slightly in a curve. I understood that this is what she was drawing. I'd heard that such things as that which was about to happen happened in Paris, and I'd learned to say "when in Rome." Mona flitted across the two-way traffic of the Pont Royal, placed her pad and charcoal by my feet.

"*Êtes-vous une artiste?*" I asked.

"No," she said. "My husband is the artist. I am a pig."

She slid her tongue in my mouth, her long spindly fingers down the front of my trousers. I left an eye open, peered down to see what she'd seen from all the way across the bridge. All she'd sketched was the river, sharp and angular like a knife.

Mona, it turned out, was a very wealthy woman who'd never gone without having her whims satisfied. We had this in common I guessed, and we became very good friends. I knew from her accent that she was not French, but she would not tell me her country of origin. "I'm European," she'd say, which made me suspicious. She introduced me to her servants as her lover, though she never again touched me the way she had above the Seine. We spent every hour we could in her enormous four-poster canopy bed. The bed had curtains that we'd close when we pretended we were on safari.

Mona was a very beautiful woman, perhaps middle-aged, perhaps older. She wouldn't tell me. She had very long hair and at night she'd twist it into small braids. The procedure took hours. I sat behind her, she between my legs, and helped.

"Tell me about your husband," I said. "Is he very important?"

"No," she said.

"No, he's not important?"

"No," she said. "No, I won't tell you."

"You won't tell me if he's important?"

"I won't tell you anything," she said.

I had begun to notice that Mona was rather mercurial. From then on, she demanded I sleep at the foot of the bed. The bed was large enough that I didn't mind. I'd learned from a servant that her husband was indeed a famous artist who was best known for his series on gorgons. This made sense. My last night with Mona, I was awoken by a strange prodding at my bottom. I turned to see her hovering above me, eyes yellow and lit, her hair a mass of sleeping snakes. She was checking my temperature.

"I never had a daughter," she told me.

"Do you think I'm your daughter?" I asked.

"No," she said. "I think you're sick." She pulled the thermometer from my bottom.

"Well?" I said.

"You're fine," she said.

"Want me to check you?" I was under the impression this was a thing one did in France.

"Of course not." She slipped beside me under the covers and stroked my hair. "Tell me how to betray you," she said.

I didn't understand what she was asking me.

"I must know," she said.

I blurted the first thing that came to mind. "If you told me lies."

"Oh sweet girl," Mona said. "I've only told you lies. Name another."

She was right to scoff, learning she had been lying to me didn't offend me in the least. I sort of suspected. "I don't know," I said, and nuzzled my nose between her cleavage. "I can't think."

When I returned from the *patisserie* that afternoon with two armloads of baguettes, I discovered she'd locked me out. An envelope addressed to me was taped to the wrought iron gate that led to the entrance of her home. I opened the envelope. She'd written me out a bill for one hundred thousand dollars, on the bottom she'd scribbled, "pay up!" She was in one of her moods and I'd had it with her. I placed the bread by the gate, flipped the envelope over, and wrote, "I hope you find what you're looking for." This seemed like the type of thing a lover was supposed to say upon departure. I made my way to town, sat for a glass of burgundy, and pondered my next move when a woman my age approached me.

"She thinks you're a masochist," she said.

"Who?" I asked, though I knew full well who she was talking about.

"My mother," the woman said. "She wants you to grovel. She'll take you back. She wants you back."

This news angered me. "I'm no masochist!" I said. I marched back up to Mona's gate, huffing and puffing the whole way. It was only when I reached my note that I realized what she'd actually done. She'd tested me hoping I'd fail, hoping I'd remain pleading outside her gate, and here I was. I took the envelope still taped to the iron gate, marked out the note I'd left, and wrote instead, "You've betrayed me. I hope you never find what you're looking for." I drew a heart with a zigzag down the center to illustrate the pain she'd caused. I wanted her to know how important she was to me. Mona suffered strongly from what I suppose was what we call the human condition. We suffer it alone, unless one is a sadist, like Mona. I picked up one of the loaves I'd abandoned earlier, bit off the end, and went on my way. I thought of our first encounter and how incredible I'd felt in her hands. I thought about betrayal and how it must always come as a surprise. Otherwise we'd prepare ourselves for it.

Perhaps due to my limited education, these new revelations about the human condition did not affect me existentially. I did not grow morose. Perhaps I was a sadist too. Instead I became sentimental and spiritual. I reflected on my experiences. I thought about God once again, and my mother. I had never been one to dwell on the past, but my new appreciation for the world, for humanity, caused me to look back fondly on my life. I had had quite a ride. But this too had its end. I'd grown weary of my travels. The earth had taken on a certain flatness, like a map, and I was merely a dotted line skipping from continent to continent, sucking the poor thing dry of all mystery. I longed for something familiar.

I decided to head back home. I was nineteen years old and still in possession of my charms. I was sleeping on the couch of a commercial fisherman who lived on Cape Breton Island. I don't feel wrong in saying that he was bearded, crotchety, and gifted with an incessantly romantic ennui. He was headed in the right direction and agreed to drop me off at a port in Gloucester. We sailed the edge of the Atlantic in his barnacled *Nantucketer*. I agreed to sleep with him in the belly of his sturdy old whaler. We never bathed, but the smell of the sea filled our nostrils and it was all that we could perceive. Existence at sea, one might imagine, is quite fluid. We did everything together—ate, sang, twisted lines, positioned booms, navigated the meandering shoals—all with such ease and tranquility. We never had a stormy night, and the fisherman told me that I was very lucky for this. Stormy nights could fill a sailor with such dreadful knowledge. "Poseidon," he said, "is fickle."

The fisherman decided, in fact, that it was me who brought the calm seas. I told him of my mother and how she often spoke of my style.

"I haven't any knowledge of style," he told me. "But you sure are one lucky dame."

When we ported, I said my goodbyes. The man was shy at first but then grew angry. He shouted at me as I speed-walked down the street, and I heard the whizzing of beer bottles as they hurtled toward me and smashed on the cobblestones. I was beginning to develop a bad impression of him, but a sweet pain soon filled my heart when I noticed his screams turn to whimpers. I remembered Mona. I realized he had not understood that I would be leaving him, even as he sailed me to my next destination. I'd learned that there is very little one person can do to assuage these feelings in another, when your very existence requires that you part ways, and their very existence requires that you stay. We all must go on.

The air smelled quite differently on land, as though we had docked on a heaping pile of decay. My own unwashed body added to this stench. I turned around, close enough for him to hear me, far enough so that he couldn't reach me with his seemingly endless supply of empty beer bottles.

"I'll miss you," I shouted.

"I'll miss you," he shouted back, wrinkled old hands cupping his mouth. He too must have caught a whiff of the earth, realized anew how solid, dense, and detached we truly were.

I purchased a small vial of mustard seed oil from a street merchant just beyond the seaport, rubbed the oil under my arms, and hitchhiked south. I had not seen my mother in a long time and I hoped she was doing well, but there was no telling with that woman.

My old street spooked me. It was autumn time and the large oak trees around my mother's apartment building had shed their leaves all along the sidewalks. I remembered this from childhood, how adults always commented on the beauty. I had never found the trees beautiful. I thought them sad, weeping, ailing; their changing colors looked like sickness to me. Many people would travel to my hometown to see this natural wonder and I would pretend to appreciate it, but autumn was my least favorite season. I thought about my unconscious motivations for returning home during my least favorite season. I was mature now and thought about these things.

I arrived at my old front door. I did not feel entitled to enter. I knocked, though if I knew my mother she would never descend the stairs to answer. I was surprised when the door opened. A short and swarthy man stood in the frame and eyed me curiously. I could hear the announcer of a soccer game on the television, shouting in Spanish.

"*¿Donde esta mi madre?*" I asked.

The man looked me up and down and then shut the door in my face. My mother was not there. I went to the neighbor's house, an older woman I remembered from childhood. She didn't recognize me right away. She squinted, but then embraced me and invited me into her home.

"Your mother left this town long ago," she told me. "She'd taken up with some man, and no one's heard from her since. But by that time..."

The old lady faltered, caught herself, but I knew what she was going to say. By that time people had already forgotten about her, because she'd spent so many years in her bedroom.

"Do you know anything about this man?" I asked her.

"No," she said.

"Did she say where she was going?"

"No," she said.

I was amazed by this information. I was also amazed with my own feelings. I thought I might cry. I left the woman's house and walked back toward my old doorsteps. I sat on the steps and moped. The short and swarthy man did not like this. He came outside with a broom and shooed me away. "*¡Vete! ¡Vete!*" he said.

"Mama! Mama!" I shouted, as though she might still be in there. I couldn't imagine another person in her room. I know it's silly, but I still expected to find our dead cat idling in his litter box.

I had nowhere to go. I had never thought about life in these terms, because there had always been someplace to go. I went to the Jews, but they'd already taken somebody else in, a new wanderer who I found repellent and unattractive, though the Jews seemed especially fond of him. He was a doctor now in pursuit of his MBA.

"He's stable," my gifted friend said. "You might want to try it yourself."

"Stability?"

"Business school."

They didn't want me. I was surprised. So many people from all over the world had wanted me. Something in my universe shifted and I was all alone. Perhaps I had always been all alone but just hadn't known, hadn't felt the weight of the thing, or assumed it was only a passing state. I guess that was the day I understood my own dreadful fate. To never be in one place long enough to know what it is to belong, and, depending on my mood, this life was a profound gift or a terrible joke.

I'm well into adulthood now and I haven't lived in the same spot for more than a few months since I was a kid. I'm tired. It's not always easy being a one-man band. I know I have every reason in the world to be angry with my mother for not raising me right, but this is not why I'm angry. She strongly implied the day I left that she'd be home when I returned. I was very disappointed when I learned she'd gone off with some man. She had never gone anywhere with me. Thinking on this fact makes my throat tighten up with a salty taste, and I often find myself red-faced, biting back tears. The days when I'm most angry, I imagine this man abandoning her on the side of the road, leaving her in a horrible, dusty town where nothing ever moves. A county of the sessile. I imagine my mother suffering in the most unpleasant, stillest place on earth, worse than the bedroom. I'm not proud of these fantasies, but I'm only human, and she hurt me so badly.

Who knows, though? There's a chance I have one more adventure left in me. Perhaps it's time I went and found that woman once and for all. Maybe at a black sand beach in Hawaii or sipping from a canteen atop a camel overlooking a desert vista, or maybe just sitting at a quaint European café, reading Saint Simon and thinking about Western civilization, I might run into my mother there. I'll tap her on the shoulder and say, "Excuse me miss; just where in the hell do you think you're going?"

Marija Stajic
SIRENS

When the bombs break the earth, it feels like your house is coming down on your head. And on your family. And you thought you were so young, and had your whole life ahead of you. And the fact that you never left Serbia didn't matter because there was so much time ahead. And the fact that you only studied and dated stupid boys. And all of a sudden, with a pilot's hand movement, with some muscle and joint contraction, with a screech of release and a smell of burnt metal, there is a whistle in the air above your head, and you're ticking the rest of your life away listening to that whistle growing meaner and louder. And the fear is unlike any fear you ever felt before, any fear you ever read about in a book. And you don't even care anymore if God exists or not, if there's heaven or an afterlife or reincarnation. You just want to live.

And when your house shakes from foundation to roof, and the crystal chandeliers swing viciously, and the glasses and porcelain break, and your great-grandmother's armoire that stood in the same spot for a century slides toward you, you wonder if you're still alive. And when you feel your heart is fighting to break out of your chest and jump and run and hide, and you're all drenched in sweat and tears, and your mother is pulling her hair out like in those heroic epic poems you studied in school, and your father is on his knees peering out of a broken window, you realize you are still alive. Then you hear another whistle. Groundhog day. And even if your sweaty palms are on your ears, you still hear men and women and children screaming in the streets, you hear cats and babies and dogs wailing alike, and cars starting and someone swearing at Christopher Columbus, and at someone's fucking American mother, and at Milosevic's mother, and you hear doors slamming, and someone's running.

Then the lights go out everywhere. A whole new layer of terror. And then you think if you're still alive, you won't be for much longer. And this must be how the grave looks like from inside. Then you hear seconds in your head, filled with lead like bombs, but they seem like minutes now. Then like hours. And suddenly everything silences. And you're thinking, this is it, I'm dead. It wasn't too bad, it didn't hurt too much. Until you hear a siren. But you don't know what it means, because, when in your twenty years of life did you ever hear a siren, and it's not like they teach sirens in school. And when a neighbor chants: "Curfew over," and his voice is first louder then fainter, and then the lights go on again, on the street, then in the house, and you see your mother weeping. And your father grabs your shoulders and asks you, Ana, are you OK. And his hands are bloody but you can't speak. And your mother hugs you so tight that you can barely breathe. And then she releases you, and you see her mouth move but you can't hear her.

David A. Taylor
HUMANE SOCIETY

Sitting in the van a block from the cat woman's house, I can see the light in her window: third from the end in a long string of brick rowhouses. Since she called in, she must be stirred up and now she's probably furiously tidying up before I get there. I pull into the alley behind Ms. Thundercats and first check on the bulldog who lives at 1814. The bulldog stays on the porch when I stop at the back gate, like he's trying to keep out of view. Tied there? Not normal behavior but not a citation offense.

After that reconnaissance, I park on the street in front of her place, walk up, and knock on the door. No response.

"Hey, Annette," I yell. "Can I come in?"

It amazes me how little most Americans know about this city. When I first came here for college, I imagined that D.C. was all monuments and white marble and every street corner had a view of the Washington Monument. When I see those images on TV now, I know immediately the handful of locations the camera crew visited.

Because I cover most of the city every day. And after three years in this job, the District strikes me mainly as poor. Poor and full of creatures needing love. But like the saying goes, "For the person with a hammer, everything looks like a nail." So when you work for the city's Animal Services, I guess...

"Coming!" The voice inside is muffled by carpets, boxes, and moldy papers. I can picture the maze from her perch in the dining room to the front door—what would be a twenty-foot path grown over with steroid-fueled kudzu. She takes a full circuit around the mammoth table and through a distant door to the kitchen that isn't blocked. She slides through the canyon, around, then... The bolt slides and the door opens and I step inside.

"Kathy, you can help me with this thing—" she says, already turning away.

In a glance I see we're back to square one with her cat problem. Feces all around, dribbles of food here and there, and fur—my god.

"Annette, you told me you weren't going to take in any more cats," I say cheerfully.

"I didn't!" She slips into the kitchen.

"I see five new ones here in this room."

"I don't know how they got in! That's another thing I was going to ask you."

That means a trip to the office to take at least five, we'll see how many. "I'm going to have to call social services again," I say. "You know that, right?" At this point I can make that assessment real quick: social services, elder protection, child protection—I have those numbers on speed dial. I light them up every day.

"But you'll be good with them, right?" she says.

I give her a stare. "Of course."

This morning Jerry left the apartment before me without a word. To me, anyway. He whispered "Good girl" to Crystal as he opened the door and he was gone. Not a good sign, I thought as I started my shift. I scrolled through the messages that came in overnight—a dozen emails and two voicemail questions transcribed by the program.

I was sitting at that computer in the tiny office upstairs. My review of the messages took just a minute—not many calls last night, and the answering service handled them all. I logged them and got ready for my morning route. Above the computer hangs a poster of a sleeping cat, with the caption, "How do you become an accomplished serial killer? Practice. Practice. Practice."

"Sergeant," said Adele as I started to leave. "Just the person I want to see." She's got a tough form of intimacy that puts me on alert. A neighborhood meeting was coming up in Petworth, she said, and she needed a body to make an appearance. A small white woman would do fine, she joked. A week from Tuesday?

Adele has something going on in her life. I judge this because lately she's been real attentive to Dotty, our office mascot, giving her extra treats. Today while she ordered me to attend a community meeting next week, Adele kept her eyes on Dotty trotting through the office, back to her crate. Adele has lived with a guy for five years, a cop in the fifth precinct. She treats his daughter like her own. She's been a steady character as long as I've known her, but now she's jumpy like I've never seen her. Her curls seem to bounce around her face, black handfuls of them. Smiling, but something's up.

I walked through the animal shelter downstairs. Two volunteers were cleaning out cages. A wave to them and I'm out the back door to my van.

This is the moment I love, with my route ahead of me—no urgent calls pulling me to a crisis, so I'm free to plan my path through my district. In my head I run through the addresses from the past month, plus the ones from last night that send up red flags.

That's as close as I get to my dream where I fly low over the city, passing over alleys and homes along my circuit, the fences and porches and little backyards of Northeast D.C., from the treeless projects of Lincoln Park to the leafy homes by the big cemetery on the hill above Bladensburg Road. I can't remember where the dream took me. In three years I have accumulated loads of addresses in my head. I have even corrected the dispatcher when she gets a number wrong. I say, "There ain't no 500 block of Meridian Place." It gets a laugh but also respect.

After checking the van, I map out a plan, jam my coffee mug in the holder, and flip the ignition. My beat begins. The dregs of rush-hour ooze past on Georgia Avenue. Let's go see the old woman hoarder who calls me the White Devil. It's been weeks since I checked in with her. I zigzag toward Rhode Island Ave.

When I told my mother that story, her eyes rolled back up into her head like a winning slot machine. She can't stand the thought of me cozying up to hoarders and people who call her daughter "White Devil." I tell her I'm getting it as a tattoo in goth lettering. I tell her my job really is about helping people as much as the animals.

It's actually the hoarders part that disturbs her. It haunts her with her own worst tendencies. She and my dad split up when I was at college, and since then whenever I visit she shoos me away from the basement door. "That's where all the bodies are," she says with a rubbery frown. All the stuff she can't bear to get rid of.

"I hate to think of you wasting all your talents on Crystal," she says, changing the topic. My mother is not a dog person. She likes Jerry well enough, but just.

Ten minutes after leaving Annette, I'm tooling through Brightwood, checking alleys where I've seen dogs chained in the past few weeks to see if their owners need a Strike Two.

I'm back of Lawrence Street looking around. Neighbors don't take abused animals seriously—they don't report it—but the people who abuse them are real time bombs. So I'm doing a public service here, not just being a bleeding heart.

I've seen some weird shit out here. Like the time I got a dispatch to where a neighbor reported a guy beating his dog. I pulled up to the address and I could see a big man sitting on the porch, hunched and tense. Across from him was a little white fluffy dog, tethered on a massive chain, like a tow chain. The dog wasn't moving. As I got closer I saw it was bleeding from the nose. Staying real still, but breathing.

Same with the guy: his arms stayed clenched, and when I spoke to him he barely said anything.

"We need to get your dog to a vet," I said. He said the dog was all right.

"Can he stand up?" I said. I felt myself tensing up.

"Sure he can." He yanked on the chain—lifted the dog to its feet long enough for me to see a leg was injured. I pointed that out. "He can stand," he said. "He's just dumb."

That sentence landed inside my chest and my stomach, hard. I started shaking. *He's just dumb*. That guy rang something inside me.

As I called it in, I kept thinking of Jerry, of how that guy would unhinge him. Of how he talked to Crystal.

Anyway I'm in the alley behind Lawrence and looking around, and that's when I come across the Pyrenees in the car. Big white blob on the backseat. Not moving. Probably been there overnight. I call it in and then I get out to try the car doors. All locked. And I can see by this point that it's clearly dead—body starting to bloat. Oh god. I'm going to have to break into this car and wrestle this dog out and into my van.

I look around but there's no one else in the alley. I slide the coat hanger in the window (most of the cars I deal with are old) and in minutes I've got it open. Then it's just me and the Pyrenees, doing a dance. Ninety pounds of stiff, bloating canine—practically my size—that I need to grapple into the van. Very sad, but no room for sadness, just heat and the struggle of limbs and gravity.

It is the most awkward and exhausting eon of my life. I feel so incredibly alone, like the only person in the city. The alley is wilderness, I realize after five minutes of wrestling Charlie (I name him that once I get him sprung from the car) into the body bag and across the dirt of the alley to the van. After I close the bag, the alley feels more like a battlefield. I'm three hours into my shift.

It takes me a few minutes in the shade to write up my dance with Charlie. Then I call the office and confirm that I'm bringing him in before the sun heats him up much more. I choose a route that takes me past the alley where we found Senteria activity a few months before.

Nothing to see there, so I go back to the office, handle Charlie, and am back out on the streets.

Later that afternoon I'm up near Lincoln Heights and the streetlights in the alley are coming on. Clouds have come in dark. D.C. hardly ever feels threatening. That, too, is hard for my mother to get. I make the mistake of telling her stories like the guy with the chain, just trying to show her how it's the people who need care. I mean, she gets that, but it makes her uncomfortable.

The wind is flipping the leaves of the saplings in the alley so their light undersides are flapping at the sky and I smell rain coming. As I turn into the alley I'm surprised it's already dark enough that my headlights light up a woman's face as she crosses quickly and goes to the street behind. She looks pissed.

Near the end of the block I see, cowering in a yard, a knot of four puppies. No more than a few weeks old. Locked in the Long fence, no shelter. Babies out in a storm. In a case like this, the owners are criminally liable. I go around front and knock. No answer.

I don't like doing it, but I can't leave these little things out in the weather. I reach over the fence and just manage to scoop up the first two, then grab the others.

I get them into the crate in the van, then pull around front to leave a note. The rain is coming down now. It's full dark. I pull onto Bennington. At the next red light, someone knocks on my window and I see the same angry eyes that the headlights caught a few minutes ago. The woman from the alley—and she's got a beef. She is yelling, furious about her puppies being stolen.

I firmly decide not to engage with her, but she steps in front of the van so I can't move.

"Gimme back my puppies!" she screams. "You stole my puppies!"

"Ma'am, I'm sorry. They were out in the open and in this storm... You know they need to have shelter, right?"

I'm talking loud through the glass so she can hear, but I'm not lowering the window. Her face is two hundred volts of rage.

"You stole my fuckin' puppies, bitch!"

I have handled many tense situations in this job and have become, I'd say, expert in defusing them. But this woman does something to dig past all that expertness.

"Ma'am, calm down!" I scream through the windshield. In that situation, I'm supposed to give her a business card so she can call the office and get her puppies back. I know that.

She starts hammering the glass with her fists and gets a smack from the windshield wipers. I put the van into reverse.

"You are *not* taking my fuckin' puppies!" She steps forward. "Get out of the van."

Something—her expression or the drop in her voice—takes me to a moment with Adele. One morning about a month ago, when Adele's new relationship had just started, I was at the office when she got in and I don't remember what I did, but it didn't matter. Her reaction was to something else, someone not in the room.

"The puppies will be safe," I say now to the crazy woman. "But you need to make a shelter in your yard. That's the law! There are lots of cheap and easy options." I'm starting to breathe better.

"Fuck that!"

I spin the wheel left and release the brake, but she steps toward the van again and I stop just short of hitting her with a fender.

"Those are *my* puppies!" She steps back at the last second. "I'll bring them inside."

"This gives you a day to get something ready for them," I yell.

The storm lightens up for a moment, like it too is taking a breath. There's a moment where I feel there's a way out of this. Then comes a fresh gust and a thousand rain pellets rake the windshield and the van's roof.

"Goddammit!" she yanks on the driver's door handle. "I'm gonna *kill* you!"

Her fury ignites mine, and it starts burning on my neck, like a searing tattoo. It takes all the strength I can muster *not* to ram my right foot on the gas and blow that woman into the pavement. Shockingly—all I can muster.

I focus on the puppies. They are right behind my seat. From the unprotected terror of the prairie-like backyard, they have been pulled into the unknown metal darkness of my van's cage.

Like them, I can't see anything ahead of me—but I have to get out of there. So I inch the van forward. I don't have room to give a shit about some mad bitch standing out in this downpour, cursing me. She has no choice but to move aside.

A block later I pull over and gulp in big breaths through my mouth. The rain is thundering on the van's roof. My shame—I have lost my professionalism, so much that I came really, really close to doing harm—makes my arms go slack and numb.

I breathe again. I think of the first batch of cats I took from Annette's house. How she called me "white devil" and we both laughed at that later. I undo my seatbelt, listen for the rain to let up. I slide back between the seats, back to the cage holding the puppies. I kneel beside them.

They're cowering against the edge, silent, breathing.

Varsha Tiwary

A PEAR A DAY
(AND OTHER PROVERBIAL TRUTHS)

My town was a dusty, dull small town known for nothing before the Big Rape happened. Rapes, of course happen in every small town in India, all the time. I am fifty years old and I do not remember a time when I was not afraid of Rape. Even before I knew the meaning of Rape, I was afraid. Of the terrible things that can befall a woman, it is the worst. Worse than death even. That is why it is our duty to take due precautions against Rape. But that is only when you look at it from individual point of view. From the societal point of view, Rape is Routine. It happens to others. It is means to an end. Normally Rapes are reported, if at all, in side margins of page five of big newspapers. Everyone knows newspapers are in the business of bad news. No one takes them seriously.

I used to be Virgin-Mother-Goddess-of-Cool and had temples to myself all over these parts. Myself, Manju, I am named for Goddess Parvati, you see. But I am just another housewife. Every morning I meditate on a *shloka* from *Bhagwad Geeta*. I do ten *Surya Namaskars* and visit Ram temple for *keertan*. Twice, I have sung devotional songs on All India Radio, Haspur. They say I have the Third Eye and the Inside Story on everything. And all kinds of feelings. Contradictory. I love Girl Child. I want to save her. I love my daughter even though she has this condition. Autism, they call it. I have duty towards my husband, Rajesh Pannu, also. He has been kind to me even though I have not borne him any sons. I am having only black tea for last four days and it makes my head ache. Forgive me, I ramble.

Let me tell you right at onset—I am patriotic Indian. My ring tone is "Jai Ho"! I go to the women's shelter every Saturday to impart to homeless, abandoned girls instruction on personal hygiene and useful crafts. I was the star campaigner of Clean India Campaign. Our ward was cleanest in the whole town and I received a badge from the honorable MLA himself. "Filth Free Haspur" was our slogan. Some big newspapers have been calling it ironic. I don't know what that means.

I am having breathing trouble these days. Otherwise I was much more active. I used to walk two miles daily and never had weight problems. But so much pollution everywhere, anything can happen. One thing after another.

That is how I knew the little girl. She and her mother came to deliver milk. Goat's milk. Doctor said that cow's milk is not so good if you have asthma. Could be allergy, cows eat rubbish, polyethylene and all. I told her to be quiet for how can you say like this about cow mother? But I listened to her for my good.

Raziya and her mother started coming to my house every evening with the goat's milk and no more headaches. No more breathing troubles. No more rashes. I would give the little girl Parle-G biscuits and a cup of tea to her mother. Of course, I made her tea from normal dairy milk as goat's milk is much more expensive. They would sit in the backyard under a banyan tree. She was nice. My daughter Minny, poor girl, stays mostly silent, unsmiling, aloof. But with Raziya, she smiled. Laughed even. They played. Why would I mind it? The mother always remembered to wash her tumbler and keep it on the ledge outside the kitchen. So you can see I have only good feelings for fellow Muslim people. People say these people will give the evil eye. But I am modern and educated. I never believed in that nonsense.

As Rapes go, this one was standard. Rape as a Lesson and warning to Muslim shepherds who stole Hindu lands. Even if Muslims claimed to have paid for it, everyone knows that they are foreigners and can have no claim over town lands. Land is such an emotive issue, you see. It is only fear for their women which can make them give up land. My husband says how these people breed! They will soon grow so many in number that we Hindus will be refugees in our own homeland. This urge to secure our lands led to the whole unfortunate incident. Now people are using that one thing to tarnish the glorious image of Hinduism. My husband's uncle knows someone in the police department, so he knows. First duty in such situations is to ensure that things are kept under control. Communal fires are not fanned. Allegations by one community against the other tend to get out of hand. Hence, for the sake of the larger good, the police were playing it low. Things went out of hand when foreign media fed by paid Delhi journalists and hyper-activist types from JNU leaked unnecessary details, leading to court orders to release the charge sheet! Allegations! Based on false complaints! By some greenhorn policewoman! Concocted. The noxious details, that any seasoned administration would have kept a lid on, were let out mischievously and everybody got hurt. It was a media conspiracy, everyone knows. So unnecessary! For nothing! All the righteous anger!

As my husband says, context is everything. Eight-year-old. Raped in temple. Four days. Four men. Said in that sensational way—makes it horrific.

This is not how it is from societal point of view. It is about historical wrongs. About who started it first. About teaching *them* a lesson. Because if you don't teach them they will teach you. Of course when I think about her face—her eyes—tears come to my eyes also. What to do? But that is not the main point.

Now my unknown town is known to everybody. Branded as the only town on earth to rally massive support for a gang of rapists. Put in this alarmist way, it sounds so crude. It is like one of those Horror stories that I like watching. Out of nowhere, black gelatinous alien spiders jump on you and suck out your lifeblood, little by little. Listen, we are good, God-fearing, law-abiding people. You cannot tarnish us like this. What can you expect from Foreign Media after all? Can they even understand the Hindu-Muslim nuances and the just anger of the majority on being deprived of their rights? Can they ever get that fanning of communal fires is far bigger danger than random lustful acts of some men?

My husband says it is only negative incidents like this that are deliberately highlighted in national and international media. When was there any positive news? Always it is made out Muslims are having problems whereas they never had any problems here. They are living like Kings! The Foreign Media wants to derail the progress we are making by causing social divides. Our beloved country is being stabbed from all quarters by external forces!

I can say with hand on my heart that the men who did it are not known to us. My husband, however, had no choice, but to stand up and protest against their arrest because till the courts decide and charges are proved, everything is an allegation and will you not stand up for a fellow Hindu if he is in trouble? They, the Muslims, always stand behind one another. Us Hindus are always divided. As you can already see, even now, it is the citified Hindus in Delhi who are organizing all the candle marches and bleeding their hearts in manufactured anguish. I tell you. These are bad times. I am totally drained. Not eaten for eight hours. Stood in the sun for five. It is the fourth day without goat's milk and my migraine and asthma are worse. It is not as if we too have not suffered enough because of all this. Still I bear it all stoically.

As a mother I have another thing to say. What kind of mother, which parents, would leave their daughter alone and let her roam all over the town? Even if she is eight years old? I never leave my daughter alone. If I have to, I lock her in. Then padlock the front gate also. Like now, I have to lock her in every day to sit on fast in support of my husband's friends.

I agree, of course, that the whole thing was unfortunate. Badly managed. Ill conceived. They should have known better. Picked up a grown-up woman.

And found a better location! Reduced the number of days! I don't know why they had to confess that they raped her dead body. So unnecessary! It's not as if the eight-year-old could feed their lust! They were only doing it as a duty to their *dharm bhais*. It is our duty to show support for them. So I sit here in the heat to show they are not alone, even if I have to lock in my Minny to take part in the rally demanding release of our accused Hindu brothers in front of the police station.

She is nine, but in Class 1, as she is slow in mind. Teacher does not understand that. She has sent me a note saying that when told to write "pear," she wrote "Rape" all over the page. I keep telling Minny how she must never write or speak dirty words. Every day, I tell her. Rape dirty. *Chee.* We never use that word. Write "pear" now. OK?

Only problem is, my daughter, she shits in her pants when I leave her alone these days. We can afford diapers, we are well-off by God's Grace. But the devil has gotten into her! Maybe from playing with that Muslim girl. She cries out her name every time the television is switched on and takes out her diaper and flings it onto the walls. Wailing. She is so disturbed! When I open the lock, the stench makes me faint.

I really think they should have left the temple alone.

M. Kaat Toy
ENTERING ATLANTIS

(excerpt from the novel, "Simone Says")

Two weeks after her job in the Fashion Office of an upscale department store in downtown Los Angeles is discontinued, Hope begins busing at Atlantis, a popular seafood and pasta place on the pier in Perpetua, an artists' colony and gay resort south of San Francisco where she has come for the summer season.

Atlantis is rugged and spacious. The floor is concrete; the walls are dark rough-hewn wood decorated with wreckage from the sea—old anchors, whale bones, and marker buoys; the wooden booths and tables are homemade; the wooden chairs are from yard sales. Through the large windows, the tips of the waves slosh on the horizon. Staring out during a lull, Hope feels seasick.

Busing is physically harder than waitressing and pays less, but there is less responsibility so Hope likes it better. She wears the required solid-colored T-shirt rolled up to her shoulders, dark blue pedal pushers rolled up to her knees, and white tennis shoes, looking faintly sporty and nautical. The waiters wear striped T-shirts, a distinction only the employees notice. The customers can't tell the waiters and bussers apart.

Malcolm, an intelligent efficient brusque gay man, about sixty-five, who has bused over forty years, trains her. Slight and clean-cut with a tan from bicycling that looks like varnish over his well-defined muscles, he is the fastest busser in town. He works six nights a week and makes a dollar an hour more than the other bussers. He insists everything be done his way and up to his speed, but he has thought it all out and has a consistent logical plan. The point is to turn the tables over fast.

Atlantis is a good place to work, and there isn't much employee turnover. Most of the waiters have been to college and most have worked there for over ten years. They are professionals. They are all gay queens who called each other "miss," "honey," and "girlfriend." Hope feels awkward referring to a grown man as "she" and understands by their lack of response she isn't supposed to.

Duane, the headwaiter, is a cute little middle-aged queen with graying brown hair, big brown eyes, a turned-up nose, and a turned-up butt. Everyone hates him for his rude condescending ways and for being barely competent at anything besides sucking up to Barney, the owner, and messing everybody up.

The waitstaff is all male because the thick white restaurant china filled with lobsters, bouillabaisse, and steamed clams in broth is too heavy for most women to carry then serve. Barney frowns on the use of portable tray tables in the dining room, and there are few places to set a tray down.

Hope likes not competing with any women for attention, but balancing a tray against her left hip with her left hand and loading it with her right, she strains her left shoulder each time she clears a table where the guests are sitting. She is expected to clear at least four dinners, sometimes six; if each dinner dish has a serving plate under it, she is holding eight or twelve plates with one arm. If the people are gone, she sets the tray on the table, but then she feels obligated to load it so heavily her back aches and her legs tremble as she carries it to the kitchen. Everyone tells her she will adjust.

The guys in the kitchen are straight. The head cook—Benny—who has a beer belly and an impish quizzical baby face—is Barney's stepson. With the cheerful confidence that comes from working a job he no longer finds challenging, he enjoys giving the waiters a bad time.

Saturday night, clearing her tray at the dishwashing station, Hope watches Benny. With fake naiveté he asks the waiters picking up their food, "What's long and hard and full of seamen?" The way he says "seamen" makes it sound like "semen."

The waiters don't answer, just put spiced apple rings and parsley on their plates with limp-wristed disgust.

"A submarine," he says, smiling at Hope.

The other busser, Adam, is a small, well-built, smoothly groomed local kid who worked at Atlantis the previous summer. In the kitchen, he talks to the waiters about the chicks and hot babes at the tables—teenaged girls having dinner with their families—and gets advice for hitting on them. The waiters will turn him into a pet and ruin him, Malcolm says. They seem to have hopes of making him gay, and he is either clueless or ambivalent, Hope thinks, to talk to them like that.

Adam cruises the dining room looking for girls, ignoring empty glasses or salad bowls and forgetting to reset tables. The gay men call him over to chat. Hope looks to Malcolm. He is steadily clearing, oblivious to Adam's wrongdoing. Only Hope feels the injustice. She can't say Adam isn't good at what he does. When he wants to, he picks up plates so quickly and precisely she can only stop and stare, immobilized by his speed. He can carry a tray full of dishes with one hand, another stack in the other hand—twice as much as she can with half the effort—and there is nothing she can do about it. She can stay in constant motion, but she cannot turn herself into an eighteen-year-old boy with that kind of muscle and endurance.

Four hours into Hope's shift, customers are piled outside the door. Every table is filled. Hope buses and sets with as much speed as she can.

Duane follows her, leaning into her face and shouting, "Pick it up! Pick it up!" which unnerves her and makes her go slower. He wouldn't do that to Malcolm or Adam, but they are faster—and they are male.

When Adam clears a table and doesn't reset it, Hope tells him to. He says, not defensively, "I forgot."

Hope can't imagine forgetting to set a table. Adam wanders off, still forgetting.

Duane calls to Hope, "Get these tables reset!" pointing to tables everywhere. "There are all of these parties that have gone out!"

"Adam is the one not resetting," she replies, reduced to sounding like a querulous child.

"You let me deal with Adam," Duane answers, but he doesn't.

Is he afraid to? Embarrassed to? Hope wonders.

Minutes later Duane tells Hope, "There's a party sitting at table A, and the table has not been cleared and reset yet," as if it is her fault he put them there.

She goes over. There really are people sitting at a table full of dirty dishes, not theirs. She apologizes.

"It's not your fault," they say. "We had reservations, and they kept us waiting."

In the kitchen the waiters give Adam dating tips—how to talk to girls, what to say to the girls' parents. He is deciding whether to keep his current girlfriend. Her car is in the parking lot. He drove it to work. He is interested, primarily, in getting laid by anyone dumb enough to have him, he makes clear.

"Get me four waters on fourteen, Hope!" a waiter calls out as he passes by. "Can you get me six waters, honey?" another asks her.

"Hope, I need four waters!"

Meanwhile Adam, who cannot carry a tune, whistles and sings. Hope has heard the phrase "tuneless whistle," but she hasn't heard one. *What is the point*? she wonders. It's just hot air blowing over his lips, dry and papery. *I hope you can fuck better than you can whistle*, she would say to him but she doesn't feel like being that friendly.

At the dining room busing station as she reorganizes dishes on a tray, Duane gives her a dirty look. He thinks she is wasting time when really she is making space to save time taking in another load.

Sucks being you, doesn't it Duane? she would like to say. *Sucks having to watch me.*

"It's fierce out there," she tells Jack, the dishwasher, in the kitchen. A middle-aged former boxer—good-looking with a flattened hook nose, a warm brown tone to his skin, and pumped-up shoulders and arms—he is also a flirt.

"What?" he asks, pretending to be deaf.

"It's fierce."

"You fear?"

"It's fierce. Duane hates my guts."

"Oh, that."

When Adam comes in, Jack, who knows Adam's parents, asks how they are. Adam, with his tuneless whistle, his flirtatiousness, and the way he is made to feel comfortable taking all the space, seems to be having a completely different night than she is. She has to figure this out: how to get along with stupid people who hate her and have power over her. It has to do with her attitude, her demeanor, which she has to change and control.

Sunday night when Hope comes in at four to set up, in the kitchen Benny is happily cutting out pictures from a girlie magazine with a meat cleaver. The pictures he prefers, which he tapes on the wall near the grill, are of women's hairy open crotches—split beavers.

"Is that fine art or gourmet cooking you're doing?" Hope asks as he lays down the cleaver and picks up the tape.

"Gourmet cooking," he says, looking at her with a brief smile.

In the dining room, two of the waiters, Stefan—the youngest, flashiest waiter who dominates the dining room with his flourishes, speed, and Hispanic good looks—and Raymond—who is fortyish with chic bleached blond hair and thick black plastic–framed Clark Kent glasses—set tables as she stacks glasses at the busing stand.

"I saw Adam downtown the other day with his shirt off," she hears Raymond brag. "*Uuhhh*," Stefan and Raymond moan, then giggle like girls.

"He said he'd miss me if he went to work somewhere else," Stefan replies.

Later in the kitchen the waiters divide up a slice of bread pudding a customer left untouched.

When they offer Adam a bite, he announces very seriously, "I don't eat that junk. My body is a temple."

"Yeah, the Temple of Doom," Raymond responds. Everyone laughs.

It is Malcolm's night off, so Hope and Adam are the only bussers.

After the first round of diners leaves, Adam tells Hope, "If you want to go now, you can. I can handle it."

When it isn't busy, Barney sends the extra busser home to save the extra wages. Duane divides the tips by the hours, so if Hope—who was the first one in, so she will be first to go—leaves, Adam will make more.

Hope tells Adam to ask Duane if she can go. Even after Duane says no, Adam, bored-looking and fidgeting, keeps telling her she can go.

"You're making me feel unwanted, Adam," she finally responds. Actually, he is pissing her off.

A few minutes later he insists again, "You can go."

"No, I can't. You wouldn't tell Malcolm that he can go. You wouldn't tell anyone but me."

"I'm just telling you to go because I thought you wanted to," he says innocently.

"You already asked Duane. Those decisions aren't up to us."

"I know," he admits. "I was hoping to get some extra time. I need the money."

They're all hoping to get extra time. They all need the money. Adam isn't even supporting himself. He lives at home. One waiter wouldn't say to another, *You can go now. I'll take your tables. It's no problem. I need the money.*

Later, while she unloads her tray in the kitchen, Raymond, running his hand through his blond hair and adjusting the corner of his Clark Kent glasses, expounds to her on an art show he has seen.

Duane tells him, "Don't talk to the bussers then complain about not getting your tables bused."

Hope, not aware that listening to Raymond has slowed her down, says, "There's a lull." There is. The waiters are standing around with nothing to do.

"There's never a lull for the bussers," Duane responds. The waiters look at him and each other.

Hope says nothing, thinking she can use that on Adam when he sits with the waiters at the end of the night while he is on duty and she cleans the dining room: "Duane says there's never a lull for the bussers, Adam." Adam is never reprimanded for hanging out in the kitchen talking to the waiters or standing behind the bar talking to the bartender while Hope and Malcolm work.

After Duane leaves the kitchen, Hope tells Jack, "I don't always think I'm appreciated around here."

Jack laughs. It's funny to think you might be appreciated. The dining room is still quiet when she goes out.

"I know you don't want me to say it," Adam begins, "but you can..."

She cuts him off. "It's not your place to tell me to go home. Either I will ask, or someone will tell me, but it is not your place."

Adam nods and keeps his mouth closed.

Luckily a crowd of customers comes in, and she is able to stay until the end of her shift; then Adam wants to trade so he can go out with his friends while she cleans up. She says no. She gets a Diet Coke and sits with the waiters while Adam works.

The following Saturday night a stray black and white cat that has been eating from the garbage cans outside Atlantis comes through the kitchen, lost and scared.

Hope calls, "Here, kitty. Here kitty, kitty," and directs it out the back door. When she returns, Benny smiles at her from behind the grill.

"I saw your pussy, Hope," he says.

"You did not see my pussy," Hope answers, pretending she doesn't understand.

"I did too. I saw your pussy."

She looks at him across the kitchen as if they really are arguing. "That wasn't *my* pussy."

At the dishwashing counter, Jack laughs. The waiters roll their eyes.

Hope picks up her tray. "It *wasn't* my pussy," she calls out just before she opens the door to the dining room which is hectic with people pouring into town for the weekend.

Adam has asked for the night off, so Hope and Malcolm are the only bussers.

They diligently carry load after load as the dining room turns over and fills up. "Smile, honey," Stefan tells her as she empties a tray in the kitchen.

She looks at him as he lines up salads. She isn't aware of not smiling—she isn't aware of anything but dirty dishes. "This is only a movie," he says.

"But I don't think I'm the *star*."

She tries to accept she has chosen this reality—she is the star of her movie. "Honey," Stefan says, dishing up the first of eight cups of clam chowder, "I'm sure all of us only have bit parts."

Later Malcolm criticizes her for filling the water pitchers for the waiters during the rush—"Let them do it themselves. It's a waste of our time"—though it is a busser's job. Duane yells at her to reset tables. She has four trays of dirty dishes in the dining room. The muscles in her calves and arms vibrate. She hates looking at her hands and seeing them quiver.

After the initial rush the waiters aren't busy; a lot of them are on tonight. They are only short on bussers, though Hope doesn't really wish Adam was there. In the kitchen, Raymond, while getting salads, sees how harried Hope is.

"So how are you this evening, Hope?" he asks, pausing to chat.

He enjoys needling people and causing trouble. He once said, as everyone talked about their sexual preferences, "I like to slap women and be slapped by men."

"A little shaky," Hope replies as she throws leftover bread into the bread recycling box.

"*Wellll*," Raymond says, raising his nose in the air and waving back his hand from the wrist, "you always were holding on by a *slender thread*."

The waiters turn to watch Hope's response. Raymond is bright, and Hope wishes he were nicer. She would like to be friends.

"*Thank you* for noticing," she says with mock grandeur. "So *few* people do." The waiters laugh, relieved she handled the attack.

At ten o'clock, the dining room closes, though it will be another hour and a half before the cleanup is over. Malcolm finds a quarter-filled bottle of wine on a table, and at the kitchen busing stand, Hope watches as he drinks it. His behavior becomes erratic. He starts clowning around and can't remember what he is supposed do. The kitchen crew goes outside and smokes dope. Jack is sent home. An hour before they finish, with a dining room half-full of dirty dishes, a prep cook, Tim, is left to finish the dishes, a job he doesn't like. Tim looks over the glass racks with his blue eyes wildly red from pot and announces he is closing down the dishwashing area.

"You can't close this early, Tim," Hope insists. He is tired and stoned. She is sympathetic but feels she can't allow this to happen. "You have to keep it open." It will kill her to sort and stack all the dirty dishes on the dishwashing counter instead of just setting them down and getting them washed.

"No fucking way, Hope." The pot released all of his hostilities. "No fucking way."

"There are too many dishes. It's too early. You can't close down."

"I don't give a fuck, Hope."

She goes out and comes back with a load of dishes. Tim is still closing.

"I'm going to tell Barney," she threatens. Everything is handled without going to Barney, but she doesn't know how to handle this. There really are too many dishes. She will never finish.

"Go ahead. Tell Barney. I don't give a fuck."

Barney is Tim's uncle.

She goes out and comes back, unloading more dishes. "No more fucking dishes, Hope."

Benny, who is in charge of the kitchen, could tell Tim to keep working, but he just looks at what is going on and walks away.

Hope puts down her tray and goes into the dining room, out of her mind with rage.

Barney sits at a table with Duane and other people. She tells him, "Tim is closing down the dishwasher."

"So?" He has had a few beers and is neither angry nor sympathetic.

"So it's too early. There are too many dishes. He can't close down. I told him he couldn't, but he's closing anyway. Could you say something to him?"

Duane is annoyed because Hope has gone to Barney. Barney stands and walks into the kitchen. She hears him say something to Tim. Barney walks out and sits down.

"Thank you," Hope says, dizzy with guilt.

She goes into the kitchen. Tim has the dishwasher open again, but he is furious, throwing dishes into the racks. She is afraid he will hit her. When they were growing up, her older brother hit her whenever he wanted. He never got punished. Their mother said she couldn't control him. *Tim isn't going to punch her out in the kitchen*, she tells herself. He can't get away with that.

Still, her mind is disintegrating with pain, hunger, and stress. She tells herself to calm down, but adrenaline dumps into her system every time she goes into the kitchen and faces Tim then returns to the dining room and sees Malcolm—who, in addition to drinking the wine, bought an end-of-the-shift drink and is drunk and hostile himself, muttering, knocking into things, slamming dishes on his tray.

She returns to the kitchen with another tray.

"We're fucking closed," Tim says. "No more dishes."

She starts to fill the glass racks, but she is trembling so hard she can't. Before she breaks something, she turns and runs out of the kitchen into the dining room, thinking she will keep loading trays until Tim finishes, but in the dining room she sees Malcolm then Duane then Raymond. She picks up a tray, but there is nowhere safe to go. She walks toward the back of the restaurant then runs. She throws her empty tray onto a table and shoves open the back door. She can't seem to control her reactions.

Outside in the dark, she sits on a parking block and lets herself sob. Raymond and Malcolm walk by, leaving for the night. They say nothing. Finally she goes in, picks up a tray, and loads it. She knows Barney won't fire anyone as long as you come to work, but what happens if you leave? In the kitchen, Tim is gone. There are stacks of dirty dishes everywhere for Jack to wash in the morning. Hope sweeps, embarrassed and afraid she will cry again.

In the dining room, Stefan helps her put up the chairs.

He asks, "Why didn't you tell Barney what was really going on? We all got in trouble, and we didn't do anything."

She is surprised. "I'm sorry. I was afraid. I didn't think Barney wanted to be bothered. I didn't think you guys would get in trouble."

Hope gets her tips, and they all go home. She doesn't understand how she draws this onto herself. She didn't get drunk or stoned or refuse to do her work, but she is the only one everyone is mad at.

Andrea Wyatt
HE'S CRAZY, EVERYBODY SAID

We met in the middle of Washington Circle as I was struggling to carry a bunch of oversized antiwar posters across the street. Posters that said *Hey, Hey, LBJ, how many kids did you kill today* with a blurry photo of a Vietnamese kid running down the street. Jean scooped the posters from my arms and carried them across the street to Moonstone, a science fiction and mystery bookshop in a crumbling Victorian house near Dupont Circle in Washington, D.C.

My friend Anita, who managed the shop, agreed to store the posters in the shop until the rally scheduled to be in front of the White House the following weekend. Days of Rage we called it. I was in a rage about the war. Everything else though seemed filled with possibilities, if we could just get out of Vietnam.

Anita and her boyfriend Phil lived in an apartment over the bookshop and she invited us upstairs. She brewed lapsang souchong tea and offered us cookies made with hashish in the shape of a peace sign. Anita's cookies were always very dry. She said there was an apartment next to theirs and she wondered if anyone we knew was interested. It was cheap, she said. This is how me and Jean came to move in together the same day we met.

He told me his name was Jean, pronounced in the French way, the "j" like the sound of the "s" in "measure" he told me; occasionally we met someone on the street who called him Richard but I didn't think much about it; it didn't matter.

He translated my five or six Eskimo mythology poems into what sounded like elegant French; he wrote them out in long hand] on heavy vellum paper— they looked grand. I planned to have them framed. He said we had to get out of America and move to Paris as soon as possible, to the 13th arrondissement where the Vietnamese live, or maybe he said wherever it was the Algerians live and we would be down with the real people, not the shopkeepers, the petit bourgeoisie, he called them, with a sneer, who were useless, no, more than useless because— and then he went on and on about obscure French history and politics that I couldn't follow even if I had wanted to.

I was a shoe store clerk at Papagallos in Georgetown, much to the disgust of my family who said I was wasting my life. It was an easy job and I had a great shoe collection. I wore short, bright-colored dresses that matched my shoes. I was twenty-three years old and I knew I looked great.

I never knew whether Jean would be at home when I arrived after work. When he wasn't there, the apartment felt like an empty stage, dusty and neglected. Sometimes he greeted me at the door, pretending to be a maître d', seating me in a grand and haughty way at our rickety wooden kitchen table. He poured a glass of red wine and served a plate of French garlic soup. I asked politely if he wouldn't like to join me. He considered my request for a moment, and then sat down. I liked watching him slice our daily baguette.

Everyone said, what's the matter with you? Why are you supporting him? What does he do all day? There's something wrong with him. He looks like a criminal, a mental patient. Is he a druggie? He was, of course, but not more than a lot of other people I knew. He looks dangerous, they said. But he did not; he looked like an angel, innocent and trusting as a baby. He's crazy, everybody said, but they never heard him recite French poetry in his faded beret, cracked black sunglasses, and extra-long silk scarf I think he stole from a downtown boutique, sitting cross-legged on our mattress, ranting about the world's failures and loss of nerve, about grief and how it never ends, about *Les Fleurs du mal* and "Le Bateau ivre," about Jean Genet, who Simone de Beauvoir called her thug of genius.

I loved hearing him talk, faster and faster and faster, his fluttering Benzedrine eyes, not able to settle, never settling on anything, his eyes flitting from side to side like moths, like flies on meat. He's crazy everybody said. But I loved how he spoke French, fast, smoky, his French accent, like Belmondo, or Godard, even though, as I later discovered, he was from Westminster, Maryland.

I loved that he was in Paris during the '68 riots, his thin shoulders moving up and down, accentuating his babble, babble, babble, as he described the French police, the street battles, smoke from his Gauloises Bleus filling up our bedroom. He couldn't stay in bed and rest more than an hour or two at a time, and even asleep, he twitched like a hound dreaming of a hunt, his hands were cold and he never wanted to eat which was OK, we had no kitchen, and he drank cup after cup of instant espresso that he prepared with bathroom tap water.

I was always shocked when the bennies or whatever drugs he was taking wore off. He would be excited and animated, and I felt like he would never let me sleep when suddenly it was almost dawn and he slumped against me just about unconscious.

I slid down quietly so he would not wake up and I held him in my arms and buried my face in his grimy, tousled hair.

Vonetta Young
AS FAR AWAY

When, in late summer 2002, Samantha told her mother Vera she wanted to go to college at Georgetown University, Vera said, "OK," with a shrug, as if it were as simple as signing some papers then moving in.

"I have to visit first," Samantha added. She stood in the doorway of their small kitchen, touching her fingertips together and shifting in her sneakers on the linoleum floor.

Vera looked at her daughter over her reading glasses and the bills that were strewn across the table in front of her. Through the thin curtains with cherry and blueberry prints, sunlight poured in, casting a spotlight on the papers. Vera exhaled, and Samantha knew it meant her mother was thinking about the time she'd have to take off work to take her. Vera did not go to college, but Samantha would, since the girl had made straight A's her whole life. She'd heard about Georgetown through a pamphlet she'd received in the mail and loved that it was in the capital city.

Vera sighed and said, "OK," again.

"Yes!" Samantha sang. She kissed her mother on the cheek, then ran to her room and called her best friend, Amy.

"Wait, where is it?" Amy asked.

Samantha rolled her eyes. "Washington, D.C."

"Wow," Amy breathed into the phone. "Isn't it dangerous there?" The pitch of her voice rose in morbid wonder.

"No," Samantha snapped. "I mean, yeah, there was 9/11, and the White House is there, but the rest of the city can't be any more dangerous than anywhere else."

"I guess..."

Samantha pictured Amy sitting in her bedroom, with pictures of Garth Brooks and the Backstreet Boys taped on the walls. Amy wasn't interested in leaving home. Looking up at her own walls, where her *The Fast and the Furious* and *Ocean's 11* movie posters were perched, Samantha could hardly breathe, she so much looked forward to living somewhere else.

Two weeks later, Vera and Samantha piled into the car for the drive from South Carolina to Washington, D.C. As her mother turned the air conditioning as high as it could go, Samantha gazed out the window at their neighborhood. The other houses looked just like hers, only with burgundy or green or blue fake shutters along the front windows, depending on the color the owners had chosen. The street was narrow, with no sidewalks. No one ever walked, so there was no need for them. As they drove closer to the interstate, the spaces between the houses grew wider, filled with trees and unkempt tall grasses.

Samantha's eyes widened the way they used to on Christmas morning as they drove across the 14th Street Bridge in Washington, D.C. Tourists and locals alike clogged the sidewalks, shielded from the sun by the shadows of big buildings, which weren't as tall as Samantha thought they would be. Cars honked at each other like ducks chatting in a pond, and an ambulance siren blared in the distance. Samantha's heartbeat quickened, matching the pace of the city around her. Vera mumbled to herself as she slammed on the brakes intermittently as cars switched lanes briskly in front of them.

When Samantha stepped out of the car in the Georgetown neighborhood, she was instantly in awe of the tree-lined, cobblestone streets. She could breathe so easily in the city. Birds chirped more crisply and confidently. The sun shined just bright enough to make everything look more beautiful, without the oppressive heat of home.

"This humidity is awful," Vera whined, wrinkling up her nose as she tried to breathe.

Samantha shrugged. Her mother was right; it was hot at home, but the air here felt like they'd walked into someone's mouth. Samantha hadn't noticed the beads of sweat forming on her cheeks until now. She wiped them away.

They found the admissions office in one of the castle-looking buildings and were directed to a room where chairs had been lined up for the presentation. They sat in the middle and silently peered at the other prospective students and parents filing in around them. There were all white boys in this group, as if someone had arranged for Samantha to be the only girl and only minority. She was used to the latter from her honors and AP classes, but being the only female body anywhere always bothered her. She could make white people forget that she was black, but it was much harder to get boys to not notice her boobs.

The boys seemed to have coordinated outfits: they all wore wrinkled, loose-fitting Polo shirts in various colors, pleated-front khakis, and leather loafers. Their mothers and fathers sat on either side of them wearing similar outfits. Samantha sighed and turned her attention to the front of the room, refusing to let her parents' divorce make her feel bad now.

Just then, a black boy and his parents came in and took seats in the front row. Samantha and Vera exchanged relieved looks.

When the talk began, Samantha sat rapt as the admissions officer went through a presentation about the history of the university, its notable alumni, and its academic programs.

"The vast majority of our juniors study abroad," the officer said. "We encourage our students to be not just good citizens of their countries—and we have students representing over a hundred nations—but to be good *global* citizens."

Samantha smiled widely. During spring break when she was stuck in the house because her mom was at work and she didn't have her license yet, she watched hours of the Travel Channel. She made lists of the places around the world she wanted to go: Brazilian beaches, big European cities that were way older than America, and hotels in Asia, where they had the best service on the planet.

"That sounds expensive," Vera whispered to Samantha, whose face fell.

As if on cue, the admissions officer continued to the most important part of the presentation: "This year, tuition and fees amount to about thirty-five thousand dollars."

All of the parents chuckled, but Vera's laugh eclipsed the others', bold and round as her tummy. Samantha closed her eyes and wished to disappear. She figured that she would qualify for a lot of financial aid since her mother was single and didn't make a lot of money. Samantha wondered if Vera was pretending this would be an unbearable burden just so she could fit in with the other parents. But they were clearly rich, so it was just an act for them, too.

Imagining the boys' wealth, Samantha fidgeted. She was smart, but she was *public school* smart, not *private school* smart. If they had paid all that money just to learn, then surely they had learned more than she had. Her mind wandered to how this would play out in classes; would she be able to ever raise her hand at all?

The admissions officer asked if there were any questions. The boy in the aquamarine Polo raised his hand and asked, "So, do you have, like, study abroad?" Samantha released a small, audible sigh of relief. At least she'd had the good sense to pay attention during the presentation.

After all the questions were answered, the admissions officer instructed everyone to file into the lobby, where the campus tour would begin. A white girl with blonde hair cut in a smooth jaw-length bob waited for them. She introduced herself as Katie. When the girl smiled, Samantha noticed that her left eye closed slightly. Katie wore a blue and white spaghetti-strapped dress with white leather flip-flops whose bottoms looked hard. Samantha looked down at her baggy white T-shirt and frayed denim shorts that touched her knees. She twisted her lips in consternation.

They followed Katie out of the building. She walked backward, pointing out to the group features about the campus and its buildings. Someone asked if she had studied abroad.

"Yes!" Katie said, smiling so big her left eye almost closed completely. "I just got back from China! It was *phenomenal*." She raked some of her almost-white hair behind her ear.

"China," Vera mumble-spat, holding her purse close to her. "I don't know why anyone would ever want to go to China. It's dirty, and it smells terrible."

Samantha looked at Vera. How would her mother know what China looked or smelled like? Vera had never left the U.S. She hadn't really been off the East Coast. Samantha knew better than to let her mother see that she was making a stank-face, so she turned her neck in the opposite direction. She gazed at the massive stones used to build the university's oldest building, constructed in the 1700s. She wondered if it might be a little bit haunted, and the thought of living with ghosts made her giggle to herself.

As the tour resumed, Vera continued to comment on just about everything: Katie's dress ("She probably should have wore pants with that Band-Aid on her knee"), shoes ("They're ugly, so they must have been expensive"), and pearl earrings ("They 'bout as big as her earlobes!"). Samantha covered her face for a moment, pretending to wipe sweat from her hairline.

Katie stopped the group at the top of a set of stairs. "Below is the Jesuit cemetery, which is considered hallowed ground."

The other parents and students peeked down and nodded, then were ready to continue. Vera clutched her ample chest.

"The blood of Jesus!" she yelped.

Samantha winced as the group turned to momentarily stare at her and her mother. She continued walking.

By the time the tour ended in front of the university bookstore, Samantha was both grateful it was over and intensely in love with the school. She could see herself walking across the lawn to class, eating with friends in the cafeteria, sitting in classrooms in the haunted old building. She would study abroad somewhere. She would get as far away as she could.

"I don't know about this place, Samantha," Vera said as she drove them out of the city.

"It's great," Samantha said definitively. She didn't need her mother's approval of where she went to college. She just needed to be accepted.

After eight hours of driving and stopping only twice for bathroom and food breaks, Vera pulled up to their house. Samantha gazed at it. Their home was tiny, with two bedrooms and one bathroom around which the two coordinated their morning routines. Samantha's parents had divorced long ago, so there was no space for her father, who lived in Tennessee with his new family. Samantha stared at the lawn. The grass was gray and brown, scorched by the summer sun and recent drought. The neighbor's cat scurried across, into the ditch along the street.

Samantha's chest swelled as she sighed. She was grateful that her mother had worked so hard to provide a home for her. Vera had sacrificed, working long overtime hours in her job as an administrative assistant in order to save for the down payment. They had shared a bedroom in the apartment of one of her mother's friends. She was nice to them, but it just wasn't the same as having their own space.

When they moved into the house five years ago, Samantha had been thrilled to finally have her own room. Over time, she decorated the walls with posters of her favorite movies, along with pictures of the leading actors from her favorite TV shows, *One on One*, *Smallville*, and *The Famous Jett Jackson*, that she'd cut out from magazines. Whenever her friends called, she hopped onto her bed after closing her bedroom door because she was happy to have a door she could close.

But Samantha wanted more. Not more *things*, but more of something she couldn't put her finger on. She had been born with a feeling that the world was bigger than her, that what she and her mother knew wasn't all that there was to know. As she grew up, she sought it out, reading endlessly and staying glued to the television. She was going to be the first person in her family to go to college, a burden she felt proud to bear. To her family, Samantha would be changing the world by doing something the other kids in the presentation found perfectly ordinary. She was thrilled to blaze the trail, especially since it meant leaving her tiny town filled with tiny ideas.

When Samantha saw the small envelope in the mailbox, she felt, physically, like someone had punched her in the gut. All breath was forced out of her lungs. She nearly screamed, but kept herself from crying. Now, she would be stuck here and, like Amy, would never, ever leave.

She went in the house and announced to Vera, "It's a small envelope—I didn't get in."

Vera frowned. "I'm sorry, baby. I know how much you wanted to go there."

Samantha nodded, finally letting tears come to the brim of her eyes. She went to her room and looked at the stack of three big envelopes she'd kept on her dresser. She'd been accepted to two state schools in South Carolina and one in North Carolina. But they weren't Georgetown. She sighed.

"Well, let me see if they were nice about rejecting me," she said.

She pushed her finger under the flap and slid the paper open. She unfolded the letter.

"*Congratulations*...? What? I got in? I got in!" She jumped up and down and ran to the living room. "I got in!"

"Praise God!" Vera shouted. She scooped Samantha into a hug. "I am so proud of you! I can't wait to tell everybody at work!" After a moment, Vera stopped and seemed to be thinking. "But are you sure you want to go? With the sniper and everything?"

Samantha had selectively forgotten about the father and son who'd gone around the D.C. area shooting people in parking lots and gas stations. Now, she shook her head.

"I'm going to be fine! I'm going!" She stopped. "There's no financial aid letter here, though. Can we afford it?"

Vera smiled proudly, showing the gap between her teeth she always said she hated. "We'll make a way."

Samantha rushed to call Amy and give her the news.

"Yay!" Amy said. "Just don't forget to come home and visit."

"I won't."

Samantha loved Amy and her mother, but she attempted to calculate how few times she could get away with coming home.

As Vera drove Samantha back to Washington, D.C., in August 2003, her face was stern. She didn't bubble with excitement the way Samantha wanted her to. Samantha thought about asking what her mother was thinking, but Vera had never been one to share her thoughts or feelings with her daughter, except when she needed to complain about work. Samantha stared out the window, watching Virginia go by.

When they arrived on campus, the parking deck swarmed with cars, trucks, and vans.

"Whoa," Vera and Samantha breathed.

Neither had expected it to be so busy, but Samantha wondered why not; she obviously wouldn't be the only one starting college. It took thirty minutes just for them to find a place to park, directed by an upperclassman wearing a T-shirt that read "Crew Team."

"What's a crew team?" Samantha asked her mother.

Vera shrugged. She jutted out her neck and squinted, as if inspecting the boy's shirt more closely would reveal the answer. "Probably something for rich people," she said, as if something rotten was on her tongue. A few seconds later, her gaze softened, surprising Samantha. "Why don't you ask him when we get out?"

Samantha thought about it, and only negative scenarios came to her mind: he would make fun of her for not knowing what it was, or he would not say anything at all, ignoring her, and she would be mortified. She pressed her lips together. This was one of those questions that she would not be able to ask, because she should already know the answer. She would have to pretend to know what crew was until someone else slipped up and asked, or until someone happened to talk about it in a way that she could put together the context clues.

As they got out of the car, another guy in a crew team T-shirt dragged over a cart. Samantha and Vera thanked him, but neither one asked what the phrase on his shirt meant.

They loaded up the cart with Samantha's luggage and hauled it out of the parking deck and down a narrow road to her dorm. By the time they got there—what felt like a football field's distance—they both were panting and sweating profusely.

"You're supposed to be young and strong," Vera laughed as Samantha bent over with her butt against the wall and her hands on her knees.

"Nope," Samantha said.

They watched other parents, mostly fathers, haul objects on their shoulders, or push their children's carts effortlessly. One girl pranced behind her father in a miniskirt and stiletto sandals, clinging only to the chain strap of her purse. Samantha and Vera rolled their eyes, then laughed.

They pushed the cart through the door and into the hall, which was bustling with kids waiting for their keys and parents waiting for their kids. Samantha avoided eye contact with anyone, unsure if she should start conversations before knowing where they lived. What if they didn't live on her floor? What if they were in the wrong dorm by accident, and she made friends with them by mistake?

After she collected her keys, Samantha and Vera with their cart squeezed into the elevator with another family.

A tall white man with dark brown hair spotted with gray stuck out his hand over the cart. "Frank Matthews," he said, revealing teeth as perfectly straight and white as he.

"Vera Jackson." She shook his hand and smiled back, showing her gap again. Samantha's eyebrows knitted.

Frank clapped the shoulder of the boy next to him. "And this is Tommy. Say hi."

Tommy mumbled, "Hi," looking down at the contents of her cart.

"Hi." Samantha wanted to feel as confident as Vera suddenly did when she shook hands with Frank. Tommy's downcast eyes sent a rumble through her stomach. She felt that her cart was missing something vital, otherwise, he would have been just as jovial to her as his father. She didn't want to say her name because she didn't want him to remember her.

"He's shy," Frank said, still smiling, but now shaking his head.

The elevator dinged and came to a stop. "This is it," Tommy said. He wedged himself out of the compartment and pulled his cart behind him.

Frank shook his head again as he stepped out. "Nice meeting you ladies."

"You too." The doors closed before Vera could get both words out. She pretended not to notice. "Well, he seemed nice."

"Yeah, right." Samantha wanted to roll her eyes, but she knew not to do it at her mother, only *with* her.

They found her room on the eighth floor, at the end of the hallway. Her name and another girl's name were written in Magic Marker on construction paper taped to the door. Theirs was the last room, next to the stairwell and emergency exit. Her heart still pounding from the interaction in the elevator, Samantha was relieved to see the placement of the emergency exit—in case of a fire, she wouldn't have to worry about running down the hall before running down eight flights of stairs.

The room wasn't big enough for the cart, so they left it in the hall and pulled Samantha's belongings out, piece by piece. When all of the suitcases and boxes were on the floor by her bed, they both stood in the middle of the concrete room and looked around, from floor to ceiling. Her roommate hadn't yet arrived, so she chose the side of the room she wanted, the one closest to the door, in case she needed to run away.

"All right, let's get you unpacked," Vera declared. She unzipped one of the suitcases at lightning speed, then walked across the tiny space and opened one of the dresser drawers. "Is the top drawer OK for your underwear?" She didn't wait for a response before taking handfuls of Samantha's cotton undergarments and placing them in the drawer.

Samantha gazed at her mother, horrified. Maybe meeting Frank had made her realize that she could date again and be happy, and she was now thrilled that Samantha would be out of the house. Samantha knew she couldn't say this out loud. She swallowed the words and bent down to unzip another suitcase and find a place for its contents, her hands shaking.

They spent an hour arranging Samantha's clothes in the closet and drawers. They put sheets on the bed and put the movie poster Samantha had brought with her on the wall. When she was satisfied with how everything was put away, Samantha sat on the bed, trembling almost imperceptibly. Vera sat next to her.

"I'm proud of you, Sammy."

Samantha smiled, and started to say thank you, but Vera continued.

"I am so happy for you. I never got to go to college or do any of the exciting things you're about to do. All I ask is that you don't forget about us at home."

Samantha wondered who "us" was since she was an only child and Vera would now be living alone. She quickly deduced that Vera meant the family in general, her aunts, uncles, and cousins who had all started jobs at the mill right after high school. She was reminded that she was opening the door to a portal her family had never entered. Her heart rammed against her chest. She breathed in and out slowly.

"I won't," she whispered. She swallowed. "I'm scared." Her eyes widened as she continued, "Maybe I should blow this whole thing and come home with you. I can go to State. What if you need me?" Samantha eyed her mother eagerly.

Vera laughed and hugged her. "I don't need you. I've been grown longer than you. And don't be scared. There's nothing to be afraid of. You deserve to be here just like everyone else." They held onto each other for several long moments before Vera pulled away. Samantha gulped down tears to keep them from coming farther up.

They walked the cart back out to the parking garage. Standing next to Vera's old car, they hugged again. Samantha held her mother tight, the weight of how much she would miss her settling heavier on her.

"I'm so proud of you," Vera repeated. "Just don't forget me."

"I won't," Samantha said, shaking her head. "I can't."

Vera kissed her cheek, and Samantha saw the tears lining her mother's bottom lids. If Vera cried, Samantha would cry, so she laughed and said, "Don't cry, Mom!"

Vera chuckled. "I'm not crying! It's just really humid here!"

They laughed again.

Samantha stood to the side as Vera backed the car out of the parking spot. They waved at each other through the rear window. Samantha stood in the parking lot until her mother's car filed in among the other parents' vehicles.

Holding her breath, Samantha counted the beats of her heart, her body inching forward and backward with each pump. As she started back for her dorm, this time taking the long way through the expansive stretch of grass on the university's front lawn, her mother's words accompanied her.

At her dorm, she entered the elevator and pressed the button. Walking down the hall, she looked at the names on all of the doors until she found the right one. She closed her eyes and inhaled. She knocked three times before the door opened.

"Tommy?"

The boy nodded.

She stuck out her hand. "I'm Samantha."

McKenzie Zalopany
STAMP BINGO

I didn't even need the money. I just wanted to be used.

Used, Mother? Erica says and gives me this new look. Her very own procured mom-look that emanates disappointment and concerned love. My eighteen-month-old grandson, Bowdie, paws at her arm to be picked up and put on her lap. I almost visibly flinch at his sudden appearance. How long has he been in the kitchen with us? I know it's bad, really bad, but I hate my grandchild. OK, hate is a strong word, because I do love him, and I would save him from a burning building, but I don't really enjoy his whole...deal.

You make it sound like being a mailperson is a S-E-X job, Erica says. I mean what does *used* even mean in this instance?

Why the H-E-L-L did you just spell out sex?

Oh, my god, she says and holds Bowdie close to her chest as if I'd just hissed in his direction. It makes me wish Gail were here to witness our daughter's mom-ness.

I meant to say useful, I want to feel less like a potato.

Bowdie giggles and says, Pah-yoyo.

You're always doing things like fixing up the house and watching Bowdie for me—you're no potato, she says.

I read this article on Facebook about people who go into retirement and then just die because their bodies are used to living in a constant state of stress.

I'm trying to live, I tell Erica, to keep myself from dying for Bowdie. So really I'm being selfless.

I don't understand why Erica is bothered by the idea of me working again. I only told her about it because I needed her help with setting up a direct deposit—something I never really had to deal with on base.

I just want to make sure you're enjoying life, taking it easy, Erica says while bouncing Bowdie on her knee. How many days a week do you work anyways? We can plan on some of your days off for a little Nana/Bow time, Erica says and starts nuzzling her head over Bowdie's face, who swats her away with a toddler Ehhh. Same, I think to myself.

I chose a job to feel more fulfilled without realizing how unfulfilling being a mail carrier is. Not in an economical sense, but in a productivity kind of way. There's a reason why mail people are on the top of the suicide statistics below dentists—their job is never done. There's always more mail. I picked it because it's similar to working in the Navy: I wear a uniform, follow orders, and sit on my ass all day.

No one really wants, needs, or uses paper mail. There's a sort of desperation among the carriers, who joke about their non-essential profession and call themselves glorified Yellow Page carriers even though we don't deliver the Yellow Pages. I hear people say, I have a backup plan, a lot.

I made up this sort of game I call Stamp Bingo. Imagine all the letters in a canvas sack as the little balls with numbers. There's a 99.9 percent chance I am going to pull out the run-of-the-mill, grocery store, patriotic, idiotic stamp. But on the 0.1 percent chance I pull something irregular, well, B-I-N-G-O, sort of.

Depending on the day, I break my boards into categories such as state birds, state flowers, lots of state things really, old-timey movie stars, presidents, all the things. It's how I keep my brain sharp, seeing as I'm no book lover. Plus I've always had a great memory of useless things. I keep a little notepad of the boards and draw what I'm going to play the day before.

Today I have memorial stamps, anything with the word Love on it stamps, cartoon character stamps, and stamps with fruit on them, all written in columns. Like I said, I have a lot of time.

There's a chilly wind today, but the Florida sun is still oppressively shining. I hate days like this, the unbalance of it, like sun showers and moonless nights. The sky is saying it's fine! I'm fine! When it's not, clearly. My car fan is on vacation and I've reluctantly switched from navy blue cargo shorts to pants. A dog barks at me, a neighbor waves, and all the stamps today depict the American flag, so I make a bingo board of animal mailboxes: manatee, dolphin, dog, pelican.

It only took me two days of forcing myself to look at the map a few times to memorize my route. I can do up to five hundred mailboxes a day, which I've learned is slow. I know some carriers who do over a thousand. Or maybe they're full of shit. Some sort of haze-the-old-woman type of talk, but honestly I don't really mingle with most of the carriers, except for Tamera.

Like me, she is widowed. Her husband died from cardiac arrest at the gym a couple of years ago. Her lack of grief makes me uncomfortable, like if she can get over it so can I. Tammy tells me the way to get over grief is to purge, keep busy, and just get back out there.

You ever hear of Thrinder? Tammy asks. I don't know much about online lesbian dating, but I know a lot of couples are looking for a third.

One of my routes is through this little bungalow-lined neighborhood that I know Gail would have loved. The houses are painted in atrociously vibrant colors and there are decks built on top of the roofs to watch the sun set beneath the Gulf. Gail used to look for the flash of green light that happened each sunset on our walks down the beach. I never saw it, but she claimed to have seen it twice.

My route ends with a bright pink bungalow with green shutters. As predicted, I hit bingo on my manatee mailbox column.

Erica was Gail's egg that I cooked. The sperm was from a donor, none of that friend crap. I wanted a guy who shot us and left. We sometimes would joke and call the donor our ghost dad. Thanks ghost dad!, we would say if Erica kicked or hiccupped in my belly. Once Erica came though the joke dropped, she was all ours and ghost dad was exorcised from the equation altogether.

It was hard for me to be pregnant though, like I was always wearing my shoes on the wrong feet. Gail pushed me to nest, to read out loud to baby, to keep a journal or scrapbook of my time pregnant. I think there's only one or two photos of me pregnant, which was something Gail made me take saying, this isn't your pregnancy, it's ours. She'll want photos of her mom pregnant!, she said.

Gail was the one who read all the baby books, got all the clothes, made the announcement.

Are we going to be authoritative or permissive parents? Do you want to be Mom or Eemah? She'd asked and I'd say, you choose.

It happened like in the movies though; I held her and there Erica was and I loved her—she looked like Gail.

Erica's household is a yelling house. She yells, her husband Garret yells, Bowdie yells, the TV yells. I am sitting on the couch watching Bowdie who is screaming his ABCs.

WHERE'S MY KEYS?

HUN, WE ARE GOING TO BE LATE.

DID YOU TELL YOUR MOTHER?

YES, I TOLD MY MOTHER.

MAKE SURE BOWDIE TAKES HIS MEDICINE.

I TOLD YOU I TOLD HER, Erica yells as she comes down the stairs.

She is dressed in an outfit that looks as if she were going to the gym, but I guess it's something young people do now—look like they are going to the gym when they go to things.

HUN WE ARE GOING TO BE LATE, Erica screams in the direction of the stairs again and kisses Bowdie who swats her away, looks at me, then realizes his mom is leaving and then clings to her legs, NOOOOOO.

He always does that when I leave, Erica reassures me as if I have never witnessed this. My daughter never grew out of her Gail-ness. Brown eyes, brown hair, freckles the bridge across her nose, and a thin top lip. Bowdie looks like he came from air not even reminiscent of Garret. Bowdie has blond hair and green eyes and full lips. Sometimes when I look at him I think, who are you? Where did you come from?

It started with little things. I'd find the soy sauce in the fridge, maybe a carton of milk in the lazy Susan. Projects would be started, then stopped, papers and coupons left in piles. The cat would be called a bird and then she'd laugh and say, I hate birds. A pot of water was once in the linen closet wedged between pool towels.

Sometimes, she would hold my face and just stare at it. I would joke and say, Hello? It's me your wife, and she'd say, That's not what I'm doing.

I've been told I'm lucky because I never had to see Gail spiral into complete oblivion. That her falling asleep and never waking up is better than her drooling in a chair for ten years. We had been so focused on her brain we forgot about the rest of her.

This morning, I caught myself talking to myself. This worries me. It's what old people do and I don't want to be that old person. Maybe if I got a dog and talked to it I would feel better, but I hate those kinds of people too—Dog-Talkers.

Today, Tamera is going on a date from Match.com. She tells me how she's never dated a man with a motorcycle. I'm just telling you in case he kills me, Tamera says and gives a strained laugh.

Gail has been gone for three out of the four years I've been retired. I don't fault Tamera for getting back out there. I just don't want to have to wake up to another blue body.

My board is MLK stamps, Marvel comic stamps, Washington Monument stamps, and stamps with yellow flowers. Sometimes it takes me days to fill a board and I've been working on this board for weeks. I'm invested.

I go house to house pulling coupons, bills, birthday cards out and scanning for one of my pieces. I dream of these damn stamps.

My last stop today is at a little Baptist church that always has a quirky sign like, I hate this church XOXO Satan.

I gave myself one more day to finish this board and still haven't hit a bingo, this is my last chance.

There are things that the brain blocks out in order to keep a sort of self-preservation. Today the sky is oppressively blue and the wind whips my face when I leave my mail truck to drop the church's mail in their box up a little walkway. I make sure not to look at the stamps until I get to the mail in order to build tension. I cannot help but see Gail's face in this blue sky. I see her on top of our blue sheets, in the blue morning light. I keep walking, crinkling the mail in my hands. When I get to the drop box the stamps are: American flag, American flag, sailboat, and Gandhi.

Erica is always telling me I need to take it easy, that I need to move on, in so many words. Remember the good times and just let Mom go, we will see her one day.

I know I gave my board one last day but I decided to keep it and play it tomorrow—it's hard to wipe the board clean, when you're missing a piece.

When I get off work my phone has three texts from Erica:

CAN YOU PLZ WATCH BOW IT'S 911

EVERY1'S OK

I WILL PAY $$$

I text her back, Sure.

The entrance to Erica's is full of family pictures from one photo shoot. Framed pictures of her, Garrett, and Bowdie in matching white outfits sitting on the beach lining the clean, white walls. I hear Bowdie yodeling nonsense when I walk through the door.

Thank you!! Erica says to me, already walking out the door, Garrett's car died again I'll be back in a little we might stop for food don't forget about probiotic and don't let Bowdie just sit in front of his iPad all afternoon love you Bow!!!

I look at Bowdie, who is chewing on one hand and using the other to navigate the template. I assume he is hungry, but the entire house is full of wheat products, non-GMOs, and whatever the hell kombucha is.

Should we go for a drive? I ask Bowdie ,who just kind of goes Blahahlaala. I'm going to take that as a yes.

I have never taken Bowdie out on my own. I was kind of a mess with Erica too. I mean that first drive from the hospital with Erica in the backseat with a noodle for a neck bobbing around almost sent me in a catatonic state. Luckily, Bowdie's neck is past that stage and I strap him in with ease. He isn't at the age where he can tattle on me for taking him to a non-mom-approved food place yet. Plus, who knows how long it'll take Erica, she usually milks me of my time when I babysit.

We go to a fast food place where Bowdie inhales chicken tender after chicken tender. I have to stop him from shoveling and choking to death. He kicks his legs happily back and forth, his shoes on the wrong feet. I'm trying to piece together the crap plastic toy that came with his meal. I don't remember ever having to assemble these things before.

Bowdie's mouth gets fuller and fuller. If he were a comic the sounds around him would go: NOM, NOM, NOM. I go to scold him to chew better but I inhale my burger bite and start choking. Like really choking. I start clawing at my throat and waving my hands, but no one in the restaurant is paying me any mind. I imagine my face going white, to red, to blue.

Bowdie lets out a loud GGEEEMAAAHH and pushes me off of my seat with the same power a mom gets when her kid is trapped beneath a car. I slam onto the ground, dislodging my food. The place ignites in applause, as if they had been paying attention the whole time.

Bowdie starts to laugh, like really laugh, and claps too.

There were two options for her arrangements in place. Option one was to be cremated and thrown in the ocean, which horrified me. Baby pee and oil and fish guts wouldn't be Gail's final resting spot. Or she wanted a little grave, which is what I chose and buried her in a shady spot in a graveyard that I didn't hate. The kind of graveyards that don't have fake flowers and little spinners lining the path. I think Erica's been twice, but I haven't really asked, don't really want to know. On the ride back to the house, I decide to take Bowdie. Almost dying in a fast food place puts things in perspective. Gail would never know Bowdie, but I guess I would. And even though I don't feel an instant connection with him, there is love there. Especially from him. I mean it was good to keep something around that didn't want you dead.

He's on my hip as we approach her grave. I planted a little gardenia bush that I like to trim and take clippings home. We sit down beneath the oak and he sings me and Gail a poor rendition of the alphabet song. I tell her how I was this close to reuniting with her until Bowdie willfully stopped it.

When we get home, Bowdie is on his iPad and I look through Erica's mail. Just more American flags, nothing for my board. At bedtime I put Bowdie down in his crib and he stands up and holds my face. I have always found nurseries disturbing, with their creepy slow music boxes and dim lighting. There are some babies that can really get to your soul with oddly adultlike looks, and right now Bowdie is barring into my eyes and then breaks the moment by sneezing in my face. He giggles and drops his hands, waving me good night.

Erica and Garrett get home a little after nine. Their car breaking down turned into dinner and a movie. I am tired, but in a way in which my body feels perfectly exhausted. I want to sleep and sleep and sleep. Erica goes to her purse and asks how much she owes me, but I say forget about it. I didn't do it for the money.

*AMY ALFIER is in the U.S. Army and is presently stationed in Stuttgart.

JEFFREY (JC) ALFIER's most recent book is *Gone This Long: Southern Poem*. *The Shadow Field*, another collection, is forthcoming from Louisiana Literature Press. His publication credits include *The Carolina Quarterly, Copper Nickel, Midwest Quarterly, Southern Poetry Review*, and *Poetry Ireland Review*. He is founder and coeditor of Blue Horse Press and *San Pedro River Review*.

TOBI ALFIER is a multiple Pushcart nominee and multiple Best of the Net nominee. Both *Slices of Alice & Other Character Studies* and a reprint of *Sanity Among the Wildflowers* were published by Cholla Needles Press. She is coeditor of *San Pedro River Review* (www.bluehorsepress.com).

*LINETTE MARIE ALLEN is an MFA candidate in creative writing and the publishing arts at the University of Baltimore. She enjoys translating her work into diverse languages and says her prior master's from the London School of Economics richly fuels her poetics. Her work has appeared or is forthcoming in *Notre Dame Review, Free State Review, The Tishman Review*, and other journals.

NANCY ALLEN is a D.C.-based criminal defense attorney, as well as a yoga studio owner and yoga teacher. Her poems have been published in *Gargoyle, Tar River Review, Sow's Ear Review, Shot Glass Journal, JMWW, New Millennium Writings* and the *Piedmont Virginian*. She lives in the mountains in Southwest Virginia.

DAVID ALPAUGH's Double-Title poems appear in *Gargoyle*'s 40th anniversary issue and in issue 68. Word Galaxy Press (an imprint of Able Muse) will be publishing a collection of his Double-Titles in 2020. He is now writing Visual Poems that fuse poetry and art, fifty-six of which have appeared so far at *Lighten Up Online, Scene4*, and *X-Peri*.

*JAMES ARMSTRONG's stories have appeared in *The Long Story, Birmingham Arts Journal, Concho River Review, The Chaffey Review*, and other publications. His plays have been published in *Canyon Voices, The Louisville Review, Yemassee*, and *The Best American Short Plays: 2012–2013*. He holds an MFA in dramatic writing from Carnegie Mellon University.

*AMY ISSADORE BLOOM is a writer and teacher. She lives in Bethesda, Maryland, with her husband and two energetic sons. Read more at bloomindc.com, Twitter @bloomindc.

A German-born UK national, *ROSE MARY BOEHM lives and works in Lima, Peru. She is the author of the poetry collections *Peru Blues or Lady Gaga Won't Be Back* (Kelsay Books, 2018), *From the Ruhr to Somewhere Near Dresden 1939–1949: A Child's Journey* (Aldrich Press, 2016), and *Tangents* (Black Leaf Publishing, 2011). Her work has been widely published in online and print U.S. poetry journals, and she is a three-time winner of the Goodreads monthly competition.

Asterisk (*) indicates first time published in *Gargoyle*.

ACE BOGGESS is author of the novels *A Song Without a Melody* (Hyperborea Publishing, 2016) and *States of Mercy* (Alien Buddha Press, 2019). His recent fiction appears in *Notre Dame Review*, *Lumina*, *The Sonder Review*, and *Superstition Review*. He received a fellowship from the West Virginia Commission on the Arts and spent five years in a West Virginia prison. He lives in Charleston, West Virginia.

When Mark Jarman chose **PAULA BONNELL**'s *Airs & Voices* for a Ciardi Prize, she discontinued the practice of law and became a full-time writer. Her poems have appeared in *APR*, *The Hudson Review*, *Rattle*, and elsewhere, aired on *The Writer's Almanac*, and in three collections: *Message* (her debut), and two chapbooks: *Before the Alphabet*, and *tales retold*. www.paulabonnell.net

***JONAH MARLOW BRADENDAY** lives on Peaks Island in Casco Bay, Maine. He goes to school at Colby College in the winter and works as a golf cart rental associate in the summer.

***JODY LANNEN BRADY** has recently come back to writing fiction after years of freelance and corporate writing. "Anything You Need" is a story she started years ago, but saw differently upon revisiting it recently. She graduated from George Mason's MFA program, and has published stories in a number of journals and anthologies.

SHIRLEY J. BREWER graduated from careers in bartending and speech therapy. She serves as poet-in-residence at Carver Center for Arts & Technology in Baltimore, and teaches creative writing workshops to seniors. Her work has appeared in *Barrow Street*, *Chiron Review*, *Comstock Review*, *Poetry East*, *Slant*, and other journals and anthologies. Shirley's poetry books include *A Little Breast Music* (Passager Books, 2008), *After Words* (Apprentice House, 2013), and *Bistro in Another Realm* (Main Street Rag, 2017). www.apoeticlicense.com

GERRI BRIGHTWELL is a British writer living in Alaska. In 2016 her novel, *Dead of Winter*, was published by Salt (U.K.). She is the author of two other novels: *Cold Country* (Duckworth, 2003) and *The Dark Lantern* (Crown, 2008). Her writing has also appeared in *The Best American Mystery Stories 2017*, *Alaska Quarterly Review*, *Southwest Review*, *Copper Nickel*, *Redivider*, and BBC Radio 4's *Opening Lines*. She teaches at the University of Alaska, Fairbanks.

***KATHRYN CHIARIELLO** writes fiction and essays. Her work was recently published in *Watershed Review*. She lives in Washington, D.C.

***CHRIS CLEARY** is the author of four novels: *The Vagaries of Butterflies*, *The Ring of Middletown*, *At the Brown Brink Eastward*, and *The Vitality of Illusion*. His work has appeared or is forthcoming in the *Virginia Quarterly Review*, *Broadkill Review*, *Oddville Press*, *Evening Street Review*, *Belle Ombre*, *North West Words*, and other publications. His short fiction has been anthologized in the award-winning *Everywhere Stories*.

JOAN COLBY's *Selected Poems* received the 2013 FutureCycle Prize, and *Ribcage* was awarded the 2015 Kithara Book Prize. Her recent books include *Her Heartsongs* (Presa Press), *Joyriding to Nightfall* (FutureCycle Press), *Elements* (Presa Press), and *Bony Old Folks* (Cyberwit Press). She has another book forthcoming from the Poetry Box Select series titled *The Kingdom of the Birds*.

GAIL BRAUNE COMORAT is a founding member of Rehoboth Beach Writers' Guild, and the author of *Phases of the Moon* (Finishing Line Press). Her work has appeared in *Gargoyle, Grist, Mudfish, Philadelphia Stories,* and *The Widows' Handbook*. She's a long-time member of several writing groups in Lewes, Delaware.

ROBERT COOPERMAN's latest collection is *That Summer* (Main Street Rag). Forthcoming from Lithic Press is *The Devil Who Raised Me*.

*KATIE CORTESE is the author of *Girl Power and Other Short-Short Stories* (ELJ Publications, 2015) and *Make Way for Her and Other Stories* (University Press of Kentucky, 2018). Her work has recently appeared in *Animal, Indiana Review, Wigleaf, Blackbird, Willow Springs,* and *The Baltimore Review,* among other journals. She teaches in the creative writing program at Texas Tech University where she also serves as the fiction editor for *Iron Horse Literary Review*.

*DANIEL COSHNEAR works at a group home and teaches through UC Berkeley Extension. He is the author of two story collections: *Jobs & Other Preoccupations* (Helicon Nine, 2001), Willa Cather Award winner, and *Occupy & Other Love Stories* (Kelly's Cove Press, 2012). In 2015, he won the Novella Award from Fiction Fix (now Flock) for *Homesick Redux*. His newest story collection, *Separation Anxiety*, will be published in 2021 by Unsolicited Press.

BARBARA CROOKER is a poetry editor for *Italian Americana* and author of nine books; *Some Glad Morning* (Pitt Poetry Series, 2019) is the latest. Her awards include the Best Book of Poetry 2018 from Poetry by the Sea, the WB Yeats Society of New York Award, the Thomas Merton Poetry of the Sacred Award, and three Pennsylvania Council on the Arts Fellowships. Her work appears in a variety of anthologies, including *The Bedford Introduction to Literature*.

MARK DANOWSKY is a writer from Philadelphia. His poems have appeared in *About Place, Cordite, Gargoyle, The Healing Muse, Shot Glass Journal, Subprimal, Third Wednesday,* and elsewhere. He is managing editor for the *Schuylkill Valley Journal*.

HEATHER L. DAVIS earned a BA in English from Hollins University and an MA in creative writing from Syracuse University. She is the author of *The Lost Tribe of Us,* which won the Main Street Rag Poetry Book Award. Her poems have appeared in *Poet Lore, Puerto del Sol,* and *Sonora Review,* among others. She lives in Washington, D.C., with her husband, the poet Jose Padua, and their daughter and son.

*ZANE DEBLOSAT (pronounced BluhSAW) of Pittsburgh, Pennsylvania, dedicates this to Professor Joycey Frauenholz who made him go back to his first love, story writing.

*ROBIN DELLABOUGH is a poet, editor, and writer with a master's in journalism from UC Berkeley. Her poems have appeared or are forthcoming in *Maryland Poetry Review*, *Blue Unicorn*, *Negative Capability*, *Westchester Review*, *Friends Journal*, *Persimmon Tree*, *Tiny Spoon*, *Footworks*, *Mildred*, and other publications. She has studied with Galway Kinnell, Sharon Olds, and Brenda Hillman; and with Kathleen Ossip, Amy Holman, and Suzanne Cleary at the Hudson Valley Writers Center. She lives in Irvington-on-Hudson, New York.

*MARGARET DIEHL has published a chapbook of poems, *it all stayed open* (Red Glass Press, 2011); two novels, *Men* (1989) and *Me and You* (1990), and a memoir, *The Boy on the Green Bicycle* (1999), all from Soho Press; as well as poems, articles, and book reviews in many publications. She works as a writer and freelance fiction editor in New York City.

ALEX MCRAE DIMSDALE won an Eric Gregory Award, the U.K.'s prize for the best poets under thirty. Her poems have been published in *The Florida Review*, *Poet Lore*, *Poetry Review*, *Magma*, *The North*, *Penumbra*, *Nth Position*, and *The Manhattan Review*. She grew up in London, and now lives in Washington, D.C. She has an MFA from Vermont College of Fine Arts.

GABRIEL DON is a multidisciplinary artist who works in a variety of media: a filmmaker, artist, photographer, musician, and writer. She has been published in numerous online and print publications. She received her MFA in creative writing at The New School, where she worked as the Reading Series and Chapbook Competition Coordinator and currently teaches writing at BMCC. Born in Australia, raised in Singapore and Dubai, Don now resides in New York City. www.facebook.com/gabrieldoninnoparticularorder/

*AARON EMMEL's stories have appeared in *Daily Science Fiction*, *Starship Sofa*, *STORGY*, and other publications. Find him online at www.aaronemmel.com.

*CATHERINE FAHEY is a poet and librarian from Salem, Massachusetts. She is the former managing editor and poetry coeditor of *Soundings East*. When she's not reading and writing, she's knitting or dancing. You can read more of her work at www.magpiepoems.com.

*GREYSON FERGUSON is a graduate of the Savannah College of Art and Design and currently resides in Tucson, Arizona. Over the past decade he's written for a number of publications, including *USA Today*, Yahoo, the *New York Times*, and CBS Interactive. When not writing, he can be found out with his dogs and sampling local whiskies.

GARY FINCKE's latest collection, *The Infinity Room*, won the Wheelbarrow Books Prize for Established Poets (Michigan State, 2019). Stephen F. Austin University will publish *The Sorrows*, his ninth collection of stories, in 2020.

*MICHAEL J. GALKO is a scientist and poet who lives and works in Houston, Texas. Both his science and his poetry explore wound healing and pain. He has poems recently published or forthcoming in *The Red Eft Review*, *Riddled with Arrows*, *Gulf Coast*, *The Mojave River Review*, *descant*, *Rockvale Review*, *Defunkt Magazine*, and *Nassau Review*.

Dr. **KATHLEEN "KATE" GILLESPIE** relies on the synthesis of stress proteins (a typical metabolite of a thesis project) for her continued creative catalytic reactions of a poetical PhD and professor who celebrates the "Poetry in Science."

*JAMES GRABILL's recent work appears at *Terrain* online, *Caliban* online, *Ginosko*, *Sequestrum*, and more. Books (Lynx House Press): *Poem Rising Out of the Earth* (1994), *An Indigo Scent after the Rain* (2003), Environmental prose poems (Wordcraft of Oregon): *Sea-Level Nerve: Books One* (2014) and *Two* (2015), with chapbooks forthcoming from Finishing Line Press and Raw Art Review. For many years in Portland, he taught writing and global issues relative to sustainability.

JAMES BERNARD GROSS has a limited-edition handmade book, *Fingerings for words: selected poems*, in nineteen library special collections including Princeton, the Beinecke, UC Berkeley, Stanford, Notre Dame, Purdue, University at Buffalo, University of Connecticut, University of Delaware, University of Rhode Island, Newberry Library, University of New Mexico, the Getty Research Institute Library, Geisel Library UCSD; in London at the British Library; and in France at the Bibliothèque Interuniversitaire de la Sorbonne. It is sold out.

HEDY HABRA has authored three poetry collections, most recently, *The Taste of the Earth* (Press 53, 2019), finalist for the 2019 Best Book Award. Her first collection, *Tea in Heliopolis*, won the USA Best Book Award; and *Under Brushstrokes* was finalist for the International Book Award. A fourteen-time nominee for the Pushcart Prize and Best of the Net, her work appears in *Cimarron Review*, *Bitter Oleander*, *Gargoyle*, *Nimrod*, and *Verse Daily*. Her website is hedyhabra.com.

*CHLOE HANSON is a PhD candidate at the University of Tennessee, where she is the poetry editor for *Grist: A Journal of the Literary Arts*. Her work has recently been featured in *The Rumpus*, *Calamus*, and *Crab Fat Literary Magazine*, among others.

SHELBY SETTLES HARPER is a writer, art enthusiast, and sometime-lawyer. Her Oklahoma upbringing and years in Colorado, Seattle, and Switzerland instilled a passion for mountains, fresh air, and adventure. Vices include Twitter, Tex Mex, country music, and hoppy IPAs. Shelby is a citizen of the Caddo Nation, an Indian tribe located in Oklahoma.

*PATRICIA HENLEY's work has appeared in *Atticus Review*, *Booth*, *The Boston Globe Sunday Magazine*, *The Atlantic*, *Best American Short Stories*, *The Pushcart Prize Anthology*, *Glimmer Train*, and other journals and anthologies. Her published work includes two novels, four collections of stories, and numerous essays.

*THOMAS HRYCYK has worked for multiple literary journals including *Fifth Wednesday Journal*. His most recent publications include a novella, *L'Amande et La Fleur* (Wapshott Press, 2016); and short stories in *Fiction International, Timber, Thrice Fiction*, and many others. He works at Tennessee State University.

DONALD ILLICH has published poetry in journals such as *The Iowa Review, Fourteen Hills,* and *Cold Mountain Review*. He won Honorable Mention in the Washington Prize book contest. He recently published a book, *Chance Bodies* (Word Works, 2018).

MIKE JAMES makes his home outside Nashville, Tennessee. He has published in numerous magazines throughout the country including *Plainsongs, Laurel Poetry Review, Birmingham Poetry Review,* and *Chiron Review*. In the spring of 2020, Luchador Press will publish his fifteenth collection, *Journeyman's Suitcase*.

*BETH UZNIS JOHNSON received an MFA from Queens University of Charlotte. Her writing has appeared in *StoryQuarterly, Southwest Review, Mississippi Review, Cincinnati Review, The Rumpus, Best American Essays,* and elsewhere. She works as an editor and writer at the University of Michigan Rogel Cancer Center and lives in suburban Detroit.

BRAD JOHNSON's second book, *Smuggling Elephants Through Airport Security* (Michigan State University Press), was selected by Carolyn Forche for the 2018 Wheelbarrow Books Poetry Prize. Work of his has also been accepted by *Carolina Quarterly, Hayden's Ferry Review, J Journal, Meridian, Poet Lore, Tar River Poetry,* and others.

*STEPHANIE JOYCE is an Arlington writer with a great stonking backlog of stories to send out.

GEORGE KALAMARAS, former Poet Laureate of Indiana (2014–2016), is the author of sixteen books of poetry, nine of which are full length, including *Kingdom of Throat-Stuck Luck,* winner of the Elixir Press Poetry Prize (2011); and *The Mining Camps of the Mouth* (2012), winner of the New Michigan Press Prize. He is a professor of English at Indiana University–Purdue University Fort Wayne, where he has taught since 1990.

TOSHIYA KAMEI holds an MFA in literary translation from the University of Arkansas. His translations of Latin American literature include *My Father Thinks I'm a Fakir* by Claudia Apablaza, *South Exit* by Carlos Bortoni, and *Silent Herons* by Selfa Chew.

RODGER KAMENETZ is an American poet and author. He is best known as the author of *The Jew in the Lotus* (1994), an account of the historic dialogue between rabbis and the XIV Dalai Lama.

*LILAH KATCHER's poetry has appeared in *Barrelhouse, Postcard Poems and Prose,* and *Poetry International*. Her flash fiction is included in the anthology *Tripping the Light Fantastic: Weird Fiction by Deaf and Hard of Hearing Writers*. She has an MFA from American University, where she was the nonfiction editor for *Folio*. She dreams of someday seeing her poems translated into American Sign Language.

*JELENA KECMANOVIC was born and raised in Sarajevo and, having escaped the Bosnian war, came to the United States in 1993. She works as a clinical psychologist and teaches at Georgetown University. Her writing has appeared in the *Washington Post*, *The Conversation*, and other newspapers and magazines. She also writes the *Psychology Today* blog "From Science to Practice."

SANDRA KOLANKIEWICZ's poems have appeared most recently in *Otis Nebulae*, *Trampset*, *Concho River Review*, *London Magazine*, *New World Writing*, and *Appalachian Heritage*.

KATHLEEN KRAFT is a poet, freelance editor, and yoga teacher. Her chapbook, *Fairview Road*, was published by Finishing Line Press, and her work has appeared in many journals, including *Five Points*, *Sugar House Review*, *Chariton Review*, *The Satirist*, and *Yoga International*. She lives in the Berkshires, Massachusetts. You can find her at kathleenyoga.com.

Dr. RANDI GRAY KRISTENSEN teaches research writing to first-year students at the George Washington University in Washington, D.C. She coedited *Writing Against the Curriculum: Anti-Disciplinarity in the Writing and Cultural Studies Classroom* (Lexington Books, 2009) and has published fiction, poetry, and memoir in *Creation Fire*, *Caribbean Erotic*, *Gargoyle*, *Under Her Skin: How Girls Experience Race in America*, and *A River of Stories from the Commonwealth Trust*, among others.

*ANDREW LAFLECHE is an award-winning poet and author of *No Diplomacy*; *Shameless*; *Ashes*; *A Pardonable Offence*; *One Hundred Little Victories*; *On Writing*; *Merica, Merica on the Wall*; and *After I Turn into Alcohol*. He is editor of *Gravitas Poetry*. Lafleche served as an infantry soldier from 2007 to 2014. He earned an MA in creative and critical writing from the University of Gloucestershire. Follow @AndrewLafleche on Twitter or visit AndrewLafleche.com for more information.

*STEPHANIE LEOW is a student at Georgetown University, studying English and linguistics. She writes and designs layout for Georgetown's womxn-oriented magazine *Bossier*, and she tutors at the Georgetown University Writing Center. She is interested in the intersection between creative writing and equitable writing education, with aspirations to be a professor and writer.

SUSAN LEWIS (www.susanlewis.net) is the author of ten books and chapbooks, including *Zoom*, winner of the Washington Prize (The Word Works, 2018), and *Heisenberg's Salon* (BlazeVOX [books], 2016). In addition to *Gargoyle*, her work has appeared in *Agni*, *Boston Review*, *The Brooklyn Rail*, *Conjunctions online*, *Diode*, *Interim*, *New American Writing*, *VOLT*, and many other journals and anthologies. She is the founding editor of *Posit* (www.positjournal.com).

CHRISTOPHER LINFORTH is the author of the story collection *When You Find Us We Will Be Gone*. He has recently published work in *The Millions*, *Whiskey Island*, *Fiction International*, *Notre Dame Review*, and other magazines.

*MILES LISS lives in the D.C. area where he teaches high school students. He's a recent graduate of the Vermont College of Fine Arts. Miles has also lived in England, India, Israel, and the Virgin Islands.

*KRISTIAN MACARON resides in Albuquerque, New Mexico, but is often elsewhere. Her poetry chapbook collection is titled *Storm*. Other fiction and poetry publications can be found in *Winter Tangerine*, *Ginosko*, Medusa's Laugh Press, *The Mantle*, *Philadelphia Stories*, and *Asimov's Science Fiction*. She is a cofounding editor of the literary journal *Manzano Mountain Review*. View her work at Kristianmacaron.com.

TRISH MACENULTY is the author of four novels, a short story collection, and a memoir. She is currently working on another memoir about taking care of her ex, titled "Two Necks, One Rope."

*KARAN MADHOK is an Indian writer and a graduate of the MFA program from the American University in Washington, D.C. He is the founder and editor of the Indian arts review, *The Chakkar*. Karan's fiction, translations, and poetry have appeared in *The Literary Review*, *Lantern Review*, *F(r)iction*, and more. He won American University's Myra Sklarew Award for the best MFA thesis (prose) and is currently working on his first novel.

*RYAN MASTERS is a writer and poet from Santa Cruz, California. His first collection of fiction, *Above an Abyss: Two Novellas*, was published by Radial Books in December 2018. Read more at RyanMasters831.com.

JOYCE ENZOR MAUST hails from the land of moss-covered boulders, mountain laurel, and state forests. Family, faith, and freedom to roam were a way of life on her parents' dairy farm. With degrees in English and physics, the daughter of a Conservative Mennonite bishop, mother to exceptional sons, and a wife to a walking history encyclopedia—she enjoys reading, discussing, and writing about almost any subject. Her works have been published in *Broadkill Review* and *Gargoyle*.

FRANETTA MCMILLIAN is a writer, visual artist, and occasional musician splitting her time between Newark, Delaware, and Avondale, Pennsylvania. Her latest zine is *Fat Black Girl in a Wheelchair*.

MARK MELNICOVE is author of two ekphrastic poetry collections—*Sometimes Times* (Two Palms Press, 2017), with printmaker Terry Winters, and *Ghosts* (Cedar Grove House, 2018), with painter Abby Shahn. He is coauthor of *Africa Is Not a Country* (2001 Africana Book Award winner) and *The Uncensored Guide to Maine*.

Named one of two hundred living individuals who best embody the work and spirit of Frederick Douglass by the Frederick Douglass Family Initiatives and the Antiracist Research and Policy Center at American University, **NANCY MERCADO** is also the 2017 recipient of the American Book Award for Lifetime Achievement. She is the editor of the first Nuyorican women's anthology published in *Voices e/Magazine*, Hunter College–CUNY. For more information, go to nancy-mercado.com.

MICHAEL MILBURN's writing has appeared most recently in *Poetry East* and *Mudlark*, and in *Gargoyle* in 2016.

*LIZ MINETTE lives in Esko, Minnesota, near Duluth. She has been writing for about twenty-five years and finds herself still doing this. Some recent publication credits include *Abbey*, *Nerve Cowboy*, *Blue Collar Review*, *Houston Poetry Fest Anthology*, and *The Thunderbird Review.*

*HANNAH MOLONEY is a freelance writer living in Kensington, Maryland, with a background in sociology and psychology. She was initially inspired to write during her travels and now her creativity is spurred by the silly stories of children attending the school where she works. Hannah is interested in the complex aspects of human interactions and relationships. She explores these through short story works of fiction and creative nonfiction.

MILES DAVID MOORE is a reporter for Crain Communications Inc. and film reviewer for the online arts magazine *Scene4*. From 1994 to 2017, he was organizer and host of the IOTA poetry reading series in Arlington, Virginia. From 2002 to 2009, he was a member of the board of directors of The Word Works. His books of poetry are *The Bears of Paris* (Word Works, 1995); *Buddha Isn't Laughing* (Argonne House Press, 1999); and *Rollercoaster* (Word Works, 2004).

*PAMELA MOORE—see page 1.

DANIEL MUELLER has authored two collections of short fiction, *How Animals Mate* (Overlook Press, 1999), winner of the Sewanee Fiction Prize, and *Nights I Dreamed of Hubert Humphrey* (Outpost 19 Books, 2013). Recent work appears in *Gargoyle*, *The Iowa Review*, *Story Quarterly*, *Booth*, *b(OINK)*, *Chicago Quarterly Review*, *Solstice*, *Free State Review*, and *Manzano Mountain Review*. He teaches at the University of New Mexico and the Low-Residency MFA Program at Queens University of Charlotte.

ELISABETH MURAWSKI'S most recent book is *Heiress*, published by Texas Review Press; it won the Poetry Society of Virginia Award.

*ALASTAIR MURDOCH is a creative writing MFA student at Manhattanville College in Purchase, New York, where he also works as a graduate assistant, editing two of the school's literary journals, *The Manhattanville Review* (online) and *Inkwell* (print). His first short story, "The Forensics Teacher," was published last year by *River River* in New York's Hudson Valley.

DONAJÍ OLMEDO was born in Mexico City, where she still lives today. English translations of her fiction have appeared in various venues, including *The Bitter Oleander*, *The McNeese Review*, and *xo Orpheus: Fifty New Myths*. She blogs at "Casa de Ateh" and edits a chapbook of the same name, in which she publishes the work of young Mexican writers.

*JORDAN PÉREZ has an MFA from American University. Her work appears or is forthcoming in *Cosmonauts Avenue*, *Winter Tangerine*, and *Mississippi Review.*

*COLLEEN KEARNEY RICH is the author of the chapbook *Things You Won't Tell Your Therapist* (Finishing Line Press, 2019). A fiction editor at *Literary Mama*, her writing has been published in *SmokeLong Quarterly*, *Wigleaf*, *matchbook*, and *Harpoon Review*, among others. She lives in Virginia.

DAVID ROMANDA was born in Kelowna, British Columbia. He currently lives in Kawasaki City, Japan. His writing has appeared in *Ambit Magazine*, *Existere*, *Gargoyle*, *Poetry Ireland Review*, and *PRISM international*.

*MARK RUBIN has published one book of poems, *The Beginning of Responsibility* (Owl Creek Press). His work has appeared in *The Gettysburg Review*, *The Ohio Review*, *Prairie Schooner*, *The Virginia Quarterly Review*, *The Yale Review*, and elsewhere. A past recipient of the Discovery/The Nation Award and a National Endowment for the Arts Fellowship, he lives and works in Burlington, Vermont, as a psychotherapist in private practice.

*LESLIE M. RUPRACHT is an editor, poet, writer, and artist living in/near Charlotte, North Carolina, since 1997. Her words and artwork appear in various journals, anthologies, exhibits, and a chapbook, *Splintered Memories* (Main Street Rag, 2012). Long-time senior associate editor of now-retired *Iodine Poetry Journal*, Rupracht also edited NC Poetry Society's 2017 and 2018 *Pinesong* anthology. Swearing off a corporate work relapse, Rupracht cofounded and hosts Waterbean Poetry Night at the Mic in Huntersville, North Carolina.

*DAWN RYAN has been writing fiction since she was an undergrad at Brandeis University. Dawn later attended Rutgers University's Newark campus MFA program in creative writing. Stories have appeared in *McSweeney's Quarterly Concern*, *Cagibi*, *Mammoth Book of Best New Erotica*, and *American Short Fiction*. Dawn is currently a public school teacher in Jersey City, New Jersey. She lives in Brooklyn with her wife and daughter.

Poet laureate of Silver City, New Mexico (Land of Enchantment) from 2017 to 2019, **BEATE SIGRIDDAUGHTER**, www.sigriddaughter.net, grew up in Nürnberg, Germany. Her playgrounds were a nearby castle and World War II bomb ruins. Her latest poetry chapbook, *Emily*, is available from Unsolicited Press (2020). On her blog "Writing in a Woman's Voice," she publishes other women's work.

NOEL SLOBODA is the author of two poetry collections and half a dozen chapbooks, most recently *Risk Management Studies* (Kattywompus, 2015). He has also published a book about Edith Wharton and Gertrude Stein. Sloboda teaches at Penn State York.

*ELLEN MCGRATH SMITH teaches at the University of Pittsburgh and in the Carlow University Madwomen in the Attic program. Her poetry has appeared in the *New York Times*, *The American Poetry Review*, *Talking Writing*, *Los Angeles Review*, and other journals and anthologies. Books include *Scatter, Feed* (Seven Kitchens, 2014) and *Nobody's Jackknife* (West End Press, 2015).

J.D. SMITH's fourth poetry collection, *The Killing Tree*, was published in 2016. His other books include the humor collection *Notes of a Tourist on Planet Earth* (2013), the essay collection *Dowsing and Science* (2011), and the children's picture book *The Best Mariachi in the World* (2008). Smith works and lives in Washington, DC.

MAYA SONENBERG has been experimenting with writing about the arts since her first published story, about a Cubist baby. Her work includes two collection of stories, two chapbooks of prose and images (most recently *After the Death of Shostakovich Père* from PANK Books), and numerous other stories and essays. She teaches in the creative writing program at the University of Washington–Seattle and can be found at https://mayasonenberg.com/ and on Twitter @MzzS36019.

*SHENANDOAH SOWASH's work has appeared or is forthcoming in *The Collagist*, *Smartish Pace*, *Vinyl Poetry*, and elsewhere. She's received fellowships from the Bread Loaf Writers Conference, the Virginia Center for the Creative Arts, the Kimmel Nelson Harding Center for the Arts, the Summer Literary Seminars, and the D.C. Commission on the Arts and Humanities.

MARILYN STABLEIN is a poet, essayist, fiction writer, and mixed media artist working in collage, assemblage, sculptural artist books, and performance art. Recent books include *Vermin: A Traveler's Bestiary* (Spuyten Duyvil); *Houseboat on the Ganges & A Room in Kathmandu: Letters from India & Nepal 1966–1972*; and *Milepost 27: Poems*, a pick for Southwest Book of the Year 2019.

MARIJA STAJIC is a Foreign Service Officer currently serving in Brussels, Belgium. She has published about a dozen stories in various literary journals and has written two novels.

KURT STEINWAND holds an MFA from the University of Tampa. He teaches children who have special needs at a middle school in Brandon, Florida. His poems have been published in *Gargoyle*, *Cincinnati Review*, *Poet Lore*, and *New Millennium Writings*. His chapbook, *Poland* (Finishing Line Press), recounts his mother-in-law's experiences as a child in Poland during the Nazi occupation and subsequent takeover by the Russians.

*MARJORIE STELMACH has published five volumes of poems, most recently *Falter* (Cascade, 2017). Her sixth book will be out this winter from Ashland Poetry Press. Individual poems have recently appeared in *Gettysburg Review*, *Hudson Review*, *Image*, *Notre Dame Review*, *Prairie Schooner*, and others. A group of her poems received the 2016 Chad Walsh Poetry Prize from *The Beloit Poetry Journal*.

*JOSEPH STERN's poetry has appeared in *The American Journal of Poetry*, *Common Ground Review*, *Main Street Rag*, and other publications. Originally from Montreal, he lives and works in Shanghai.

DAVID A. TAYLOR's collection, *Success: Stories*, received the Washington Writers' Publishing House fiction prize. His fiction has appeared in *Potomac Review*, *Jabberwock*, *Washington City Paper*, and anthologies, as well as *Gargoyle*. His nonfiction includes most recently *Cork Wars*, from JHU Press. David also writes for documentaries and teaches with the Johns Hopkins Science Writing Program. He lives in D.C.

Born and raised in South Africa, *K.P. TAYLOR* came to the United States at twenty-nine to work at an amusement park for a summer and never left. His writing has been featured in *Lotus-eater*, *The Write Launch*, and *Kōan* (Paragon Press) and is forthcoming in *Hobart*, *Ginosko*, and *Running Wild Anthology of Stories*. He currently lives in Pennsylvania with his wife, their son, and several cats.

MARK TERRILL is a well-traveled American poet, translator, and prose writer who has resided in Northern Germany since the mid-1980s. Forthcoming from Verse Chorus Press is a new full-length collection of poems and prose poems, *Great Balls of Doubt*, illustrated by Jon Langford.

VARSHA TIWARY is grateful to the city of D.C. for its generous culture of writing workshops/groups. Varsha's stories, memoirs, and essays have appeared in DNA-Out of Print fiction shortlist (2017), Kitaab, Basil O'Flaherty, *Muse India*, *Jaggery Lit*, *Manifest-Station*, *Spark*, *Usawa*, *Café Dissensus*, *Emerge*, *Kaani*, and *Shenandoah*. She has just moved back to New Delhi.

M. KAAT TOY (Katherine Toy Miller) of Taos, New Mexico, has published a prose poem chapbook, *In a Cosmic Egg* (Finishing Line Press, 2012), and a flash fiction book, *Disturbed Sleep* (FutureCycle Press, 2013). Her prose story manuscript, "Many Worlds: Some American Odysseys," is forthcoming from Shanti Arts Publishing (2020).

GAIL WHITE's fourth poetry collection, *Asperity Street*, was published in 2015 by Able Muse Press. She won the Howard Nemerov Sonnet Award for 2012 and 2013. She lives in Breaux Bridge, Louisiana, with her husband and cats.

SALLY WILDE is a ghostwriter and advertising copywriter in Washington, D.C.

ANDREA WYATT's books include *Three Rooms*, *Poems of the Morning*, *Poems of the Storm*, *Founding Fathers: Book One*, *The Movies*, *Jurassic Night*, and *Baseball Nights*. She coedited *Selected Poems by Larry Eigner*, *Collected Poems by Max Douglas*, and *The Brooklyn Reader*. Wyatt works for the National Park Service in the Maintenance Division of the National Mall and Memorial Parks.

VONETTA YOUNG is a black woman writer based in Washington, D.C. She generally explores in her work the themes of complex family dynamics, the intersection of race and class, and the desire for belonging. Her essays and fiction have been published in *Catapult*, *DASH*, *Lunch Ticket*, and *Cosmonauts Avenue*, among others. She is twice a graduate of Georgetown University. Follow her on Twitter @VonettaWrites.

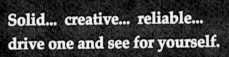

LAST WORDS

"Art hurts. Art urges voyages—and it's easier to stay at home." —Gwendolyn Brooks

"Start writing, no matter what. The water does not flow until the faucet is turned on." —Louis L'Amour

"I once jokingly told someone that every book is like a relationship. They're four or five years long. They're serious. They demand a lot of attention. But I remember thinking that I wanted to have one with someone who's not so crazy and peculiar and demanding." —A.M. Homes

"To travel is to discover that everyone is wrong about other countries." —Aldous Huxley

"To acquire the habit of reading is to create for yourself a refuge from almost all the miseries of life." —W. Somerset Maugham

"You see, the interesting thing about books, as opposed, say, to films, is that it's always just one person encountering the book, it's not an audience, it's one to one." —Paul Auster

"You are not a miserable and momentary body; behind your fleeting mask of clay, a thousand-year-old face lies in ambush. Your passions and your thoughts are older than your heart or brain." —Nikos Kazantzakis

"What people are ashamed of usually makes a good story." —F. Scott Fitzgerald

"Flags are bits of coloured cloth that governments use to first shrink wrap people's brains and then as ceremonial shrouds to bury the dead." —Arundhati Roy

"Illusions are important. What you remember can be as important as what really happens." —Javier Marias

"Have no fear of perfection. You'll never reach it." —Salvador Dali

"The writer must believe that what he is doing is the most important thing in the world. And he must hold to his illusion even if he knows it is not true." —John Steinbeck

"The world is never the same once a good poem has been added to it." —Dylan Thomas

"Reading is the sole means by which we slip, involuntarily, often helplessly, into another's skin, another's voice, another's soul." —Joyce Carol Oates

"A book, too, can be a star, a living fire to lighten the darkness, leading out into the expanding universe." —Madeleine L'Engle